Canadian Wood-Frame House Construction
Second Metric Edition

Canada Mortgage and Housing Corporation (CMHC)
offers a wide range of housing-related information.
For details, contact your local CMHC office.

CMHC subscribes to the sustainable development theme of
the federal government. Quantities of our publications are
limited to market demand; updates are produced only when
required; and recycled on environmentally friendly stock
and environmentally safe inks are used wherever possible.

Cette publication est aussi disponible en français sous le titre *Construction de
maison à ossature de bois — Canada. Deuxième édition métrique* (LNH 5031)

Canada

First Metric Edition published 1984, Second Metric Edition 1988.
Reprinted 1989, 1991

ISBN: 0-660-12647-8
Cat. No. NH17-3/1988E

Produced by the Public Affairs Centre, CMHC

Printed in Canada

The technical information and related tables printed in this book reflect Canadian construction conditions and do not necessarily conform to building regulations and standards in areas outside Canada.

Canada Mortgage and Housing Corporation, the Federal Government's housing agency, is responsible for administering the National Housing Act.

This legislation is designed to aid in the improvement of housing and living conditions in Canada. As a result, the Corporation has interests in all aspects of housing and urban growth and development.

Under Part V of this Act, the Government of Canada provides funds to CMHC to conduct research into the social, economic and technical aspects of housing and related fields, and to undertake the publishing and distribution of the results of this research. CMHC therefore has a statutory responsibility to make widely available information which may be useful in the improvement of housing and living conditions.

This publication is one of the many items of information published by CMHC with the assistance of federal funds.

CONTENTS

Preface   ix
Location and Excavation   1
   Marking the Excavation Area   1
   Excavation Size and Depth   1
   Placement of the House   3
   Backfilling   4
   Related Publications   5

Concrete Work   6
   Ready-Mix Concrete   6
   On-Site Mixing   6
   Placing Concrete   7
   Curing Concrete   7

Footings, Foundations and Slabs   9
   Footings   9
      Wall footings   9
      Column footings   10
      Stepped footings   11
   Foundations   11
      Cast-in-place foundation walls   12
      Concrete block foundation walls   16
      Preserved wood foundations   18
   Slabs   21
      Basement floor slabs   21
      Slabs-on-ground   23
   Footings and Foundations for Crawl Spaces   24
   Garage Foundations   25
   Foundation Drainage   26
   Related Publications   28

Protection and Care of Materials on the Building Site   29

Lumber and Other Wood Products   30
   Grade Marks   30
   Lumber Grades   30
   Composite Structural Members   31
   Sheet or Panel Products   31
   Related Publications   33

Framing the House   34
   Platform Construction   35
   Balloon Construction   35

Floor Framing   36
   Sill Anchors   36
   Columns and Beams   36

Beam and Joist Installation 37
Foundation Wall and Joist Connection 38
Floor Joists 42
Floor Performance 44
Subfloor 44
Floor Framing at Projections 45

Wall Framing 47
Platform Framing 47
Balloon Framing 51

Ceiling and Roof Framing 53
Pitched Roofs 54
Pre-assembled roof trusses 55
Site assembly of pitched roofs 56
Gable-end framing and projections 63
Flat Roofs 66

Roof Sheathing and Coverings 68
Roof Sheathing 68
Installation of roof sheathing 68
Roof sheathing details 69
Roof Coverings 70
Asphalt shingles on slopes 1:3 or greater 71
Asphalt shingles on low slopes of 1:6 to less than 1:3 73
Wood shingles 74
Handsplit shakes 75
Finish at ridge and hips 76
Built-up roofs 76
Sheet metal roofing 78
Concrete and clay tile roofing 78

Wall Sheathing and Exterior Finishes 80
Types and Installation of Sheathing 80
Wall Sheathing Paper 83
Exterior Cladding 83
Metal and vinyl sidings 83
Hardboard siding 85
Lumber siding 85
Plywood panels 88
Hardboard panels 89
Corner treatment for siding 89
Wood shingles and machine-grooved shakes 90
Stucco side-wall finish 91
Masonry veneer 92

Exterior Trim and Millwork 94
Eave Projections 94
Eave and Gable-End Intersections 96

Window Frames and Sashes 96
Exterior Door Frames and Doors.......................... 98
Related Publications 100

Framing Details for Plumbing, Heating and Wiring 101
Cutting the Framing Members.............................. 101
Framing Details for Plumbing Systems 103
Framing Details for Heating Systems....................... 106
    Warm-air systems....................................... 106
    Hot-water systems 108
    Electric baseboard heating systems..................... 108
Framing Details for Wiring 108
    Box location 112
    Switches 112
Related Publications 112

Vapour and Air Barriers 113
Placement 114

Thermal Insulation..................................... 117
Types of Insulation 117
Amount of Insulation..................................... 118
Insulation of Foundations................................ 118
Insulation of Floors 121
Insulation of Walls 122
Insulation of Truss or Rafter-Type Roof-Ceilings 125
Insulation of Joist-Type Roof-Ceilings 126
Related Publications 128

Fire and Sound Control................................. 129
Smoke Alarms... 130
    Location and installation 130

Ventilation 132
Roof Space Ventilation 132
Size of Vents... 133
Crawl Space Ventilation and Ground Cover 134

Interior Wall and Ceiling Finishes 135
Gypsum Board Finish 135
Other Finishes 138

Floor Coverings 139
Wood Strip Flooring 139
Wood Tile Flooring 141
Underlay for Resilient Flooring 141
Installation of Resilient Floor Covering 141
Seamless Resin Constituent Resilient Flooring 142

Carpeting 142
Ceramic Tile 142

Interior Doors, Frames, and Trim 144
Installation of Door Hardware 146
Window Trim Installation 148
Base Mouldings 148
Millwork 148
Kitchen Cabinets 149
Closets 149

Stairs 152
Stair Design Terminology 152
Ratio of Rise-to-Run 154
Stairway Design 156
Stringers 156
Newels, Handrails and Guards 157
Basement Stairs 157
Exterior Steps and Stoops 158

Flashing 159

Eaves Troughs and Downspouts 163

Garages and Carports 164

Chimneys and Fireplaces 166
Chimneys 166
Fireplaces 168

Surface Drainage, Driveways and Walkways 171
Surface Drainage 171
Driveways 171
Walkways 172

Protection Against Decay and Termites 173

Painting 174

Maintenance 175
Related Design Publications 175

Appendix A
Tables 177

Appendix B
Roof Truss Designs with Nailing Schedules 215

Glossary 225

Index 234

Preface

This publication explains in detail how a wood-frame house is put together in Canada. It presents the most commonly employed construction methods and provides suggestions for the selection of suitable materials. The book does not attempt to cover all the variations which may be used in different parts of the country, but where the details of construction vary, the fundamental principles outlined in this book still apply.

It is hoped that this book will be a useful guide to a wide range of people interested in house construction and that it will be helpful in the training of building-trade apprentices and students of building technology. The information in this volume is presented in a manner that may be understood by those without previous construction experience. The text is liberally supplemented with illustrations to make it easier to understand, and the appendices contain useful tables to aid in the construction of a wood-frame house. Where more detailed information is required, the *National Building Code of Canada* should be consulted. Additional resource books are also listed at the end of some of the chapters.

The practices described in this book meet or exceed the minimum requirements set out in the *National Building Code of Canada 1985*. Those practices that exceed the Code's requirements are considered to be desirable rather than merely acceptable practice.

All measurements in this book are in metric units since an increasing number of construction drawings give metric dimensions, and Canadian manufacturers continue to convert products and their descriptions to metric sizes.

The Institute for Research in Construction of the National Research Council Canada, Forintek Canada Corporation, the Canadian Wood Council and the Canadian Portland Cement Association have co-operated with Canada Mortgage and Housing Corporation in the preparation of this manual. Their assistance has been invaluable in determining the scope and content of the book and in suggesting changes and corrections to the drafts.

Location and Excavation

Marking the Excavation Area

Before the exact location of the house on the site is decided, it is important to check local regulations for minimum setback and side yard requirements, as these can be determining factors in placing the house. In some cases, setback from the street may be established by lining up with existing houses on adjacent properties.

After the site is cleared, the perimeter of the house is marked using as reference the exact location of the corners of the lot. These are determined by a certified survey. The corners of the house are marked by small wood stakes accurately located at each corner with nails driven into their tops indicating the outside line of the foundation walls.

As these stakes will be eventually lost during excavation, additional markings are needed. Offset markings may be located by extending the lines of the foundation walls from the established corners, and fixing these offset markings either with stakes on the ground or marks on surrounding, but permanent, objects. These markings are used after the excavation to set up an arrangement of batter boards (Fig. 1,A). However, if the foundation shape is simple, the site area unconstrained and the excavation carefully done, the batter boards can be erected at this point.

The area to be excavated is staked out usually 600 to 700 mm wider than the corners of the house. This extra width is needed for easy handling and erection of the formwork, placement of the drain tile, application of dampproofing and placement of the insulation.

An alternative approach to marking the perimeter of the excavation, especially when the foundation shape is not a simple rectangle, is to spray fluorescent paint directly on the ground.

Excavation Size and Depth

In most cases, the quickest and least expensive way to excavate is to use a bulldozer or power shovel. Before this is done, however, all top-soil should be stripped and stored for reuse. The subsoil from the excavation is usually carried away for disposal unless grading requirements allow its use on the site. The depth of the excavation and, consequently, the elevation of the foundation usually depend on the elevation of the street, sewer and water services, the profile of the lot and the level of finished grade around the perimeter of the house. The elevation of adjoining houses and surface drainage patterns must also be considered.

Two more considerations affect the depth of the excavation: the basement headroom and the elevation of the floor above grade. The headroom in the basement should be at least 1.95 m to the underside of beams or joists, but a headroom of 2 m is preferable. If the basement is to be used as a living space, however, the headroom should be

2.3 m, the same height as the other floors. The elevation of the first floor should allow for a minimum distance from finished grade to the beginning of exterior finishing (normally starting at the foundation top) of 150 mm for masonry and metal siding, and 200 mm for wood siding, plywood, hardboard and stucco (*Fig. 2*). This is intended to minimize damage to siding by melting snow and rainwater bouncing off the ground.

The finished grade should be sloped away from the foundation wall of the house and provision made to carry the surface water off the property. A swale (a gently sloping ditch) is used for this purpose where the drainage slope around the house meets a reverse slope. For example, if a lot slopes up from front to rear, the swale would be located at the rear of the house so that the surface water would flow along the swale around the house and out toward the street. The rough

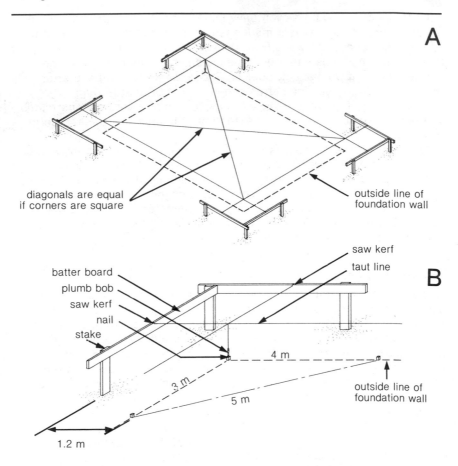

Figure 1. Establishing the lines of the house: A, marking the excavation area; B, measuring for squareness of building corners using triangulation method.

grade around the house should be kept at least 100 mm below the line established for the finished grade to allow for subsequent placing of topsoil or paving material.

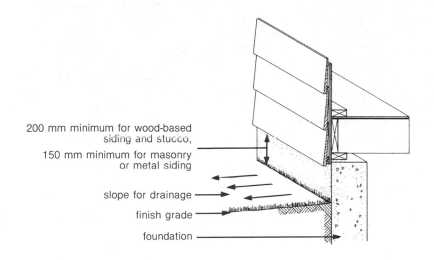

200 mm minimum for wood-based siding and stucco,

150 mm minimum for masonry or metal siding

slope for drainage

finish grade

foundation

Figure 2. Finish grade sloped for drainage.

When a granular base is to be used under the basement floor slab, the excavation should be made deep enough to accommodate this base. Normally, this depth is also sufficient to accommodate the thickness of the footings. If the site is well-drained and only a damp-proofing membrane is used without the granular base underneath, the excavation is stopped at the elevation established for the top surface of the footings. When this is done, the footings are formed by trenching, and adequate space must be provided for the drainage pipe beside the footing.

The steepness of the back slope of the excavation is determined by the subsoil encountered. With clay or other stable soil, the back slope can be nearly vertical. When sand is encountered, the banks must be cut back.

Placement of the House

After the excavation is completed, the next step is to establish the lines and elevation for the footings and foundation walls. Figure 3 shows a convenient arrangement of batter boards for this purpose.

Using the previously established location of the foundation walls, three stakes of suitable length are placed at each corner at least 1.2 m beyond the lines of the foundation. Boards are then nailed horizontally as shown in Figure 3 so the tops of all the boards are level and at the same elevation. Twine or stout string (called carpenter's chalkline) is stretched across the tops of opposite boards at two corners and adjusted exactly to follow the line of the outside edge of the foundation wall. By cutting saw kerfs 6 to 8 mm deep or driving nails where the lines touch the boards, the lines may be replaced if broken or disturbed. After similar cuts are made in all of the batter boards, the lines of the house will be established.

There are two methods to determine if the building corners are square. The first is to measure the diagonals. If the diagonals are equal, the building corners are square *(Fig. 1,A)*. Another method, called triangulation, is to measure along one side of the corner a distance in multiples of 300 mm and along the adjacent side the same number in multiples of 400 mm. The diagonal or hypotenuse will have an equal number of multiples of 500 mm when the corner is square *(Fig. 1,B)*.

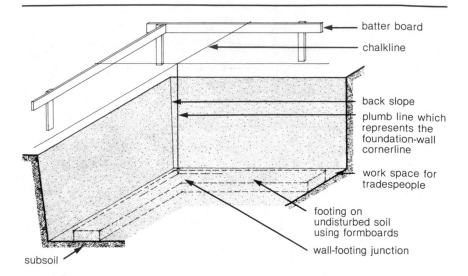

Figure 3. Method of setting batter boards and establishing corners for excavation.

Backfilling

Backfilling of foundation walls should not be carried out until floor joists and subfloor are in place. This applies to concrete, masonry and preserved wood foundation walls. Table 1 presents the maximum height of the finished grade for both laterally supported and laterally unsupported foundation walls.

Sudden pressures against foundation walls brought about by loads of backfill material may cause the walls to move, resulting in damage such as cracking in a concrete block wall. It is important, therefore, that backfill material be deposited gradually and uniformly around the perimeter in small lifts, with each lift being compacted to the appropriate density before the next lift is placed. Care should also be taken to ensure that the dampproofing membrane or externally-mounted insulation is not damaged.

Related Publications

A Glossary of House-Building and Site-Development Terms
        Canada Mortgage and Housing Corporation NHA 1165
Metric Conversion Tables
        Canada Mortgage and Housing Corporation NHA 5159
National Building Code of Canada
        Associate Committee for the National Building Code, National
        Research Council of Canada, 1985
New Housing in Existing Neighbourhoods
        Canada Mortgage and Housing Corporation NHA 5569
Site Planning Criteria
        Canada Mortgage and Housing Corporation NHA 5214

Concrete Work

Concrete, both plain and reinforced, is used for a variety of purposes in houses, such as concrete foundations, basements and garage slabs-on-ground.

Ready-Mix Concrete

Ready-mix concrete is available in most locations. When ordering ready-mix concrete for footings and foundation walls, it is important to specify a minimum of 15 MPa air-entrained concrete. For basement floors, slabs-on-ground, exterior steps and driveways, a minimum of 20 MPa air-entrained concrete should be specified. Air entrainment of 5 to 8 per cent will produce a concrete that contains a system of minute air bubbles. Air-entrained concrete is more easily placed and worked than plain concrete and, most important, when cured it is many times more resistant to damage from frost action.

On-Site Mixing

The practice of adding water to concrete at the construction site to facilitate its placement should be avoided. Additional water will lower strength, increase permeability and decrease freeze-thaw resistance. If more workability is required, the concrete supplier should be asked to adjust the mix, as the concrete may need a plasticizer to improve workability and placement.

When mixing must be done on site, water and aggregate should be clean and free of organic material or other substances which might damage the concrete. The aggregates should also be well-graded. All concrete should be air-entrained to improve durability and resistance to frost action.

The air-entraining admixture should be added in strict accordance with the manufacturer's recommendations, as too much admixture will decrease the strength of the concrete. It is recommended that the manufacturer's representative be contacted, if possible, for advice about the proper proportion for a specific use. Air-entraining admixtures should be used only if the concrete is mixed in a motorized mixer.

For concrete in footings and foundation walls, not more than 20 L of water should be used for each 40 kg sack of cement. For other concrete work, not more than 18 L of water should be added to each 40 kg sack of cement. These amounts are based on average moisture content in the aggregate.

The proportions of fine and coarse aggregates, cement and water should be adjusted to produce a mixture that will work readily into angles and corners without allowing the material to segregate or free water to collect on the surface. The concrete mixes shown in Table 2 are generally considered acceptable.

Placing Concrete

Whenever possible, concrete should be placed into the forms continuously in horizontal lifts not exceeding 300 to 450 mm in depth. Concrete should not be allowed to fall into the forms from a height of more than 1.5 m, as this causes the concrete to segregate. For higher drops, the concrete should be deposited through a suitable vertical pipe. Buggies, wheelbarrows or chutes may be used to move the concrete if all points in the forms are not accessible to ready-mix trucks. The chutes should be metal or metal-lined with round bottoms and slopes of a maximum of 1 vertical to 2 horizontal and a minimum of 1 vertical to 3 horizontal.

The concrete should not be deposited in a pile but should be spread out and levelled by raking or shovelling. Vibrators may be used to consolidate the concrete but should not be used to assist placement. Concrete can also be placed by pumping, if proper equipment is used.

If it is necessary to interrupt the placing operations, the surface of the concrete placed in the forms should be levelled off and the concrete allowed to set partially. The surface should then be roughened to provide a good bonding surface for the next lift. When work resumes, the surface should be cleaned and slightly dampened prior to placing the concrete. Grout of 1 part of cement to 2 parts sand should be spread about 12 mm thick over the roughened surface to provide a good joint between the two lifts. The new lift should be placed immediately after the placement of the grout.

When being placed, the concrete should be uniformly compacted by means of tamping hand tools (puddling sticks) or, preferably, by a vibrator.

When the air temperature is at or below 5°C or when there is a possibility of it falling to that level within 24 hours, concrete operations should, if possible, be suspended. If concreting is carried on, however, the concrete must be kept at a temperature of not less than 10°C or more than 25°C while being mixed and placed, and it must be maintained at a temperature of not less than 10°C for a minimum of 72 hours while curing. To do this, the water to be mixed into the concrete may have to be heated. The concrete should not be placed against frozen soil, and any ice and snow should be removed from the formwork.

Curing Concrete

Curing involves keeping freshly-set concrete moist or preventing it from drying out and shrinking for several days after placing. The cracking of concrete walls and floors can often result from improper attention to curing. Proper procedures for curing must be followed, therefore, if concrete is to achieve its potential strength, watertightness and durability.

The curing of walls should be carried out after the forms are removed for at least another day if the temperature of concrete is kept above 21°C, and for another 3 days if the temperature of concrete is kept between 10°C and 21°C.

A good method of curing is to place a soil soaker hose around the top of the wall allowing water to run down the wall. When water curing cannot be carried out (for example, in cold weather), spray-on curing compounds that inhibit evaporation may be used. If a dampproofing compound is applied to the wall, no further curing of that face is required.

In hot weather, concrete should be protected from rapid drying. During hot dry weather, wood forms should be sprinkled with water while they are in place in order to prevent excessive drying out.

In freezing weather, freshly placed concrete may be protected with a thick layer of straw or other insulating material. In addition, it may be necessary for the concrete to be protected by an enclosure and the space heated with fuel-burning heaters to ensure appropriate temperatures during the curing period.

Concrete slabs-on-ground can be cured by use of water sprays, by covering with burlap kept continuously moist or by covering with poly-ethylene sheeting or other means to prevent moisture loss. Unless curing is carried on for about a week after placing the concrete, the exposed surface of the slab may show unsightly shrinkage, cracking or be otherwise weakened.

Footings, Foundations and Slabs

Footings

Footings receive the house loads through posts or foundation walls and then transmit these loads to the soil. The type and size of footing should be suitable for the soil conditions and far enough below ground level to be protected from frost action. Frost action can also be avoided by providing good drainage around the foundation and away from the building.

The distance of the footing base from the finished grade should generally be no less than the depth of frost penetration. Table 3 shows the minimum depths for several soil conditions. Where fill has been used, the foundation should extend below the fill to undisturbed earth or be designed to suit the condition of the fill.

Wall Footings The size of the wall footings should comply with building code requirements. Table 4 presents the size of concrete footings on average stable soil. However, if the distance of the water table from the bearing surface is the same as the width of the footing, the footing sizes listed in Table 4 should be doubled. Unless soil conditions and design allow for sharply-cut trenches, side forms should be used for footings.

Footings should project beyond each side of the wall at least 100 mm, and the thickness of the footings without reinforcement should be at least 150 mm *(Fig. 4)*. If the soil is of low loadbearing capacity, wider reinforced footings may be required.

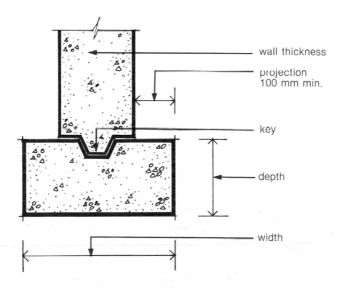

Figure 4. Size of footings.

If the footing excavation is uneven and in places too deep, the ground level may be raised with concrete placed on undisturbed soil. Excavated material should not be used as a base.

Pipe trenches directly under wall footings should be backfilled with concrete.

Column Footings Footings for posts or columns *(Figs. 5 and 6)* should be placed so that the members they are supporting will be centred. Footings vary in size depending on the allowable soil pressure and the load they support. On average stable soil, common sizes are 0.4 m² (about 650 × 650 mm) for one-storey houses and 0.75 m² (860 × 860 mm) for two-storey houses. The minimum thickness of column footings without reinforcement should normally be at least 150 mm. Footings for fireplaces and chimneys are usually placed at the same time as other footings.

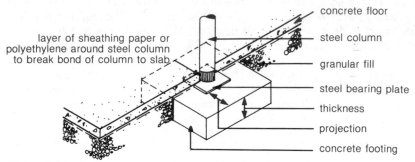

Figure 5. Steel column supported on steel bearing plate resting on footing. Base of column embedded in concrete floor. Table 4 provides minimum footing sizes for normal conditions.

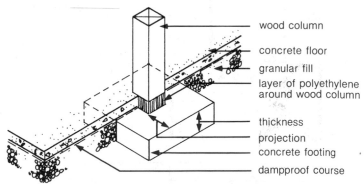

Figure 6. Wood column supported on concrete footing. Polyethylene layer separates wood from concrete. Base of column may be soaked in wood preservative.

Stepped Footings On steeply sloping sites, or where an unstable soil is encountered in part of the excavation, stepped footings may be required. The vertical part of the step should be placed at the same time as the footing. The bottom of the footing is always placed on undisturbed soil or compacted granular fill with each run level.

The vertical connection between footings at the step should be of concrete at least 150 mm thick and the same width as the footings *(Fig. 7)*. On steep slopes, more than one step may be required. Except in rock, the vertical distance between steps should not exceed 600 mm, and the horizontal distance between steps should be not less than 600 mm. For very steep slopes, where these limitations cannot be maintained, special footings may be required.

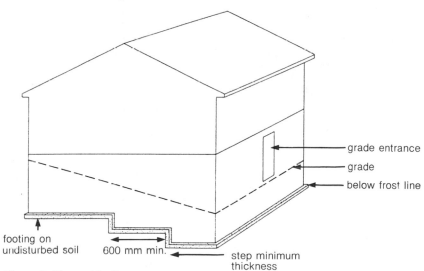

Figure 7. Stepped footings.

Foundations

The foundation wall carries the floor, wall, roof and other building loads (including snow and occupant loads) down to the footings. The two materials commonly used are cast-in-place concrete and concrete blocks, although preserved wood is also a practical option. Precast concrete or steel foundations may also be used.

Wall thickness of concrete and concrete block walls may vary from 150 to 300 mm depending upon their depth below grade and the lateral support provided by the floor framing system. Table 1 shows minimum foundation wall thickness for solid concrete and concrete masonry units in stable soils.

Where unstable soils are encountered, the construction of foundation walls should follow proven local practices or be specifically designed by an engineer.

Cast-in-Place Foundation Walls Concrete should be placed continuously without interruption. During the placing operation, it should be tamped or vibrated to remove air pockets and to work the material under window frames and other blocking.

Anchor bolts for sill plates should be placed while the concrete is still in a plastic condition. Anchorage is commonly accomplished by 12.7 mm thick anchor bolts spaced not more than 2.4 m apart *(Fig. 8)*. Anchor bolts should be embedded at least 100 mm into the foundation wall. The end of the anchor bolt embedded in the concrete should be deformed or bent to prevent withdrawal.

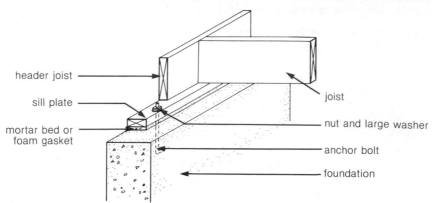

header joist

sill plate

mortar bed or foam gasket

joist

nut and large washer

anchor bolt

foundation

Figure 8. Method of anchoring floor system to concrete walls, showing anchor bolt for wood sill.

Formwork for Foundations Crushed stones are normally used around the perimeter and under the basement slab for drainage, and it is advantageous to spread that layer of stone around the footings in advance to provide a clean, dry surface on which to work.

Formwork for concrete walls must be tight, well-braced and tied to withstand the pressure of the concrete before it sets. Reusable forms are made of plywood or steel and make use of steel form ties to hold the two sides of the formwork together *(Fig. 9)*. The ties are usually broken off to remove the forms when the concrete has set. If these convenient forms are not available, the formwork may be made with lumber (tongue-and-groove or shiplap) or plywood, together with the necessary framing members. They can be built in sections and then erected.

Combination steel form ties and separators are generally used both to hold the forms together and to maintain the necessary width. Where wire ties are used, wood spacer blocks of a length equal to the finished thickness of the wall are placed between the faces of the form. Where wood spacer blocks are used, they must be removed and not left in the concrete. The wire ties hold the forms rigidly against the separators. Chalklines or nails may be used on wood forms to show the elevation at which the concrete will be placed.

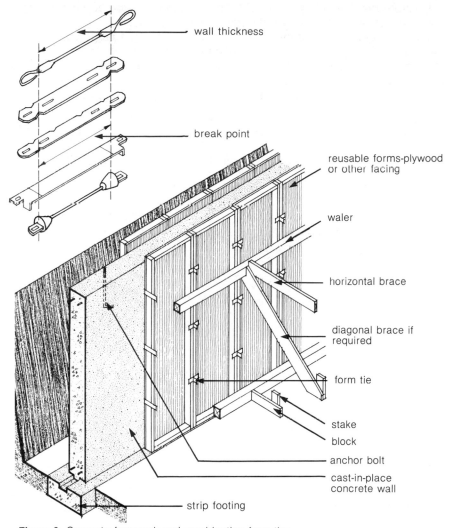

wall thickness

break point

reusable forms-plywood or other facing

waler

horizontal brace

diagonal brace if required

form tie

stake

block

anchor bolt

cast-in-place concrete wall

strip footing

Figure 9. Concrete formwork and combination form ties

Frames for basement windows, doors and other openings, along with the boxes that will form notches for the ends of floor beams, are set into place when the formwork is built. Framing and bracing are used to keep the forms vertical and in place until the concrete has set *(Fig. 10)*. It is important to check the diagonals of the frames to ensure that the frames are square.

If wood beams at or below grade are not preservatively treated to prevent decay, the wall notch or pocket for such beams should be big enough to allow at least 12 mm of clearance at the sides and ends of the beam for air circulation *(Fig. 11)*. These air circulation requirements do not apply to steel beams.

Where a masonry chimney is to be incorporated in the outside walls, provision should be made at this stage of construction.

Forms should not be removed until the concrete has acquired sufficient strength to support loads imposed during early construction. At least two days are required, but a week is preferable, particularly in cold weather.

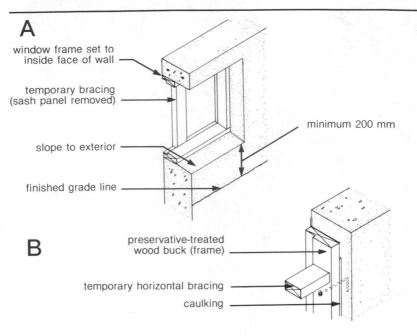

A

window frame set to inside face of wall

temporary bracing (sash panel removed)

minimum 200 mm

slope to exterior

finished grade line

B

preservative-treated wood buck (frame)

temporary horizontal bracing

caulking

Figure 10. Concrete frames and braces: A, window installed in cast-in-place concrete wall; B, around door frame.

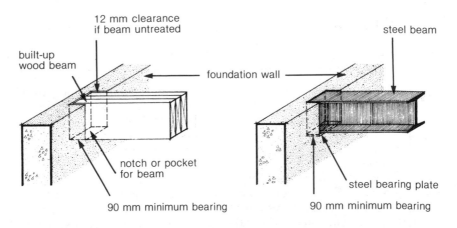

12 mm clearance if beam untreated

steel beam

built-up wood beam

foundation wall

notch or pocket for beam

steel bearing plate

90 mm minimum bearing

90 mm minimum bearing

Figure 11. Notches or beam pockets in foundation walls.

Control Joints If uncontrolled cracking of concrete slabs and walls is to be avoided, steel reinforcing rods or properly located and formed vertical control joints should be used *(Figs. 12 and 13)*. Wall joints are formed by nailing strips of wood about 20 mm thick, bevelled from 20 to 12 mm in width, to the inside of both interior and exterior wall forms. The purpose of these grooves is to provide a controlled plane of weakness in the wall, thus predetermining the location of shrinkage cracks. Control joints are necessary in walls longer than 25 m. Shorter walls are also susceptible to cracking and can use control joints to advantage as well.

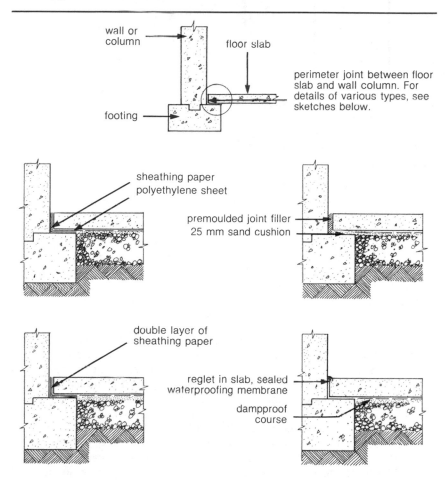

Note: Different combinations of slab/footing and slab/wall isolation joints may be used together, as desired.

Figure 12. Perimeter joint for floor slab.

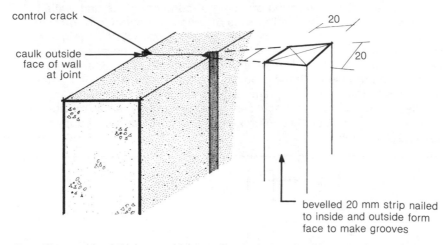

control crack

caulk outside
face of wall
at joint

20

20

bevelled 20 mm strip nailed
to inside and outside form
face to make grooves

Note. The combined thickness of inner and outer strips should equal approximately one-fifth of the wall thickness.

Figure 13. Control joint in basement wall.

Control joints should be located first at the natural planes of weakness, such as windows and doors, and then within 3 m from the corners, and 6 m apart. The sides of windows or door openings, if present, should be chosen as joint locations. After removal of the wall forms, the groove in the exterior face of the wall should be carefully caulked with a good-quality joint sealer. The dampproofing material, applied after the caulking operation, should be compatible with the caulking material used. A supplier should be contacted for advice regarding the compatibility of caulking materials.

Dampproofing Concrete walls below grade should be dampproofed with a heavy coat of bituminous material applied on the exterior surface from the footings to the finished grade line. Such a coating is usually sufficient to make the wall watertight against ordinary seepage that may occur after a rainstorm. Added protection from moisture can be provided by special dense glass-fibre insulation which is applied to the outside of the basement wall. In poorly-drained soils, waterproofing may be necessary and should consist of an impermeable membrane such as two layers of bitumen-saturated felt. The two layers of felt should be attached to the wall and each other with liquid bitumen.

Concrete-Block Foundation Walls Concrete blocks are available in various sizes and shapes, but those most widely used come in modular sizes 200 mm high, 400 mm long, and 150, 200, 250 or 300 mm wide. The actual size is 10 mm less than the modular size to allow for the joint.

Block courses (rows) start at the footing and are laid up with 10 to 12 mm mortar joints. No joint should exceed 20 mm, and all joints should be tooled smooth to resist water seepage. Full bed and head joints should be used in the bottom course. Succeeding courses may be laid with mortar applied only to the contact surfaces of the block. When pilasters (column-like projections) are required by building codes to strengthen a wall or support a beam, they protude into the basement space and should terminate lower than the perimeter of the foundation and at the bottom of the beams that they support.

Special concrete blocks, such as universal, pier or sash blocks, should be used to frame the sides of openings for basement doors and windows *(Fig. 14)*. For example, sash blocks have a keyed face or recess into which the frames are connected, thus providing rigidity and preventing air infiltration. Proper sill and lintel details should also be used to achieve the same effect.

Block walls should be capped either with 50 mm of solid masonry or concrete, or with a mortar filling in the top course of blocks. Alternatively, where termites are not found, a wood plank 38 mm thick and the same width as the wall may be used. At grade, another separation should be introduced to prevent convection currents in the cores of hollow masonry walls. This separation can be achieved with a strip of

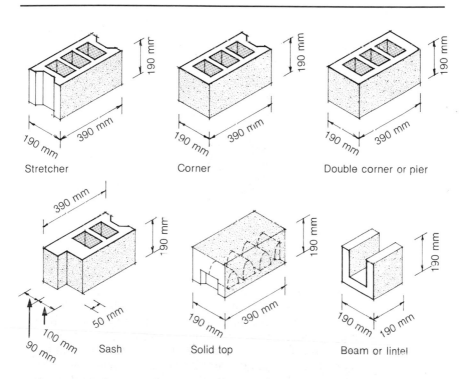

Figure 14. Concrete blocks for foundation construction.

polyethylene between courses. In all cases, the siding should overlap the foundation wall by at least 12 mm so that rainwater cannot reach the top of the foundation. Pilasters supporting beams should be capped with 200 mm of solid masonry.

Freshly-laid block walls should be protected from below-freezing temperatures. Freezing of the mortar before it is set will result in low adhesion, low strength and joint failures. Mortar mix proportions should conform to those shown in Table 5.

Concrete-block walls should be parged on the outside with at least 6 mm of portland cement plaster. A cove should be formed at the joint between the footing and the wall *(Fig. 15)*. The wall should then be dampproofed by the application of at least one heavy coat of bituminous material over the parging up to the proposed ground level. For added protection where quantities of water accumulate in the soil, two layers of a bitumen-saturated membrane may be mopped on and coated overall with a heavy coating of bituminous material. This covering will prevent leaks if minor cracks develop in the blocks or joints between the blocks.

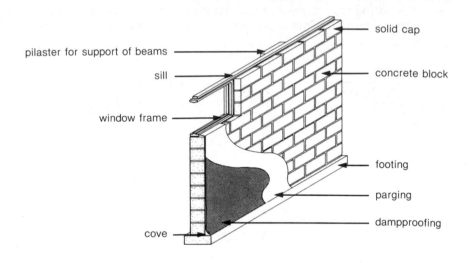

Figure 15. Concrete block wall.

Preserved Wood Foundations Preserved wood foundations are constructed by the same methods employed in house framing. The foundations usually consist of a pressure-treated wood footing plate resting on a granular drainage layer; pressure-treated bottom and top plates, studs and blocking with pressure-treated plywood as outside cladding, and a polyethylene sheet for added dampproofing. The space between the studs may be filled with insulation and the interior finished to provide a well-insulated living space partly or entirely below ground level.

In preserved wood foundations, all wood exposed to decay (that is, subject to moist conditions from the surrounding earth) must be pressure treated with chemical preservatives in accordance with Canadian Standards Association (CSA) Standard 080.15. The chemicals permanently impregnate the wood cells to levels of penetration and concentration that make the wood highly resistant to attack by decay organisms and insects such as termites. The dried wood is odourless with only slight colour. Properly treated lumber and plywood can be identified by a certification mark showing that the material has been treated by a plant certified according to CSA Standard 0322 *(Fig. 16)*.

The certification mark contains the following information:

ⓈⓅ	— identifies the certifying agency.
0322	— identifies the standard, CSA 0322, under which the material is certified.
PWF and FBT	— identifies the intended use of the material
L/B and/or P/C	— the plant is licensed for lumber and/or plywood certification.
CCA (or ACA)	— identifies the preservative used.
2577	— the first two digits identify the treating plant, the last two the year of treatment.

Figure 16. Facsimile of certification mark.

Wood foundations are suitable for low-rise single or multiple dwellings. They can be built with a conventional concrete slab floor, a wood floor on sleepers resting on a granular drainage layer, or a suspended wood floor *(Fig. 17)*. They must be designed to carry not only the vertical load of the house and its floor and roof loads but also the horizontal loads of the backfill material. The required size, species and grade of studs and thickness of plywood depend on stud spacing and backfill height and the number of storeys supported.

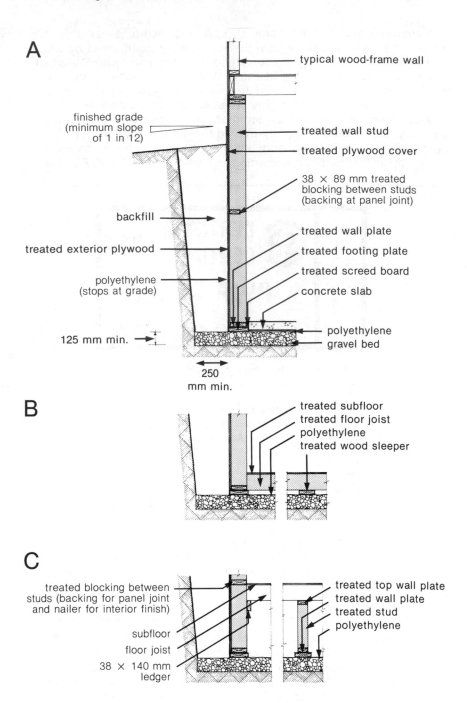

A

typical wood-frame wall

finished grade
(minimum slope
of 1 in 12)

treated wall stud

treated plywood cover

38 × 89 mm treated
blocking between studs
(backing at panel joint)

backfill

treated wall plate

treated exterior plywood

treated footing plate

treated screed board

polyethylene
(stops at grade)

concrete slab

polyethylene

125 mm min.

gravel bed

250
mm min.

B

treated subfloor
treated floor joist
polyethylene
treated wood sleeper

C

treated blocking between
studs (backing for panel joint
and nailer for interior finish)

treated top wall plate
treated wall plate
treated stud
polyethylene

subfloor

floor joist

38 × 140 mm
ledger

Figure 17. Preservative-treated wood foundations: A, with concrete floor slab; B, with wood sleeper floor; C, with suspended wood floor; D, on concrete strip foundation.

D

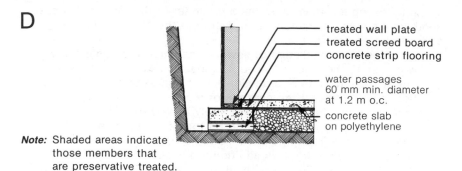

treated wall plate
treated screed board
concrete strip flooring

water passages
60 mm min. diameter
at 1.2 m o.c.
concrete slab
on polyethylene

Note: Shaded areas indicate
those members that
are preservative treated.

Figure 17 cont'd.

Slabs

Concrete slabs are used for basement floors and for houses or portions of houses constructed at grade. In small buildings, they are
generally supported by the ground below and not by the structure at
the perimeter.

Basement Floor Slabs Basement floors are usually installed after the
roof construction is completed, the building enclosed, sewer and water
lines installed and the basement floor drain in place. While curing,
concrete gives off moisture which can seriously affect finish flooring
or millwork. The basement should be ventilated to allow moisture to
escape before finish flooring or millwork is installed.

Basement floor slabs should be at least 75 mm thick and sloped
toward the floor drain. There should be at least one drain, and if a
laundry area is provided, the drain should be located near it.

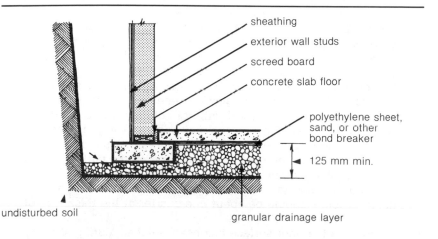

sheathing
exterior wall studs
screed board
concrete slab floor
polyethylene sheet,
sand, or other
bond breaker
125 mm min.

undisturbed soil

granular drainage layer

Figure 18. Concrete footing resting on granular drainage layer.

The following summary provides a reminder of the requirements, the good practice and the sequence of events in the construction of concrete basement floor slabs.

1. Complete the installation of sewer lines and other subsurface work before the slab is placed. Compact backfill in trenches.

2. Put at least 125 mm of crushed rock or coarse gravel under the floor slab to restrict the passage of moisture by capillary action from the ground up to the slab. Apply a layer of 0.15 mm polyethylene sheet or Type S roll roofing on top of the granular fill to dampproof the floor. The sheets should be lapped at least 100 mm at the joints (Fig. 18). This additional precaution is especially desirable when a finish floor will later be attached to the slab by an adhesive. Only when the site is particularly dry may this step be omitted. Where the the water table is high, insulating the slab becomes necessary to prevent excessive heat loss through the basement floor.

3. Basement floor slabs should not bear directly on wall or column footings but should be isolated from them by a minimum 25 mm sand cushion or other means (Fig. 12).

4. In order to allow for slight movement of the floor slab due to shrinkage of the slab during the drying and settling of the sub-base, a premoulded joint filter or double layer of sheathing paper (Fig. 12) between floor slab and wall or column should be provided.

5. After the concrete has been placed and consolidated, it should be struck off with a straightedge to the proper elevation. This can be determined by measuring down from the bottom of properly-levelled floor joists. In order to eliminate local high or low areas and to embed large aggregate particles, the surface is then immediately smoothed using a large float of either the darby or bull type. Tools used for air-entrained concrete should have a magnesium surface. Care must be taken not to overwork the concrete, as this will result in a less durable surface.

6. After the water sheen has disappeared and the concrete has stiffened slightly, edging, jointing and floating operations can begin. Any of these operations performed while bleed water is present will cause serious dusting or scaling.

7. If unsightly random cracking in the slab is to be avoided, proper control jointing or grooving may be necessary. Control joints should be placed on line with interior columns and at changes in width of floor slab (Fig. 19). The maximum spacing of control joints should be between 4.5 and 6.0 m in either direction. Joints may be formed in the freshly placed concrete by cutting grooves with a jointing tool, or preferably they may be cut into the slab with a power saw as soon as the concrete is firm enough. The depth of joints should be about one-quarter of the thickness of the floor slab.

8. As soon as the floor surface has been finished, curing should begin. Curing should continue for at least five days at air tempera-

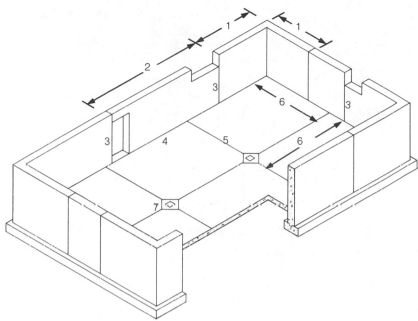

Note: The diamond-shaped joints (7) may be omitted if column footings are below floor level and the column is wrapped with two layers of sheathing paper or joint filler to break the bond.

1. control joints within 3 m of corners
2. spacing of joints 6 m max.
3. joints incorporate side of opening.
4. perimeter joint between floor and wall.
5. control joint in floor slab.
6. floor slab joint spacing of 4.5 to 6 m.
7. control joint around column footings. (see note)

Figure 19. Location of control joints.

tures of 21°C or higher, or for seven days at temperatures of 10°C to 21°C. Curing may be carried out by ponding water on top of the slab (by temporarily plugging all floor drains) or by covering with burlap, which is kept continuously wet. If this is not practical, liquid membrane-forming curing compound sprayed on the concrete surface may be used. If the finish is to be tile, caution should be used, as curing compounds may not be compatible with adhesives.

Slabs-on-Ground As the requirements for slabs-on-ground are similar to basement slabs *(Fig. 20)*, the steps and precautions described above apply here as well. An important difference is the need to establish the finish floor level at a sufficient height above the natural grade so that the finished grade will provide good drainage away from the house. The top of the slab should be at least 150 mm above finished grade.

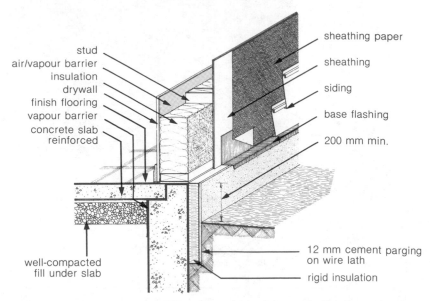

stud
air/vapour barrier
insulation
drywall
finish flooring
vapour barrier
concrete slab
reinforced

well-compacted
fill under slab

sheathing paper
sheathing
siding
base flashing
200 mm min.

12 mm cement parging
on wire lath
rigid insulation

Figure 20. Independent concrete floor slab and foundation wall. Slab is supported on 125 mm of coarse fill and on a ledge formed in the foundation wall.

It is also important to remember that all debris, stumps and organic matter from the unexcavated areas under the building should be removed to provide a smooth surface free of soft pockets. As well, the soil should be tamped where loose.

A water repellent type of rigid insulation should be installed around the perimeter of the wall. The slab should also be reinforced with approximately 3.6 mm thick reinforcing steel bars spaced 600 mm on centre in both directions. (The steel bars have a product designation of 10M.) Alternatively, a welded wire mesh can be used that forms a grid of 152 mm squares in which the thickness of the steel is 3.4 mm. (The product designation of this grid is 152 × 152 MW9.1 × MW9.1.)

A topping is generally not needed since the finished surface resulting from mechanical trowelling is very smooth. When a topping is used, it should consist of 1 part cement to $2^1/_2$ parts well-graded sand. A layer 20 mm thick is placed after the concrete slab has set; the layer should be trowelled to a smooth level finish.

Footings and foundations for houses with slabs-on-ground have similar requirements as those for crawl spaces and are constructed in the same manner.

Footings and Foundations for Crawl Spaces

Houses with a crawl space are supported on a foundation wall that is carried at least 150 mm above the exterior finished grade.

Trenches are dug for the foundation walls and the footings placed at a depth below grade determined by soil conditions and frost penetration. (See Table 3.) The sizes of the footings are generally the same as those used to support basement walls. The foundation walls may be built of concrete, concrete masonry units or preserved wood, but since the inside grade is never much lower than the outside grade, the thickness of the foundation walls is usually less than those enclosing a basement. Table 1 shows minimum foundation wall thickness for stable soils.

Footings for columns supporting the floor beams should be placed on solid undisturbed ground, and this may require some excavation. Concrete or masonry columns are generally used to support the beams and the excavated area backfilled around the base of the columns and footings when the crawl space floor is levelled.

Where the crawl space floor is below the level of the outside finished grade, the foundation walls should be dampproofed. Drain tile is then installed around the footing and connected to a drain. The floor of the crawl space and access trenches is graded toward the drain, and a ground cover of 0.15 mm polyethylene or Type S roll roofing is installed over the surface with the joints lapped at least 100 mm. The ground cover prevents ground moisture from entering the crawl space area. The crawl space should also be ventilated. See the chapter on Ventilation.

Crawl space insulation, which can be installed either at its perimeter or in the floor joist, is discussed and illustrated in the chapter on Thermal Insulation.

Garage Foundations

Foundations for garages are usually concrete or masonry, although concrete slabs-on-ground are also used. The minimum depth below grade for a garage foundation should not be less than shown in Table 3.

If fill is required below the floor, a granular material is preferable and should be well compacted to avoid settlement after the floor is laid. With a base of 150 mm of crushed stone or gravel, the concrete floor should be 75 mm thick; without a coarse granular base, the floor should be 125 mm thick. Unless a floor drain is installed, the floor should be sloped toward the entrance.

Detailing, placing and curing of concrete garage floors should be carried out as described for basement floor slabs. Control joints should be used to produce panels as nearly square as possible. For a single car garage, one transverse joint should be sufficient.

The foundation walls should not be less than 150 mm thick and should extend at least 150 mm above grade.

Sill plates should be anchored to the foundation wall or slab with anchor bolts spaced about 2.4 m apart and with at least two bolts in each sill piece. Extra anchors may be required at the sides of the main door.

Foundation Drainage

In most locations, it is necessary to drain away any subsurface water to prevent damp basements and wet floors. Where drainage is required, drain tile (pipe) is laid around the perimeter of the wall footings, or a granular drainage layer is used. Drain tile may be made of either plastic or concrete.

The drain tile should be laid on solid undisturbed soil around the footing, making sure that the top of the tile is below the level of the

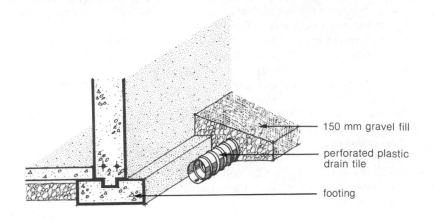

150 mm gravel fill

perforated plastic drain tile

footing

Figure 21. Drain tile at foundation wall.

basement floor or crawl space, with a slight slope to the outlet. The tile is then covered with 150 mm of gravel or crushed rock *(Fig. 21)*.

The drain tile should be connected with a tight joint pipe to a storm sewer or other satisfactory outlet. Adequate drainage to prevent the buildup of hydrostatic pressure is essential. A sump may be necessary in some cases. On wet sites, special drainage features, such as lateral drain tiles under the floor slab, may be needed to avoid this condition.

If a preserved wood foundation is used, a granular drainage layer should be employed in combination with a sump. The bottom of the excavation is sloped so that it drains to the sump, which is subsequently drained by gravity or mechanical means. The granular drainage layer should extend at least 300 mm beyond the footing plate and, if thicker than 200 mm, should be compacted.

This granular drainage layer technique is applicable to any type of foundation. With concrete footings placed on undisturbed soil, water passages of 60 mm in diameter and at regular 1.2 m intervals should be put in the footing to permit the draining of water to the sump *(Fig. 22)*.

As with foundation walls, surface drainage should be directed away from basement windows. Basement windows that extend below ground level require window wells *(Fig. 23)*. Galvanized sheet steel, corrugated for added strength, is commonly used for this purpose. This type of

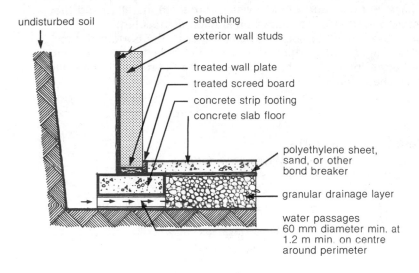

undisturbed soil

sheathing

exterior wall studs

treated wall plate

treated screed board

concrete strip footing

concrete slab floor

polyethylene sheet, sand, or other bond breaker

granular drainage layer

water passages 60 mm diameter min. at 1.2 m min. on centre around perimeter

Figure 22. Concrete footing resting on undisturbed soil.

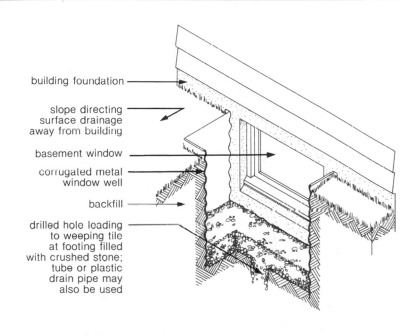

building foundation

slope directing surface drainage away from building

basement window

corrugated metal window well

backfill

drilled hole leading to weeping tile at footing filled with crushed stone; tube or plastic drain pipe may also be used

Figure 23. Window well at basement wall.

window well is available in a variety of sizes to suit various window openings. For concrete window wells, forms are installed and the concrete placed after the backfill has been compacted.

When the backfill is not a granular material, the bottom of the window well should be drained by a tube or hole 150 mm in diameter drilled down through the backfill material to the drain tile and filled with crushed stone.

Related Publications

Construction of Preserved Wood Foundations
   Canadian Standards Association, CAN3-S406

Protection and Care of Materials on the Building Site

The protection of building materials on the site and their storage before use are very important. If materials are stored without protection in inclement weather, damage may be caused that could be reflected in wastage of material and troublesome maintenance.

As far as possible, material should be delivered to the site just before it is to be used. This is especially true of exterior window and door frames and exterior trim materials. Interior finishing materials may be stored in the house once the roof is on.

In the normal staging of construction, the framing lumber and sheathing materials are delivered to the job after the foundation is complete. Structural and framing materials in place before the house is enclosed may be subject to wetting during rainstorms, but the wetting is mostly on the exposed surfaces and can dry out quickly in subsequent dry weather without causing damage.

Lumber stored in close piles, however, may soak up and retain water, and drying out will be very slow. This condition should be avoided as it may lead to stain and decay. Piles of lumber should be placed on skids raised off the ground and covered with sheets of waterproof material to shed water.

After the framing is started, the roof shingles may be delivered. Asphalt shingles should be stored so that bundles can lie flat without bending. Curved or buckled shingles will result in a roof which is not attractive.

Window and door frames are usually the next items to be installed after the roofing. If the frames are delivered before they can be installed, they should be sheltered until they are used. Good frames are costly items, and exposure to the weather may nullify their good construction. This is especially true where the frames are delivered with the window sash installed.

Insulation, interior wall and ceiling finish, wood siding and similar items can easily be stored in the house. Heavy materials such as gypsum wallboard should be distributed over the floor area so as not to overload the floor joists. Heavy loads, concentrated on one spot for any appreciable time, may cause permanent deflection in the floor joists.

Hardwood flooring, interior trim and millwork should not be stored in the house until after the basement floor has been completed and allowed to dry, as the moisture given off may cause the kiln-dried material to swell, resulting in excessive shrinkage after the materials are installed.

Lumber and Other Wood Products

The primary component of wood-frame construction is dimension lumber. It forms the structural shell which encloses and divides spaces and to which finishes are applied. In addition to lumber, other wood products are frequently used in the construction of the shell and in the interior and exterior finishes. All of these products are intended for specific uses and are manufactured to meet certain standards.

The lumber that is commonly used for framing is 38 to 102 mm thick and is called dimension lumber. Timber is the name given to lumber thicker than 114 mm; there are also decking, boards and finish lumber groupings. Table 6 presents the grades, common grade mixes, principal uses and grade categories for the various sizes of dimension lumber.

Grade Marks

Lumber for construction uses is grade stamped in Canada with identifying markings to show that it conforms to the National Lumber Grades Authority (NLGA) grading rules for Canadian lumber. The grading and grade marking of lumber must also conform to CSA Standard 0141, "Softwood Lumber." Grade stamps usually show the name or symbol (or both) of the grading agency, the species or species combination designation, the grade, the moisture content at the time of manufacture and the mill number.

"S-GRN" in the grade mark signifies that the lumber was surfaced at a moisture content higher than 19 per cent to a size which would allow for natural shrinkage during seasoning. "S-DRY" in the mark indicates the lumber was surfaced at a moisture content not exceeding 19 per cent while "MC 15" indicates a moisture content not exceeding 15 per cent.

Facsimiles of Canadian grade marks are shown in Tables 7 and 8.

Lumber Grades

Each piece of lumber is examined and assigned a grade depending on its physical characteristics. In addition to visually-graded lumber, machine-stress-rated (MSR) lumber is available in Canada. MSR lumber is identified in grade stamps by its structural properties and, for most wood-frame construction purposes, is independent of species.

Many softwood lumber species in Canada are harvested, manufactured and marketed together. Those having similar properties so that they can be used together easily are combined into a single species combination and marketed under a group designation. The Canadian commercial species combinations and their characteristics are shown in Table 9.

The top grade of most species is Select Structural, which is used only where high strength, stiffness and good appearance are all required. Lumber marked No. 1 grade often contains some percentage of Select Structural material, but permitted knots are slightly larger.

No. 2 lumber may have larger knots than No. 1, but they are tight knots and the grade is excellent for floor and roof framing members. No. 3 has still more and larger defects; it is adequate for sills, plates or non-loadbearing studs. The lowest grade is Economy, which is used primarily for non-structural purposes such as stakes and temporary bracing.

Four other grades also appear on the lumber stamps of 38 × 89 mm lumber. Stud grade is stiff, straight lumber suitable for vertical wall members. Construction grade falls somewhere between No. 1 and No. 2. Standard and Utility are still lower grades, but somewhat better than economy.

Minimum grades for various uses of lumber in wood-frame construction, such as stud wall framing, plank frame construction, posts and beams, sheathing and subflooring are set forth in the National Building Code of Canada. Tables giving maximum allowable spans for visually-graded lumber and for MSR lumber when used as joists and rafters are available from the Canadian Wood Council. In this publication, Tables 11 through 19 present the maximum allowable spans for ceiling, floor and roof joists as well as roof rafters using Nos. 1, 2 and 3 grades of lumber.

Metric sizes of softwood lumber are the same as those in use in Canada under the imperial system of measurement, but their sizes are expressed in millimetres of actual thickness and width after surfacing. The concept of "nominal size" is not used. Table 10 relates the current metric dimensions to the imperial equivalents actual and nominal.

Composite Structural Members

Dimension lumber and other wood products are often combined in the manufacture of composite structural members by the use of glue or mechanical fasteners or both. The most common example is the engineered pitched roof truss. Less common, but of increasing application, is the parallel-chord truss with metal, wood, plywood or waferboard webs (Fig. 24).

All these products provide greater flexibility in design by virtue of their larger spans and their capability to house services. In addition, when used for the roof structure, they can accommodate higher insulation levels.

Sheet or Panel Products

In addition to dimension lumber, other wood products in the form of sheets and panels are used in wood-frame construction. Plywood and waferboard, for example, are used to add stiffness to the structural components of the roof, wall and floor, apart from forming a uniform surface for the application of other materials. Fibreboard, particleboard and hardboard are also used in many aspects of interior and exterior finishing.

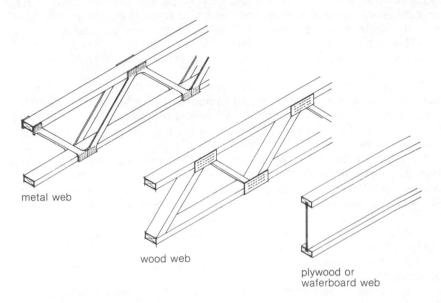

metal web

wood web

plywood or
waferboard web

Figure 24. Parallel trusses.

Plywood is one of the most commonly and extensively used wood products, being used in the construction of the shell (subfloor, roof sheathing, and so on), exterior finishing, some interior finishing and cabinetry.

Plywood is made of thin layers or plies of wood glued together with the grain of each ply running in a counter direction. Common thicknesses range from 6.0 to 18.5 mm. Like dimension lumber, plywood is graded for particular uses. For instance, there are interior and exterior grades of plywood; the interior grade will delaminate if exposed to moisture.

Waferboard has the same uses as plywood: subflooring, roof sheathing and wall sheathing. Waferboard is made of wide wood shavings compressed and glued together.

Fibreboard is made of wood fibres bonded together under pressure. It is available both in a plain and an asphalt-impregnated form; the impregnated version is used primarily for wall sheathing.

Particleboard is generally used in underlay or interior finishing such as shelving and other cabinetry. It is often covered with a plastic laminate or other protective and decorative material and used for the manufacture of cabinet doors. The same material is often used as the base for plain or preformed kitchen countertops.

Hardboard is made of wood fibre, like fibreboard, but is denser and harder. It is present in many furniture and cabinetry products. Hardboard siding with a prefinished colour is an alternative to wood, vinyl or aluminum siding. Also large panels with prefinished and textured surfaces are often used to create special effects inside or outside the building.

Related Publications

Lumber Specifications
    Canadian Wood Council, Datafile WS-1, 1985

Framing the House

The structural shell of a one or two-storey house must be erected before any other work can commence. The shell consists of the foundation, floors, walls and roof *(Fig. 25)*. In some cases, interior walls may be loadbearing, and they must be erected at the same time as the exterior walls. The shell must be made rigid in all directions, especially during construction when it has not obtained its final design rigidity. Temporary bracings and cross bracings should be introduced to allow construction to proceed without accidents or damage.

Before starting the framing of the house, it is important to consider the levels of insulation to be used in the different elements of the structural shell, as framing dimensions may have to be increased to accommodate higher levels of insulation. Table 36 presents the recommended insulation levels for different climatic regions.

The platform and balloon methods of framing are two ways of constructing a wood-frame house.

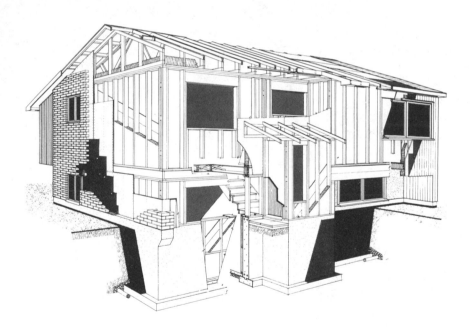

Figure 25. Cutaway of a wood-frame house.

Platform Construction

The most commonly used method for framing a house is platform construction. The chief advantage of this approach is that the floor system, assembled independently from the walls, provides a platform or working surface upon which the walls and partitions may be assembled and erected. Since the studs are one storey in height, walls can easily be prefabricated off the site or assembled on the subfloor in sections and erected one storey at a time without the use of heavy lifting equipment. The bottom and top plates, which are an integral part of the wall framing, provide fire stops at the floor and ceiling and also nailing support for wall sheathing and interior finish.

Balloon Construction

Balloon framing differs from platform framing in that the studs used for exterior and some interior walls are continuous, passing through the floors and ending at the top plates which support the roof framing. Since the connections between the floor joists and studs in balloon framing do not lend themselves to prefabrication or easy assembly on the site, this method of framing houses is rarely used. However, some of the techniques involved in balloon framing may be used with the platform framing method. For example, ceiling joists for dropped ceilings may be supported on a 19 × 89 mm ribbon let into the studs, or floor joists may be similarly supported where the level of the floors is offset at an adjoining wall in split-level houses. In some two-storey houses, the centre loadbearing wall in an otherwise platform-framed house is balloon-framed to provide convenient passage for heating ducts and pipes.

Floor Framing

In a wood-frame house, the floor framing consists of sills, beams and joists. In the interior, loadbearing stud walls are sometimes used instead of posts and beams to support the floor joists and the centre-bearing partition. All framing lumber should be well-seasoned and have a moisture content not exceeding 19 per cent at the time of installation.

Sill Anchors

The sill plate should be levelled carefully. If the top of the foundation is level, the sill plate may be laid directly on the foundation and the junction caulked. Alternatively, the sill plate may be placed on an 89 mm wide closed-cell foam gasket or other air-impermeable material. If the top of the foundation is uneven or not level, the sill plate may be laid in a full bed of mortar and anchored to the foundation wall.

Columns and Beams

Wood or steel columns are generally used in the basement to support the beams, which in turn support the inner ends of the first-floor joists as well as loads from upper floors transferred through walls and posts.

Round, adjustable, structural-steel columns fitted with plates at both ends are commonly used. The top plate should be as wide as the beam it supports and either be bolted to the flange where a steel beam is used or nailed to a wood beam. Columns may be adjusted to length after installation to compensate for movement in the soil or settling caused by shrinkage in the framing members.

Rectangular wood columns at least 140 × 140 mm may be solid or built-up of 38 mm lumber. Generally, 82 mm nails spaced at 300 mm on centre are used to fasten the built-up members together. Wood columns should be the same width as the beam they support and cut to ensure bearing at top and bottom. Each column is nailed to the beam at the top and separated from the concrete base at the bottom by dampproofing material such as 0.15 mm polyethylene or Type S roll roofing.

Columns are usually spaced 2.4 to 3.0 m on centre, depending on the loading and strength of the beam they support.

Either wood or steel beams may be used in house construction. One advantage of steel is the absence of shrinkage. For steel beams, the I-beam is the commonly used shape. Wood beams are of two types: solid or built-up. The built-up beam *(Fig. 26)* is usually made of three or more pieces of 38 mm lumber set on edge and spiked together from each side with 89 mm nails. The first two nails are driven near the end of each piece of lumber. Additional nails are driven not more than 450 mm apart in each row. Butt joints in each member are located over a supporting post or within about 150 mm of the quarter points in the span. (See Tables 20 and 21.)

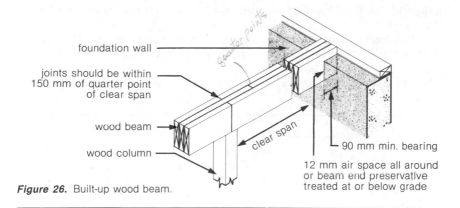

foundation wall

joints should be within 150 mm of quarter point of clear span

wood beam

wood column

greater points

clear span

90 mm min. bearing

12 mm air space all around or beam end preservative treated at or below grade

Figure 26. Built-up wood beam.

Ends of beams should bear at least 90 mm on masonry walls or columns. There is a decay hazard, however, where beams are so tightly set into wall notches that moisture cannot escape readily. Therefore, the ends of wood beams, located at or below grade and framed into masonry or concrete walls, should be treated to prevent decay or have a 12 mm air space at the ends and sides. Wood beams that are not treated should also be separated from the concrete with an impermeable membrane where they are below 150 mm of the ground.

Beam and Joist Installation

The simplest method of beam and joist framing is to have the joists rest on top of the beam *(Fig. 27)*, in which case the top of the beam is level with the top of the sill plate *(Fig. 26)*. This method is used where the basement must have adequate headroom below the beam.

Where more clearance under a wood beam is desired, 38 × 64 mm ledger strips are securely fastened to each side of the beam to support the joists *(Fig. 28)*. A 38 × 38 mm splice at least 600 mm long is nailed to opposing joists or the joists are notched, lapped and nailed to each other to provide support for the subfloor *(Fig. 29)*. Care should be taken to obtain full bearing on top of the ledger strip. Joists may also be

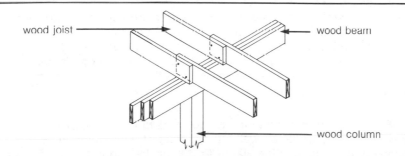

wood joist

wood beam

wood column

Figure 27. Joists supported on top of wood beam and fastened to the beam by toenailing. Two 82 mm nails used for each joist.

supported by joist hangers or other structural connectors attached to the beam.

Joists framed into the side of a steel beam may be supported on the bottom flange or on a 38 × 38 mm ledger strip bolted to the web with 6.3 mm bolts spaced 600 mm on centre. The joists should be spliced *(Fig. 28)* and a 12 mm space provided on top of the beam to allow for joist shrinkage.

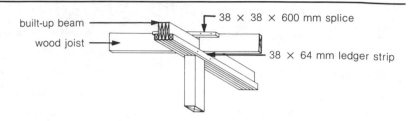

built-up beam

wood joist

38 × 38 × 600 mm splice

38 × 64 mm ledger strip

Figure 28. Joists supported on ledger strip nailed to beam with two 82 mm nails per joist. Splice nailed to joists with two 82 mm nails at each end.

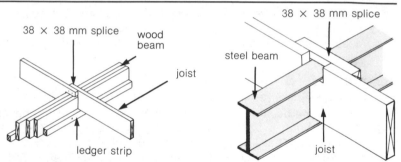

38 × 38 mm splice   wood beam

joist

ledger strip

38 × 38 mm splice

steel beam

joist

Figure 29. Joists supported on ledger strip nailed to beam with two 82 mm nails per joist. Joists lapped and nailed together with two 82 mm nails. When a steel beam is used, joists rest on the bottom flange and are joined at the top with a 38 × 38 mm splice.

Foundation Wall and Joist Connection

The two general types of floor joist construction used over the foundation wall conform either to platform or balloon-frame construction. Platform framing is by far the most common type used.

In platform framing, two methods of wall and joist connection are used and are generally referred to as the sill-plate method and the joist-embedded method.

Sill-Plate Method. This method can be used with either concrete or concrete block foundation walls. It consists of a wood sill plate anchored to the foundation wall *(Fig. 30)* for the support and fastening of the joists and header at the ends of the joists. The sill plate is usually supported on the top of the foundation wall, and in this case

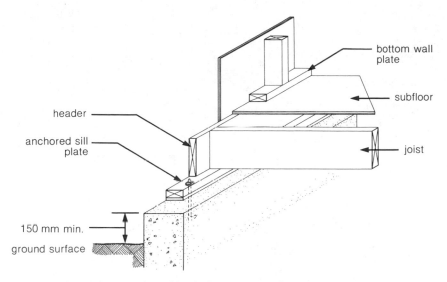

Figure 30. Sill-plate method used in platform construction.

the bottom of the sill plate should be at least 150 mm above the
finished grade.

Where it is desirable to lower the elevation of the main floor, the top
of concrete foundation walls may be reduced to 90 mm in thickness. If
siding or stucco is used as an exterior finish, the wall framing is supported on a sill plate anchored to the top of the wall, and the floor
joists rest on a separate sill plate located on a ledge formed in the
wall *(Fig. 31)*. Where a masonry finish is used, such as brick veneer,
the masonry is supported on the top of the foundation wall, and the
wall framing is supported on the floor framing *(Fig. 32)*. If the thickness
of the wall is reduced as referred to above, the height of the reduced
section should not exceed 350 mm.

Joist-Embedded Method. This method *(Fig. 33)* can be used only with
cast-in-place concrete foundation walls. Beams, joists and headers are
positioned before the concrete is placed. Floor framing is temporarily
supported on the inside concrete form and wedges used to level the
framing. Filler pieces placed between the floor joists and along the
end walls retain the fluid concrete between the joists. These filler
pieces are set flush with the inner face of the foundation wall. Joist
headers and end joists serve as outside forms for the concrete. Beam
ends are treated to prevent decay when they are located at or below
grade. The concrete is then placed so that at least two-thirds of the
depth of each joist is embedded in the concrete, thus providing suitable anchorage for the floor-framing members. The filler pieces are
removed, together with the wall forms, when the concrete has set. The
same method can be used when the finish of the exterior wall is
masonry *(Fig. 34)*.

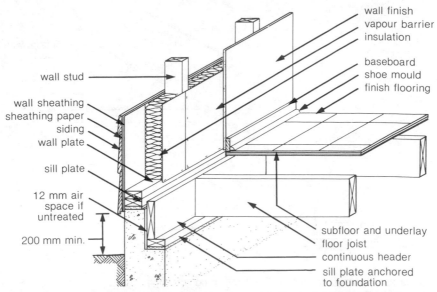

wall finish
vapour barrier
insulation

baseboard
shoe mould
finish flooring

wall stud

wall sheathing
sheathing paper
siding
wall plate

sill plate

12 mm air
space if
untreated

200 mm min.

subfloor and underlay
floor joist
continuous header
sill plate anchored
to foundation

Figure 31. Floor joists supported on a ledge formed in the foundation wall. Joists are toenailed to header and sill plate. Sill plate is anchored to top of foundation wall with anchor bolts. Wall plate supporting the wall framing is fastened to the sill plate with 76 mm nails spaced 400 mm on centre.

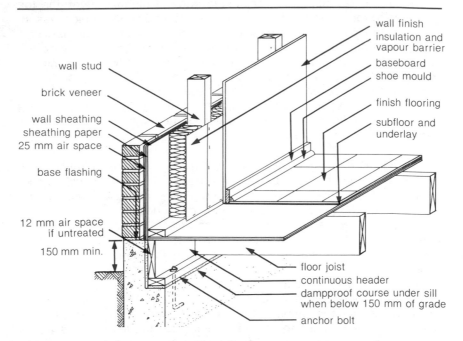

wall finish
insulation and
vapour barrier

baseboard
shoe mould

wall stud

brick veneer

finish flooring

wall sheathing
sheathing paper
25 mm air space

subfloor and
underlay

base flashing

12 mm air space
if untreated

150 mm min.

floor joist
continuous header
dampproof course under sill
when below 150 mm of grade

anchor bolt

Figure 32. Floor joists are supported on ledge formed in foundation wall. Joists are toenailed to header and sill plate. Masonry veneer supported on top of foundation wall. Wall framing supported on top of the subfloor.

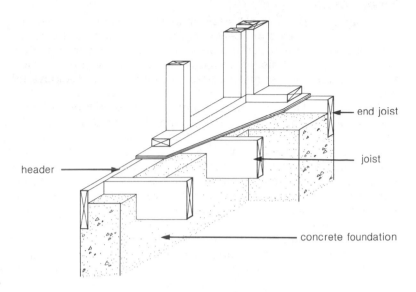

Figure 33. Floor joists embedded in the top of the foundation wall.

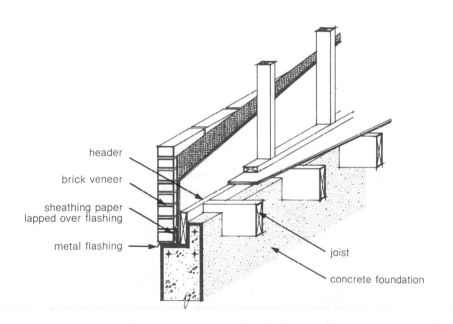

Figure 34. Masonry support using joist-embedded method of floor framing.

Floor Joists

Joists are selected to meet strength and stiffness requirements. Strength requirements are dependent upon the loads to be carried. Stiffness requirements, on the other hand, are intended to limit cracking of ceiling finishes under live loads and, even more important, to limit vibrations from moving loads, often a cause of annoyance to occupants.

Wood floor joists are generally of 38 mm thickness and either 140, 184, 235 or 286 mm depth. The size depends upon the loading, length of span, spacing between joists, the species and grade of lumber used and the deflection which may be allowed. Tables 12 and 13 show the spans which are allowable for the various grades and species of lumber and for different loading conditions. The allowable spans shown in these tables are measured between inside edges of the joist supports and have been calculated on the basis of lumber dressed to standard Canadian sizes.

Where a sill plate is used, the joists are installed after the sill plates have been levelled on the mortar bed and anchored to the foundation wall. As already described, where joists are embedded in the top of the foundation wall, they are installed before the foundation wall is placed. The joists are located and spaced in accordance with the design.

Joist spacing of 400 mm on centre is most commonly used, although for heavy loads or when space is limited, 300 mm spacing of shallower joists may be substituted. Conversely, if floor thickness is not a limitation, deeper joists at 600 mm spacing may prove more economical.

Any joists having a slight bow edgewise should be placed with the crown on top. A crowned joist will tend to straighten out when the subfloor and floor loads are applied.

A header joist is end-nailed *(Fig. 35)* or toenailed *(Fig. 31)* to each joist. In platform construction, each joist including the end joist parallel to the exterior walls is toenailed to the sill *(Fig. 35)*. The inner ends of the joists are supported on top of the beam *(Fig. 27)* or framed into the side of the beam *(Fig. 28)*.

When a loadbearing wall runs parallel to the joists, it should be supported by a beam or loadbearing wall in the basement.

Floor plans often require a loadbearing wall to be located at right angles to the floor joists but offset from the joist support. Loadbearing interior walls at right angles to floor joists should be located not more than 900 mm from the joist support when the wall does not support a floor, and not more than 600 mm from the joist support when the wall supports one or more floors, unless the joist size is designed to support such concentrated loads.

Non-loadbearing partitions parallel to the joists should bear on joists or on blocking between the joists. This blocking should be 38 × 89 mm lumber and spaced 1.2 m or less.

When framing for large openings, such as stairwells or fireplaces, trimmer joists are doubled if they support header joists more than 800 mm long. Header joists longer than 1.2 m should also be doubled. Where unusually large openings occur, trimmer joists that support

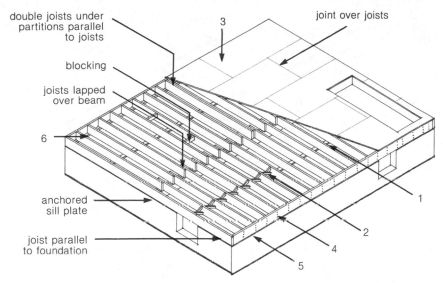

double joists under
partitions parallel
to joists

3

joint over joists

blocking

joists lapped
over beam

6

1

anchored
sill plate

2

joist parallel
to foundation

4

5

Figure 35. Floor framing: (1) 19 × 89 mm continuous wood strapping nailed at bottom with two 57 mm nails; or (2) 38 × 38 mm cross bridging at midspan nailed with two 57 mm nails. (Where joist span is within 460 mm of maximum, both (1) and (2) are required, unless a finished ceiling is installed when (1) is omitted); (3) subfloor nailed with 51 mm nails to joists; (4) header joist end-nailed to joists with three 82 mm nails; (5) header toenailed to sill plate with 82 mm nails 600 mm o.c.; (6) floor joists toenailed to sill plate with two 82 mm nails, one on each side.

---

header joists more than 2 m long and header joists that are more than 3.2 m in length should be designed in accordance with accepted engineering practice.

Nailing and assembly methods generally used in the framing of floor openings are shown in Figure 36.

Joist hangers are often used to support long joist headers and tail joists.

Joists may be kept from twisting by cross bridging, blocking, strapping or a ceiling finish fastened to the underside of the joists. Where a board-type finish is not used, necessary restraint should be provided at intermediate locations between the supports and at distances not greater than 2.1 m.

Intermediate support may be provided by one of the following methods:

1. 19 × 64 mm or 38 × 38 mm cross bridging or 38 mm solid blocking fastened between joists together with continuous wood strapping of 19 × 64 mm nailed to the bottoms of the joists; continuous wood strapping, however, is not required where a ceiling finish is provided.

2. The use of glue in addition to the nails when fastening the plywood or waferboard subfloor provides sufficient strength and eliminates the need for cross bridging and strapping.

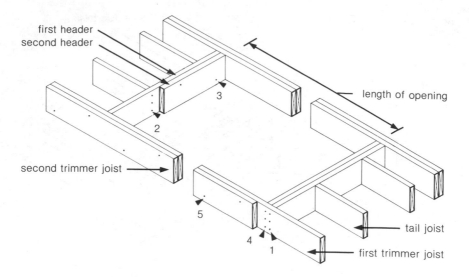

Figure 36. Framing for floor openings where double headers and double trimmers are used: (1) first trimmer nailed to first header with three 101 mm or five 82 mm nails; (2) first header nailed to tail joists with three 101 mm or five 82 mm nails; (3) second header nailed to first header with 76 mm nails spaced 300 mm apart longitudinally; (4) first trimmer nailed to second header with three 101 mm or five 82 mm nails; (5) second trimmer nailed to first trimmer with 76 mm nails spaced 300 mm apart longitudinally.

Floor Performance

If the span of the floor joists comes within approximately 460 mm of the maximum span permitted in Tables 12 and 13, the floor (while structurally adequate) may be perceived by the user as "bouncy" or "springy." The performance of such floors will be improved by installing transverse load-distributing framing, such as ribbon bridging combined with cross bridging, or solid blocking the same depth as the joists.

Subfloor

Subflooring should consist of (a) plywood, (b) waferboard or (c) square-edge, shiplap or tongue-and-groove lumber no wider than 184 mm. The minimum thicknesses of plywood, waferboard and lumber for sub-flooring are shown in Table 22.

Plywood is often used as subflooring under wood-strip flooring or as a combination subfloor and underlay for resilient flooring, carpet or ceramic tile. When used as a combination subfloor and underlay, the side joints should be supported on 38 × 38 mm blocking fitted between the joists unless the edges of the panels are tongue-and-grooved.

Plywood panels should be installed with the surface grain at right angles to the floor joists and with the end joints staggered and nailed along the edges at 150 mm on centre and 300 mm at intermediate supports. Ringed underlay nails, which are designed to resist withdrawal and "nail popping," should be used where the panels provide a combination subfloor and underlay. (See Table 23 for details of fastening sheathing and subflooring.)

Floor stiffness can be substantially increased, and floor squeaks minimized, by applying elastomeric glue between the floor joists and the plywood subfloor. In this method, the plywood and joists act together as a series of composite, stiff T-beams that help prevent differential deflection between joists. Further stiffening results from the application of elastomeric glue in the plywood tongue-and-groove joints.

Waferboard panels may also be used as subflooring and should be covered with an underlay where a vinyl floor covering is used. The panels should be staggered and nailed in the same way as plywood.

All plywood and waferboard panels used for subflooring and under-layment should be the exterior type, manufactured with waterproof adhesives.

An underlay is not required where the edges of the subflooring are supported.

For lumber subfloor, 19 mm thick boards are generally used, although this thickness may be reduced to 17 mm where joists are spaced at 400 mm on centre. The boards should be applied so that the end joints occur over the joists. End joints are usually staggered throughout the floor. Boards may be applied at right angles to the joists or diagonally at an angle of 45°. When the subflooring is laid at right angles to the joists, strip finish flooring should be placed at right angles to the subflooring unless an underlay is used. Diagonal sub-flooring permits finish strip flooring to be laid either parallel to or across the joists. The boards should be nailed with two 51 mm nails at each support. Lumber subflooring must be covered with a panel-type underlay where the floor is finished with resilient flooring.

Floor Framing at Projections

Floor joists sometimes project beyond the foundation wall to provide support for a bay window or additional floor space in the upper rooms. The cantilevered portion of the floor framing should not exceed 400 mm for 38 × 184 mm joists and 600 mm for larger joists. In either case, this projection should not carry loads from additional floors. If the cantilevered floor joists are to carry additional loads, they must be specifically designed for the appropriate loads in accordance with accepted engineering practice. The subflooring is carried to and sawn flush with the outer framing members. Figure 37 shows a typical second-storey projection.

Insulation should be fitted carefully and placed on top of the soffit finish under the cantilevered floor and up the inside face of the joist header and end joists. The vapour barrier should be placed on the

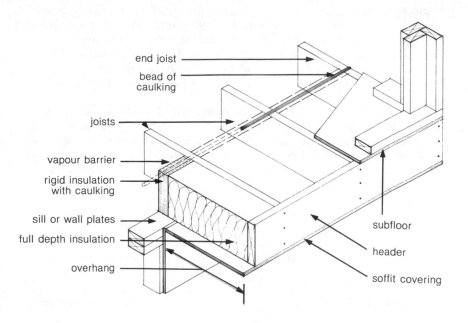

Figure 37. Floor framing at projections.

---

warm side of the insulation and neatly fitted and fastened in place.

If the joist depth is great enough, the space between the insulation and subfloor is usually left open to let the warm air in the ceiling area circulate between the joist spaces. In this way, the floor in the projected area is heated both from below and above, resulting in an even and comfortable floor temperature throughout the room.

To prevent external air infiltration into the projected area, the soffit under the overhang and other parts of the trim should be carefully fitted and caulked where necessary or wrapped with an air barrier.

Wall Framing

The term "wall framing" includes the vertical and horizontal members of exterior walls and interior partitions. These members, referred to as studs, wall plates and lintels, serve as a nailing base for all covering materials and support the upper floors, ceiling and roof. All framing lumber should be well-seasoned and have a moisture content not exceeding 19 per cent (See Table 24 for nailing practice.)

Exterior wall studs are the vertical members to which the wall sheathing and cladding are attached. They are supported on a bottom plate or foundation sill and in turn support the top plate. Studs usually consist of 38 × 89 mm lumber and are commonly spaced at 400 mm on centre. This spacing may be changed to 300 mm or 600 mm on centre depending on the load and the limitations imposed by the type and thickness of the wall covering used. (See Table 25.) Wider studs (38 × 140 mm) may be used to provide space for more insulation. Insulation beyond that which can be accommodated within an 89 mm stud space can also be provided by other means, such as rigid insulation or batts between 38 × 38 mm horizontal furring strips or by attaching rigid insulation sheathing to the outside of the studs.

The studs are attached to horizontal top and bottom wall plates of 38 mm lumber that are the same width as the studs.

Lintels are the horizontal members placed over window, door and other openings to carry vertical loads to the adjoining studs. Lintels are usually constructed of two pieces of 38 mm lumber separated with spacers to the width of the studs and nailed together to form a single unit. The preferable spacer material is rigid insulation. The depth of a lintel is determined by the width of the opening and vertical loads supported. (See Table 26.) Larger depth lumber may be used throughout for convenience and faster construction.

Platform Framing

The method of framing wall sections horizontally on the subfloor prior to erection is widely used. The top and bottom plates are end-nailed to each stud with two nails at least 82 mm in length. Studs are doubled at openings, the jack stud being cut to receive the lintels which are placed and end-nailed through the outer studs.

Wall sheathing is usually applied to the framing prior to erection, thus eliminating the need to scaffold for this operation. Some types of sheathing, such as asphalt-impregnated fibreboard, plywood and waferboard, will provide adequate bracing to resist lateral loads and keep the wall square; others, such as rigid glass-fibre, polystyrene or polyurethane board, will not. In this latter case, the wall should be reinforced with a diagonal wood or metal bracing let into the studs. The wall sections are then raised and put in place, temporary braces added and the bottom plates nailed through the subfloor to the floor framing

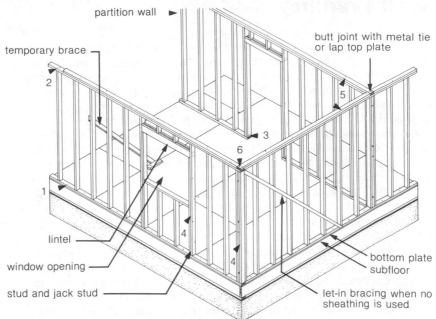

Figure 38. Wall framing used with platform construction: (1) bottom plate nailed to joist or header joist with 82 mm nails 400 mm on centre; (2) top plate end-nailed to stud with two 82 mm nails; (3) stud toenailed with four 63 mm nails or end-nailed to bottom plate with two 82 mm nails; (4) doubled studs at openings and multiple studs at corners and intersections nailed with 76 mm nails 750 mm on centre; (5) top plates nailed together with 76 mm nails 600 mm on centre; (6) top plates at corners and loadbearing partitions are lapped and nailed together with two 82 mm nails or the plates are butted together and tied with a metal plate fastened to the top plates with three 63 mm nails on each side of the joint.

members *(Fig. 38)*. The braces should have their larger or flat dimension upward and should permit adjustment of the vertical position of the wall.

Once the assembled sections are plumbed, they are nailed together at the corners and intersections. A second top plate, with joints located at least one stud space away from the joints in the plate beneath, is then added. This second top plate usually laps the first plate at the corners and partition intersections and, when nailed in place, provides an additional tie to the framed walls. Where the second top plate does not lap the plate immediately underneath at corner and partition intersections, these may be tied with 0.91 mm galvanized steel plates at least 75 mm wide and 150 mm long, nailed with at least three 63 mm nails to each wall.

Interior partitions supporting floor, ceiling or roof loads are called loadbearing walls; others are called non-loadbearing or simply partitions. Interior loadbearing walls are framed in the same way as exterior walls. Studs are usually 38 × 89 mm lumber spaced at 400 mm on centre. This spacing may be changed to 300 mm or 600 mm depending on the loads supported and the type and thickness of the wall finish used. (See Table 25.)

Partitions can be built with 38 × 64 mm or 38 × 89 mm studs spaced at 400 or 600 mm on centre depending on the type and thickness of the wall finish used. Where a partition does not contain a swinging door, 38 × 89 mm studs at 400 mm on centre are sometimes used with the wide face of the stud parallel to the wall. This is usually done only for partitions enclosing clothes closets or cupboards to save space. Since there is no vertical load to be supported by partitions, single studs may be used at the door openings. The top of the opening may be bridged with a single piece of 38 mm lumber the same width as the studs. These members provide a nailing support for wall finish, door frames and trim.

A multiple-stud post made up of at least three studs, or the equivalent, is generally used at exterior corners and intersections to secure a good tie between adjoining walls and to provide nailing support for the interior finish and exterior sheathing. Corners and intersections, however, must be framed with at least two studs.

Figures 39 and 40 illustrate exterior corners and partition intersections commonly used.

Nailing support for the edges of the ceiling finish is required at the junction of the wall and ceiling where partitions run parallel to the ceiling joists. Figures 41 and 42 illustrate the types of nailing support commonly used.

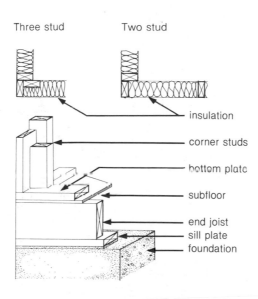

Figure 39. Multiple stud arrangements at exterior corner. In the two stud arrangement, a plasterboard clip is used at the corner for support.

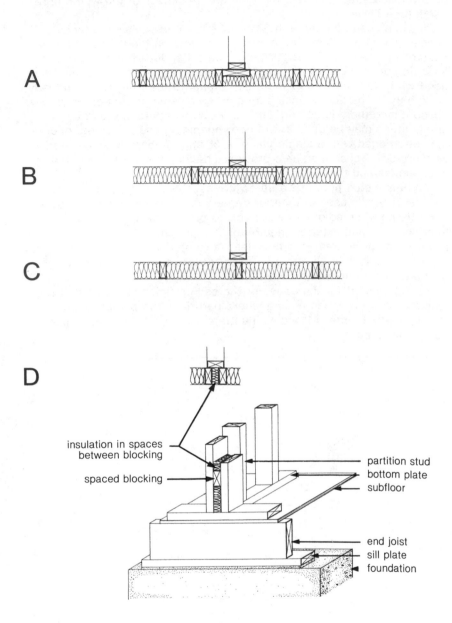

Figure 40. Multiple stud arrangements at the intersection of an interior partition with an exterior wall: A, two studs used; B, bracing or blocking is used; C, the partition is attached to exterior wall after drywall has been installed; D, insulation must be installed before sheathing is applied.

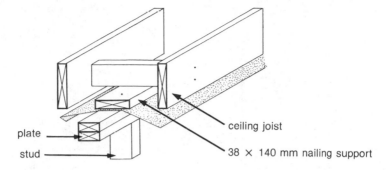

plate

stud

ceiling joist

38 × 140 mm nailing support

Figure 41. Horizontal nailing support for interior finish. Nailing support provided by 38 mm lumber nailed to top plates with 76 mm nails at 300 mm on centre.

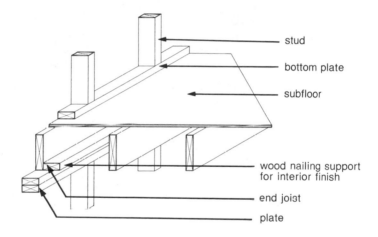

stud

bottom plate

subfloor

wood nailing support
for interior finish

end joist

plate

Figure 42. End-wall framing and nailing support for interior finish using platform construction method.

Balloon Framing

In balloon-framed construction, both the studs and first-floor joists rest on the foundation sill plate *(Fig. 43)* and the centre beam or bearing wall. Studs are toenailed to these supports with four 63 mm nails; the joists in turn are nailed to the studs with two 76 mm nails. When lumber subfloor is laid diagonally, blocking is required between the joists at the wall lines to support the ends of the boards.

Second-floor joists bear on a 19 × 89 mm ribbon that has been let into the studs, and the joists are nailed to the studs. The end joists

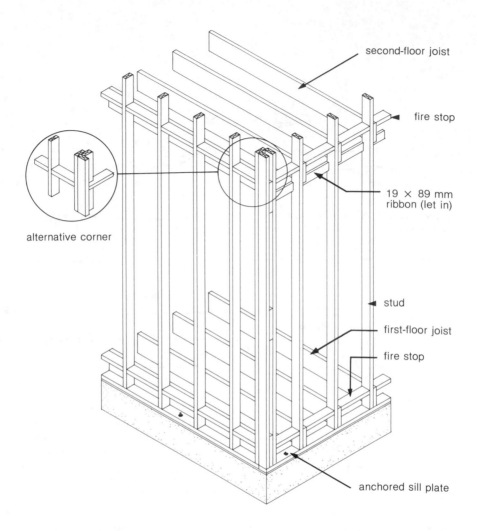

second-floor joist

fire stop

19 × 89 mm
ribbon (let in)

alternative corner

stud

first-floor joist

fire stop

anchored sill plate

Figure 43. Wall framing using balloon construction method.

parallel to the exterior walls on both first and second floors are similarly nailed to the studs.

When framing the floor, blocking should be inserted between joists at the wall to support the ends of diagonal subfloor boards. As the spaces between the studs are not interrupted by wall plates (as in platform framing), fire stops are required at floor and ceiling levels to eliminate continuous passages in the wall and thus resist the spread of fire. Lumber blocking 38 mm thick is commonly used for this purpose. Fire stops, however, are not required where the wall space is filled with insulation.

Ceiling and Roof Framing

There are two basic types of roofs — pitched and flat — and each type has many variations.

The slope of a roof is expressed as a ratio of rise-to-run with the vertical component always being shown first. For slopes less than 45°, the first number should always be shown as one. A ratio of 1:5, for instance, indicates a rise of 1 mm for every 5 mm of horizontal dimension, or 1 m for every 5 m. For slopes steeper than 45°, the second number (that is, the horizontal component) should always be one to facilitate easy verification. A ratio of 5:1 expresses a rise of 5 mm for a horizontal dimension of 1 mm, or 5 m for each 1 m. The use of mixed units, such as 1 mm in 10 m, should be avoided.

Expressed as a ratio, the standard slope reference of 4 in 12 (or 400 mm in 1200 mm) becomes 1:3; similarly, 3 in 12 becomes 1:4. In special cases, where a high degree of accuracy is required, angular expressions of slope are acceptable.

For purposes of definition, flat roofs might be classed as those having less than 1:6 slope. Pitched roofs vary in slope from 1:6 to 1:1 or more (for example, 2:1), depending on the roof covering and the use of attic space.

The dimensions of roof joists and rafters for the various grades and species of lumber and for the different live loads encountered are given in Tables 14 to 19.

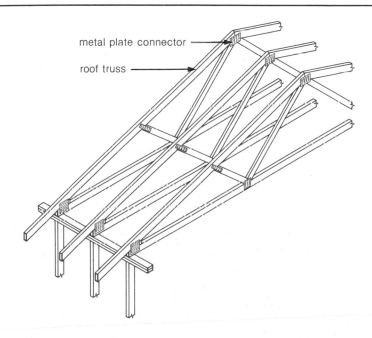

metal plate connector

roof truss

Figure 44. Roof framing using lightweight roof trusses.

Pitched Roofs

Roof trusses are most often pre-assembled, although they can be constructed on site. Appendix B presents a number of different designs for the on-site construction of pitched roof trusses. Pitched roofs can also be stick-built, although this is a time-consuming process. Of the pitched roofs, the gable roof is the simplest to construct, especially with the use of lightweight roof trusses *(Fig. 44)*. Other configurations, such as the hip roof and L-shape roof, though more complex, can also be framed with trusses *(Fig. 45)*.

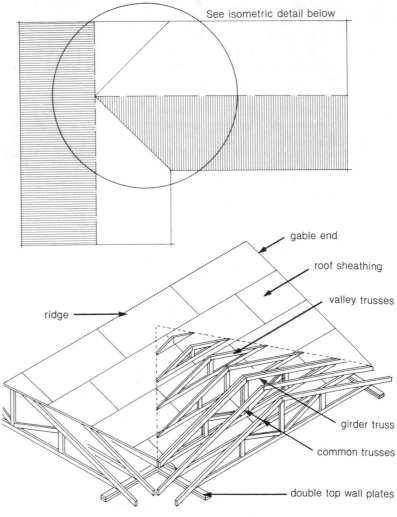

See isometric detail below

gable end

roof sheathing

valley trusses

ridge

girder truss

common trusses

double top wall plates

Note: For clarity, some structural members of some of the common trusses have been omitted, and roof sheathing appears continuous.

Figure 45. L-shape trussed roof.

Pre-Assembled Roof Trusses Pre-assembled roof trusses offer many advantages in that they save material and speed up the process of enclosing the house. They provide, in one step, a surface for the roof sheathing, a surface for the ceiling finish material and a space for insulation. Ventilation of the attic space is easily accomplished through the eaves or gables or both, and at or along the ridge. In most cases, trusses are designed to span from exterior wall to exterior wall with no intermediate loadbearing walls to support the roof loads *(Fig. 46)*. Thus, the entire house may be used as one large workroom during construction. This increases the flexibility of interior planning, as partitions can be placed without regard to structural requirements. Additional flexibility and speed is gained with preassembled components and add-on features such as garage roof trusses, porch roofs,

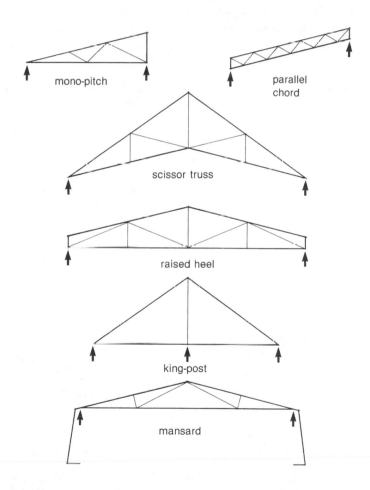

Figure 46. Types of prefabricated roof trusses.

simulated mansards and window canopies, which can also be supplied by the truss manufacturer.

Metal-plate-connected trusses can be delivered to the construction site and placed on a flat, clean portion of the site. Trusses under a 6 m span are usually installed by hand. Trusses longer than 6 m require special lifting techniques to avoid damage.

The trusses must be lifted into position with care to prevent excessive lateral bending. The first to be put in place is the gable truss, which is braced to the ground and wall. Each additional truss is lifted into position, generally 600 mm on centre, toenailed to the top plates and temporarily braced *(Fig. 47)*. When all trusses are positioned, they are braced permanently *(Fig. 48)*. The stiffness of the roof is increased after the sheathing has been applied.

Site Assembly of Pitched Roofs For on-site construction, the simplest roof to frame is the gable roof *(Fig. 49,A)*. All rafters are cut to the same length and pattern, and erection is straightforward. A variation of the gable roof may include dormers for additional light and ventilation in second-floor rooms *(Fig. 49,B)*. The shed dormer provides greatest possibilities for light, floor space and headroom *(Fig. 49,C)*. However, openable windows and fixed skylights that can be fitted on a slope between rafters will provide ventilation and light without the complexity and cost of framing a dormer. With the hip roof design, shown in Figure 49,D, common rafters are fastened to the ridge board while hip rafters supply the support for the jack rafters.

Important considerations in framing a liveable attic space are insulation and proper air and vapour barrier sealing; these subjects are dealt with in the chapter on Thermal Insulation. The choice of framing

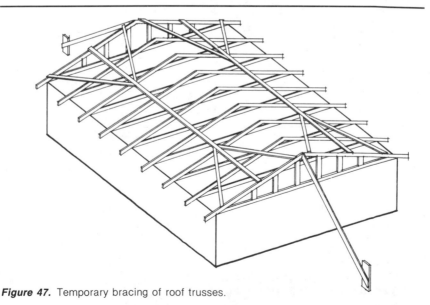

Figure 47. Temporary bracing of roof trusses.

members for structural strength, based on Tables 14 and 19, may not provide sufficient depth for insulation and necessary ventilation space. Larger size members or a modified framing technique will be needed to meet current standards.

Ceiling Joists are used to support the ceiling finish and to act as ties between exterior walls and, in some cases, opposing rafters. They may also provide support for roof loads transferred to them by dwarf walls (knee walls) used as intermediate support for rafters, in which case they need to be appropriately increased in size. (See Table 11 for ceiling joist spans.) When the joists also support floor loads, their size

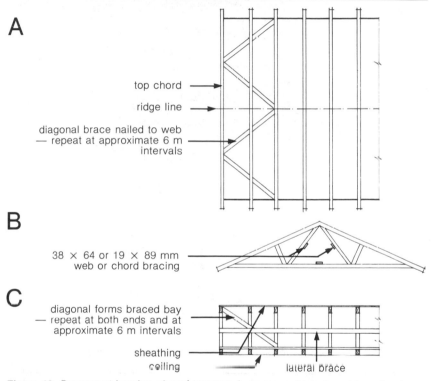

A

top chord

ridge line

diagonal brace nailed to web
— repeat at approximate 6 m
intervals

B

38 × 64 or 19 × 89 mm
web or chord bracing

C

diagonal forms braced bay
— repeat at both ends and at
approximate 6 m intervals

sheathing

ceiling

lateral brace

Figure 48. Permanent bracing of roof trusses: A, permanent bracing of top chord plane; B and C, permanent lateral bracing to web member or bottom chord plane.

should be determined by the floor joist tables (See Tables 12 and 13).

In pitched-roof framing, the ceiling joists are nailed in place after the interior and exterior wall framing is complete but before the rafters are erected, as the thrust of the rafters will otherwise tend to push out the outside walls. Ceiling joists are generally used to tie the lower ends of rafters in pitched roofs that slope 1:3 or more. To prevent the rafter ends from moving outward, the ceiling joist is nailed to the side of each pair of rafters *(Fig. 50,A)*. The joists are lapped and nailed

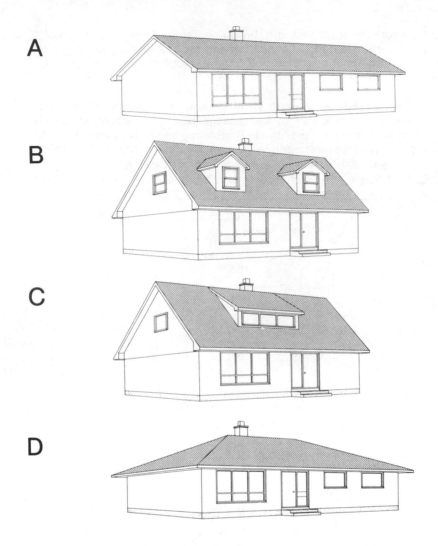

Figure 49. Types of pitched roofs: A, gable; B, gable dormer; C, shed dormer; D, hip.

together or spliced at the centre loadbearing wall, thus providing a continuous tie across opposing rafters. The number of nails used in the connections depends upon the roof slope, rafter spacing, snow load and width of the house. (See Table 27 for nailing practice.)

The additional roof load imposed by dwarf walls that run at right angles to the ceiling joists (*Fig. 51*) should be taken into account when the size of the joists are determined. An increase in the depth of the joists to the next standard depth will usually provide the additional strength required where the roof slope is more than 1:4. When the slope is 1:4 or less, the size of the ceiling joists is determined from span tables for roof joists (Tables 14 to 17).

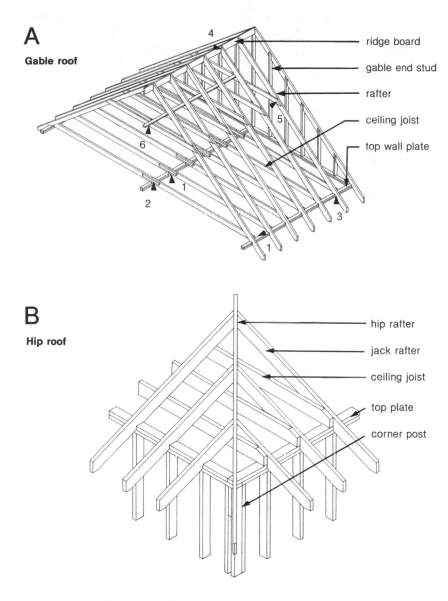

A

Gable roof

4

ridge board

gable end stud

rafter

5

ceiling joist

6

top wall plate

1

2

3

1

B

Hip roof

hip rafter

jack rafter

ceiling joist

top plate

corner post

Figure 50. A, ceiling and roof framing with ridge board; (1) ceiling joists toenailed to top wall plate with two 82 mm nails, one each side; (2) ceiling joists butted with splice plate over centre-bearing partition. Joists also nailed to each part of rafters (see Table 27 for nailing practice); (3) rafter nailed to plate with three 82 mm nails; (4) each rafter toenailed to ridge board with four 57 mm nails or end-nailed with three 82 mm nails; (5) collar brace used as intermediate support for rafters nailed to each pair of rafters with three 76 mm nails at each end; (6) 19 × 89 mm strip nailed to top of collar braces at their centre with two 57 mm nails when the braces are more than 2.4 m long; B, jack rafter nailed to hip rafter with two 82 mm nails.

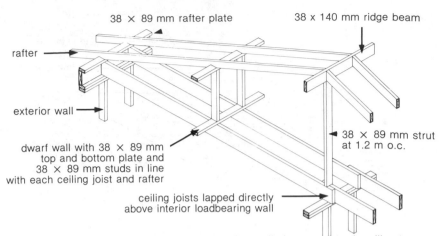

Figure 51. Rafter heel supported on a rafter plate nailed to top of each ceiling joist with two 101 mm nails.

Since hip rafters are about 55 mm deeper than the common or jack rafters, they reduce the space along the end walls to the extent that in low-slope roofs, there may not be enough room to install the outside ceiling joist at normal spacing from the wall. In this case, doubled joists are used and positioned to suit the available space *(Fig. 52)*. Tail joists are then added and toenailed to the outside wall plate and end-nailed to the doubled joists. The spacing of these tail joists is usually the same as the spacing of the main ceiling joists.

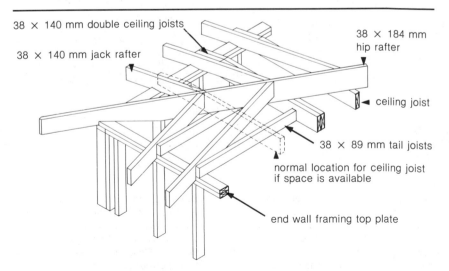

Figure 52. Doubled ceiling joists and tail joists used where hip rafter reduces clear space near the end wall.

Rafters are cut to length with the proper angle cut at the ridge and eaves and with notches (known as birdmouths) provided for the wall or rafter plates. The heel or lower part of the rafters should bear directly over the exterior wall. Depending on the plan of the roof and the shape of the outside walls, the rafters are placed:

(a) directly on the wall plates *(Fig. 50)*;

(b) on a rafter plate nailed to the top of the ceiling joists *(Fig. 51)*, or

(c) on a loadbearing wall supported on the exterior wall plate *(Fig. 53)*.

The last method is used where a portion of the outside wall is set back. In this case, the ceiling joists are extended beyond the exterior wall and nailed to the side of the rafters. This provides lateral support for the bearing wall and resists outward and downward movement of the ends of the rafters.

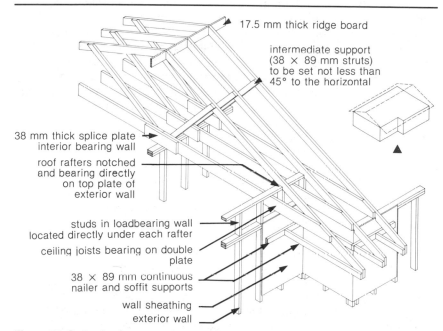

17.5 mm thick ridge board

intermediate support (38 × 89 mm struts) to be set not less than 45° to the horizontal

38 mm thick splice plate interior bearing wall

roof rafters notched and bearing directly on top plate of exterior wall

studs in loadbearing wall located directly under each rafter

ceiling joists bearing on double plate

38 × 89 mm continuous nailer and soffit supports

wall sheathing

exterior wall

Figure 53. Rafter heel supported on loadbearing wall. Ceiling joists project beyond the wall line and are nailed to the rafters (see Table 27 for nailing practice). Roof struts 38 × 89 mm used as intermediate support for rafters. Struts are nailed to the side of the rafter with three 82 mm nails and toenailed to bearing wall with two 82 mm nails.

A ridge board *(Fig. 50)* or a ridge beam (*Fig. 51*) is used to ensure a level ridge line and for ease in erection and alignment of the rafters. Rafters are erected in pairs and nailed to the ridge board or beam. The lower ends are toenailed to the wall plate. Each pair of rafters is usually located directly opposite each other. However, they may be offset at the ridge by their own thickness. This offsetting is required to maintain vertical alignment of the rafters when the lower ends are tied to ceiling joists that have been lapped (rather than butted together) at the centre loadbearing wall *(Fig. 51)*.

Roofs which slope less than 1:3 should be vertically supported at the peak..This can be accomplished by providing a 38 × 140 mm ridge beam, supported at 1.2 m intervals by 38 × 89 mm vertical struts *(Fig. 51)*. A loadbearing wall may be used instead of the ridge beam. Since these methods of support reduce the outward thrust of the roof, continuous ties between the lower ends of opposing rafters are not necessary.

Intermediate Support for Rafters is generally installed between the ridge and exterior walls to reduce the span of the rafters. This reduces the size of the rafters which are required as the span is taken from this intermediate point to the ridge or eave support.

For rafters in roofs which slope 1:3 or more, intermediate support is generally provided by a 38 × 89 mm collar brace nailed to the side of each pair of rafters. Since these braces are in compression and sub-ject to buckling, they should be supported against lateral deflection when more than 2.4 m long. This can be done by nailing a 19 × 89 mm continuous member at right angles to the collar braces near their centre with three 76 mm nails at each end *(Fig. 50)*.

Intermediate support for rafters in roofs which slope less than 1:3 is usually provided by a dwarf bearing wall *(Fig. 51)* built in the same way as a loadbearing partition, except that a single top plate may be used where the rafters are positioned directly over the studs.

Struts may also be used as intermediate supports for rafters in pitched roofs. A 38 × 89 mm strut *(Fig. 53)* is nailed to the side of each rafter and supported on a loadbearing partition. The angle of the struts should not be less than 45° to the horizontal.

Rafters which run at right angles to the ceiling joists may be sup-ported at an intermediate point by a dwarf wall sitting on a beam placed between the ceiling joists. The underside of the beam is raised at least 25 mm above the ceiling finish by blocks inserted under the ends of the beam at the exterior walls and centre loadbearing partition. The space thus formed prevents the beam from damaging the ceiling finish when deflected at its centre by the roof loads.

A beam similarly installed may also be used as intermediate support for hip and valley rafters. In this case, a roof strut is used to transfer the load from the hip or valley rafter to the beam.

Where intermediate support is required for a few rafters in the end section on a hip-type roof, a simple form of support can be provided by a beam (sometimes called a "strongback") consisting of two 38 × 89 mm members nailed together, set on edge and nailed to the bottom of the rafters. This beam is in turn supported at points along its length by 38 × 89 mm struts radiating from a common point of support on the centre loadbearing wall. The angle of any strut should not be less than 45° to the horizontal. The ends are cut to fit the selected angle and securely nailed in place.

Hip and Valley Rafters should be about 50 mm deeper than the common rafters *(Figs. 50,B and 54)*.

This additional depth provides full contact with the angle-cut of the jack rafters. In hip roofs, the jack rafters are nailed to the hip rafters and wall plate. Where a valley occurs, the jack rafters are nailed to the valley rafter and ridge.

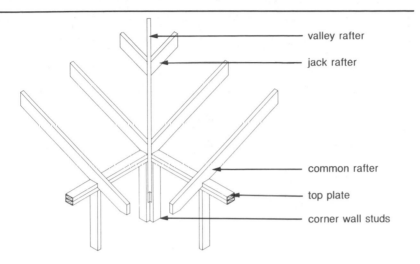

valley rafter

jack rafter

common rafter

top plate

corner wall studs

Figure 54. Framing at a valley.

Dormers, such as small gable dormers, are framed so that the rafters at each side are doubled to support the side studs and valley rafters. The top end of the valley rafters are supported by a header *(Fig. 55)*. The most common method of construction is to install the roof sheathing before the dormer is framed and then saw the sheathing flush with the framing members around the opening. A bottom plate added on top of the sheathing supports the side studs enclosing the dormer and also serves as a nailing base for the wall sheathing. If future expansion is contemplated or additional rooms are to be built in the attic, consideration should be given to framing the roof to accept future dormers when the house is built.

Gable-End Framing and Projections After the roof framing members are up, the gable-end studs are cut to fit and nailed in place. Studs in unfinished attics may be placed with the wide face parallel to the wall. The ends of the studs are then cut to fit the angle of the rafter and are toenailed to the wall plate and to the underside of the rafter with four 63 mm nails at each end *(Fig. 56)*.

Construction of roof projections commonly used at the gable ends is shown in Figures 56 and 57. As with eave projections, the soffit is covered with 6 mm sanded plywood or pre-finished aluminum or vinyl

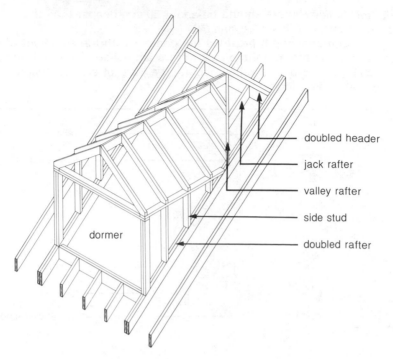

Figure 55. Typical dormer framing. After roof sheathing is applied, blocking is added between side studs at roof line to provide nailing support for wall sheathing.

doubled header

jack rafter

valley rafter

side stud

dormer

doubled rafter

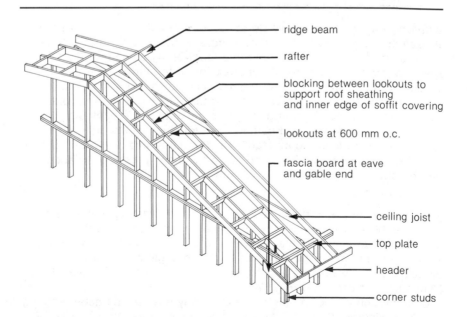

ridge beam

rafter

blocking between lookouts to support roof sheathing and inner edge of soffit covering

lookouts at 600 mm o.c.

fascia board at eave and gable end

ceiling joist

top plate

header

corner studs

Figure 56. Wide projection at gable end supported by "lookout" rafters.

sheets, and fascia board is added to the outside framing member.

Roofs which project less than 400 mm over the gable-end wall usually terminate with a framing member sometimes called the rake rafter *(Fig. 57)*. A 19 mm nailing strip is fastened to the rafter located above the gable-end wall. Blocking spaced at 600 mm on centre is used to support the soffit covering. This blocking is toenailed to the nailing strip and end-nailed to the rake rafter. The soffit covering is then installed and nailed to these supports. A fascia board is added in the manner previously described.

Gable-end projections extending more than 400 mm beyond the wall are usually supported by framing members called "lookouts" *(Fig. 56)*. The gable-end studs are placed with the narrow face parallel to the sheathing, and a top wall plate is added. The lookout members, usually the same size as the rafters, are spaced at 600 mm on centre. The ends are supported by end-nailing to the first rafter and to the header, and toenailing to the wall plate. Blocking is then fitted between the lookouts at the wall line to support the roof sheathing and inner edge of the soffit covering. The soffit covering is nailed to these supports, and a fascia is added as previously described. The length of lookout members should be about twice the width of the roof overhang. A double rafter is used to support the inner ends of the lookout members when they project into the roof more than one rafter spacing.

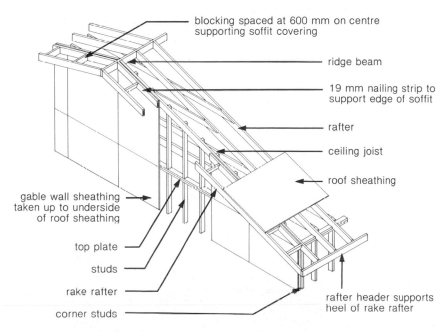

blocking spaced at 600 mm on centre supporting soffit covering

ridge beam

19 mm nailing strip to support edge of soffit

rafter

ceiling joist

roof sheathing

gable wall sheathing taken up to underside of roof sheathing

top plate

studs

rake rafter

corner studs

rafter header supports heel of rake rafter

Figure 57. Narrow projection at gable end. Rake rafter supported by ridge beam, rafter header, blocking and roof sheathing.

Flat Roofs

Flat roofs are generally less practical and less durable than pitched roofs, especially in heavy snowfall areas. They are sometimes used to cover extensions of the main house and in combination with upper floor decks. Carports and garages are frequently covered with a flat roof.

In flat-roof construction where rafters also serve as ceiling joists, the term "roof joist" is used. The size of these roof joists is established on the basis of both roof and ceiling loads (Tables 14 to 17). Rafters chosen for structural adequacy may not, however, provide adequate depth for insulation and ventilation of the roof space. In such cases, wider lumber or another framing detail should be used.

Roof joists for flat roofs are usually laid level, with roof sheathing and a roofing covering on top. The underside of the roof joists is used to support the ceiling. A slope of at least 1:50 should be provided for roof drainage by tapering each joist with a ledger strip on the underside of the joist at the bearing wall or by adding a tapered strip to the top of the joists.

The house design may call for an overhang of the roof beyond the wall or for a parapet wall carried above the roof. Insulation may be added just above the ceiling. In this case, the space above the insulation should be ventilated not only to help prevent condensation in the winter but also to help remove hot air in the summer. Alternatively, rigid insulation may be installed on top of the roof sheathing and the roof covering placed on the insulation. In this case, the space above the ceiling is not ventilated. Figure 58,A shows a simple type of flat roof in which roof joists are level, eliminating the need for separate ceiling joists.

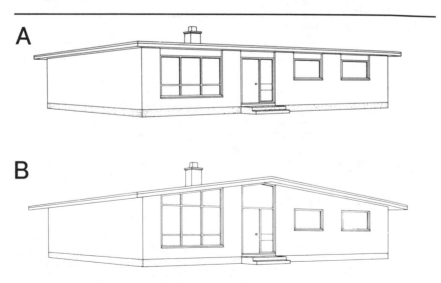

Figure 58. Two flat-roof designs. Rafters may also serve as ceiling joists.

When an overhang is called for on all sides of the house, lookout rafters are ordinarily used *(Fig. 59)*. These lookout rafters, which are usually twice as long as the overhang, are toenailed to the wall plate and end-nailed to the first roof joist. If the lookout rafters project into the ceiling area more than one joist space, two roof joists are nailed together to form a header. One outside rafter header is then added and end-nailed to the lookout rafters and roof joists.

This serves as a nailing support for the roof sheathing, fascia board and soffit covering. Such overhangs are generally from 400 mm to 600 mm but do not exceed 1.2 m.

Sloped roofs, as shown in Figure 58B, may have a ceiling finish attached to the roof joists with the ceiling following the pitch of the roof to form a "cathedral" ceiling.

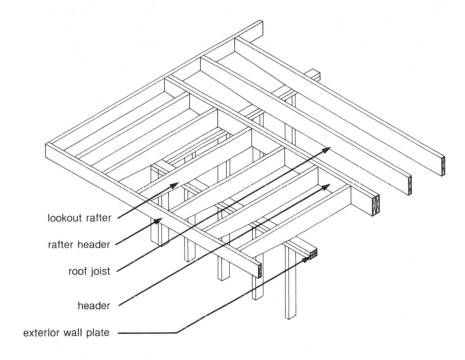

lookout rafter

rafter header

roof joist

header

exterior wall plate

Note: Insulation is generally placed between the roof-ceiling joists. A ventilated space of at least 63 mm must be provided between the top of the insulation and the underside of the roof deck. This can be achieved by placing 38 × 38 mm cross purlins over the top of, and at right angles to, the roof-ceiling joists. The 38 × 38 mm members may be shimmed to provide the required roof slope. Figure 107 shows a cross-section of the completed roof.

Figure 59. Typical construction of flat roof with overhang.

Roof Sheathing and Coverings

Roof Sheathing

Roof sheathing is applied over roof trusses or rafters and usually consists of plywood or waferboard panels or lumber. Sheathing provides a nailing base for the roof covering and laterally braces the roof framing.

Installation of Roof Sheathing When plywood is used for roof sheathing, it is laid with the face grain at right angles to the framing *(Fig. 60)*. Sheathing-grade (unsanded) plywood is used for this purpose. To obtain a good tie across the roof framing, the end joints of the panels should be staggered on the framing members. The butting edges of the panels should be separated by at least 2 to 3 mm to prevent buckling when minor expansion occurs during wet weather.

The thickness of the plywood or waferboard used for roof sheathing depends to some extent on the spacing of the rafters, roof joists or trusses and whether or not the edges of the sheets are supported. To prevent damage to roof covering when thinner plywood is used, the joints running across the framing should be supported by 38 × 38 mm blocking, nailed securely between the roof framing members, or by metal H-clips inserted between sheets. The latter method is widely used as the installation is simple and economical. Minimum thicknesses for plywood and waferboard roof sheathing are shown in Table 28. Staple fastening for 9.5 mm roof sheathing must be 1.6 mm thick, 38.1 mm long with a 9.5 mm crown, and be driven with the crown parallel to the framing *(Table 29)*. Thicker roof sheathing, no less than

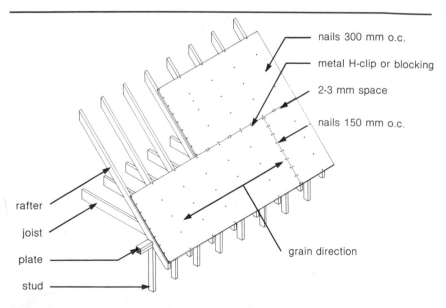

Figure 60. Application of plywood roof sheathing.

15.5 mm, is required for built-up roofing on a flat roof where it is used as a walking deck.

Under materials requiring solid and continuous support, such as asphalt shingles and built-up roofing, lumber sheathing must be laid closed *(Fig. 61,B)*. The boards are usually 19 mm thick, but this thickness may be reduced to 17 mm where supports are spaced at 400 mm on centre. Boards 184 mm or less in width are nailed to the framing members with two 51 mm nails per bearing. Those wider than 184 mm should be nailed with three 51 mm nails per bearing. Boards wider than 286 mm should not be used for roof sheathing. For a wood shingle roof, the roof boards may be spaced the same distance apart on centre as the shingle exposure. This method *(Fig 61,A)*, commonly used in damp climates, permits freer movement of air around the boards and under the shingles, thus reducing the possibility of decay.

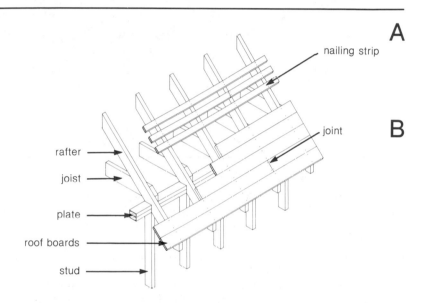

Figure 61. Installation of wood-board roof sheathing: A, spaced method, B, closed method.

Roof Sheathing Details Where openings occur in the roof structure for interior chimneys, the roof sheathing and framing members should have a clearance of 50 mm from the finished masonry on all sides for fire protection *(Fig. 62)*. This clearance may be reduced to 12 mm for exterior chimneys. Roof sheathing should be securely nailed to the rafters and headers around the opening.

Roof sheathing at valleys and hips should be fitted to give a tight joint and should be securely nailed to the valley or hip rafter *(Fig. 62)*. This will give a solid and smooth base for the flashing.

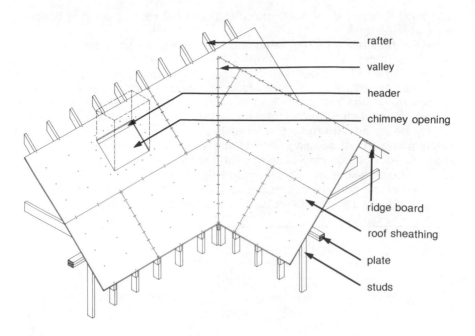

Figure 62. Roof sheathing detail at a valley and at a chimney opening.

Roof Coverings

The roof covering is installed as soon as the roof framing and the sheathing has been completed and before any other interior or exterior finishing work starts. This sequence produces a weatherproof working space within the building early in the construction process so that other trades can begin; it also protects the lumber and interior panel products from excessive moisture.

Roof coverings should provide a long-life, waterproof finish that will protect the building and its contents from rain and snow. Many materials have withstood the test of time and have proven satisfactory under various conditions.

Asphalt shingles are by far the most frequently used roof covering for pitched roofs. Galvanized steel or aluminum roofing is also common in some regions. At normal roof pitches, metal roofs will generally shed the snow, a desirable characteristic in heavy snowfall areas. Roll roofing, wood shingles, handsplit shakes, sheet metal and concrete or clay tile are also used, each for an appropriate situation. For flat or low-pitched roofs, built-up roofing with a gravel topping or cap sheet is frequently used. The choice of materials may be influenced by cost, local code requirements or local preferences based upon past experience.

The minimum and maximum slopes for the different types of roof coverings are presented in Table 30.

In shingle application, the exposure distance Is Important, and the exposure depends on the roof slope and the type and length of shingle used. The minimum slope of roofs is 1:6 for asphalt shingles (using a low-slope application), 1:4 for wood shingles and 1:3 for handsplit shakes and asphalt shingles (using normal application). Built-up roof coverings are rarely used on roofs where the slope exceeds 1:4.

In order to avoid water damage caused by melting snow, which sometimes forms into ice dams at the eaves, shingle or shake-covered roofs should have additional protection when the overhang is less than 900 mm. This protection usually consists of either Type S (smooth surface) roll roofing laid with the joints lapped at least 100 mm and cemented together, or of a continuous sheet of 0.15 mm polyethylene. Placed over the roof sheathing, this protection sheet extends from the edge of the roof to a line at least 300 mm beyond the inside of the inner face of the exterior walls, thus preventing water infiltration through joints in the roof sheathing (Fig. 63,A and B).

Methods of flashing shingled roofs at valleys, chimneys and intersecting walls are described in the chapter on Flashing.

Asphalt Shingles on Slopes 1:3 or Greater The minimum recommended grade for asphalt strip shingles is the No. 210 shingle. Square-butt strip shingles are usually 310 × 915 mm or 335 × 1000 mm in size, have three tabs and should be laid with 130 mm or 145 mm of their width exposed to the weather. Since there are approximately 21 to 26 strips in a bundle, a bundle will cover about 3 m².

Bundles should be piled flat for storage so that strips will not curl when the bundles are opened. Care should be taken in piling shingles on the roof; if too many are piled together, the load capacity of the framing may be exceeded.

The method of laying an asphalt-shingle roof is shown in Figure 64. Eave protection is first provided by one of the methods already described. A starter strip at least 300 mm wide is then placed along the eaves under the first course of shingles, so that it extends at least 12 mm beyond the eaves, rakes and fascia board to form a drip edge. This projection prevents water from backing up under the shingles by capillary action. A shingle strip laid with the tabs facing up the roof slope is often used for this purpose. Type M (mineral-surfaced) roll roofing may be used as a starter strip and when continued up the roof slope will also serve as eave protection. The starter strip is nailed along the bottom edge at 300 mm intervals. The first course of shingles is then laid with the butt edge in line with the bottom of the starter strip.

Several chalklines will help align the shingle courses so that tabs and tab notches will be in a straight line for good appearance. Each shingle strip should be nailed with four large-head roofing nails of sufficient length to penetrate through or 12 mm into the roof sheathing. Good nailing is important. When a nail penetrates a crack or a knothole, another nail should be driven alongside into sound wood. Cementing the tabs of strip shingles is recommended for all areas.

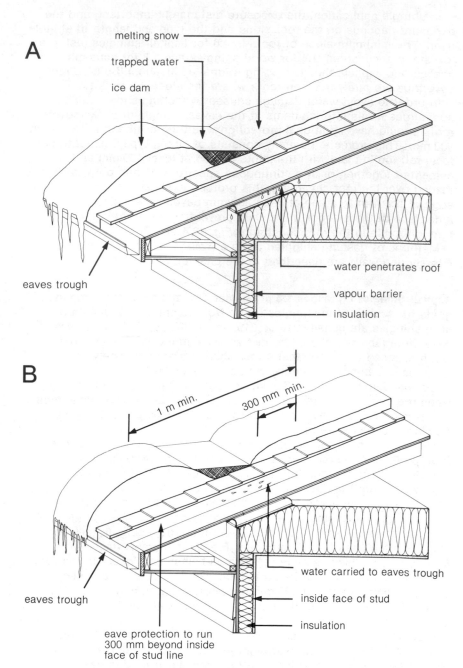

Figure 63. A, Snow and ice dams. Ice dams often build up on the overhang of roofs and in eaves troughs, causing water from melting snow to back up under shingles at the eaves; B, eave protection prevents water trapped by ice dams from entering the roof.

Plastic cement can be used for this purpose with a spot approximately 25 mm in diameter being placed under the centre of each tab. Most shingles are manufactured with an adhesive strip on the underside of the tabs. Interlocking and other special shingles should be laid according to the manufacturer's directions.

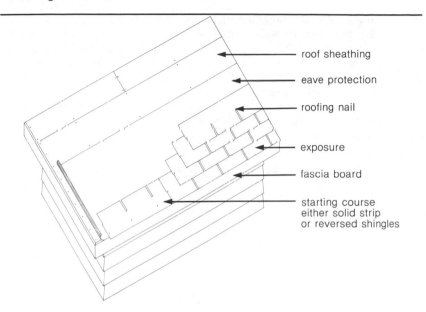

Figure 64. Application of asphalt shingles.

Asphalt Shingles on Low Slopes of 1:6 to less than 1:3 Additional precautions must be taken on low slopes to ensure a waterproof roof covering. Except for the first two courses, three thicknesses of shingles are used on the entire roof including hips and ridges. This is achieved by using an exposure of not more than one-third the full height of the shingle. A starter strip is first installed as described for higher-sloped roofs, but laid on a continuous band of cement not less than 200 mm wide. The first course of shingles is then cemented to the strip with a continuous band of cement that is 100 mm wider than the shingle exposure. For example, a 250 mm band of cement should be used when the shingle exposure is 150 mm. The succeeding courses of shingles are laid on a band of cement 50 mm wider than the shingle exposure, so that a 200 mm band is used when the exposure is 150 mm.

To avoid defacing the exposed surface of the shingles with cement, the band should be located between 25 mm and 50 mm above the butt edge of each succeeding course of shingles. Each shingle strip should be nailed in place with four nails.

If cold application cement is used, it should be applied at the rate of approximately 0.5 L/m² of cemented area. Hot application cement is applied at the rate of approximately 1 kg/m^2 of cemented area. The above technique is necessary only for slopes lower than 1:4 since there are special low-slope shingles of sufficient length for the three thicknesses necessary at this roof pitch.

Wood Shingles Wood shingles commonly used for houses are No. 1 and No. 2 grade. Red or white cedar are the principal species of wood used for shingles, as their heartwoods have high decay resistance and low shrinkage. The width of wood shingles varies, but the maximum width is 350 mm with a minimum width of 75 mm.

Figure 65 illustrates the proper method of laying a wood-shingle roof. As is the case for asphalt shingles, underlay and roofing felt is not usually required for wood shingles, but eave protection, as described previously, should be installed. Maximum exposure for wood shingles is shown in Table 31.

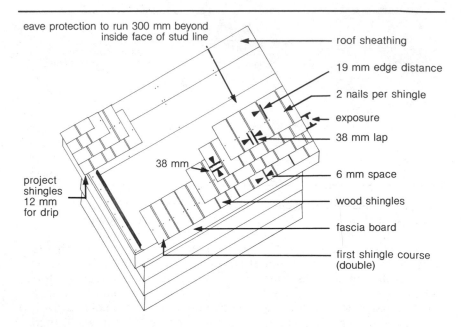

eave protection to run 300 mm beyond inside face of stud line

roof sheathing

19 mm edge distance

2 nails per shingle

exposure

38 mm lap

project shingles 12 mm for drip

38 mm

6 mm space

wood shingles

fascia board

first shingle course (double)

Figure 65. Installation of wood shingles.

The first shingle course should be laid double with the upper shingles overlapping the joints in the course beneath and both rows extending about 25 mm beyond the fascia boards at the eaves. This precaution will prevent water from backing up underneath the shingles. Shingles should be laid 6 mm apart to allow for swelling when wet. The joints between shingles in one course should be offset at least 38 mm from the joint between shingles in the course below. The joints in succeeding courses should be spaced so that the joint in one course is not in line with the joints in the two previous courses laid.

Only two nails should be used for each shingle. The distance of the nails from the butt edge of the shingle being nailed should be the shingle exposure plus 38 mm, with an edge distance of about 19 mm. For example, if the shingle exposure is to be 125 mm, add 38 mm, and thus the nail should be 163 mm from the butt edge of the shingle being nailed. Shingles are fastened with hot-dip galvanized or other corrosion-resistant shingle nails. Flat grain shingles wider than 200 mm are sometimes split and nailed as two shingles to avoid problems with cupping and warping.

Handsplit Shakes Cedar handsplit shakes may be applied over spaced and closed roof sheathing. When spaced sheathing is used *(Fig. 61,A)*, 19 × 89 mm (or wider) strips are placed on centres equal to the weather exposure at which the shakes are to be laid, but never more than 250 mm. In areas where wind-driven snow conditions prevail, closed roof sheathing is recommended.

Proper weather exposure is important. As a general rule, 190 mm exposure is recommended for 450 mm shakes, and a 250 mm exposure for 600 mm shakes. The minimum recommended roof pitch for handsplit shakes is 1:3.

A 900 mm strip of No. 15 roofing felt should be laid over the sheathing boards at the eave line. The beginning or starter course of shakes should be doubled; for extra texture, it can be tripled. The bottom course or courses can be of 380 mm or 450 mm shakes, the former being made expressly for this purpose.

After each course of shakes is applied, a 450 mm wide strip of No. 15 roofing felt should be laid over the top portion of the shakes, extending onto the sheathing. The bottom edge of the felt should be positioned above the butt at a distance equal to twice the weather exposure. For example, 600 mm shakes laid with 250 mm exposure would have felt applied 500 mm above the shake butts. Thus, the felt will cover the top 100 mm of the shakes and extend out about 350 mm onto the sheathing *(Fig. 66)*. Shakes should be spaced approximately

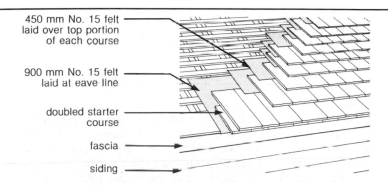

450 mm No. 15 felt laid over top portion of each course

900 mm No. 15 felt laid at eave line

doubled starter course

fascia

siding

Figure 66. Installation of handsplit shakes.

6 mm apart. Side joints should be offset 40 mm over adjacent courses. When straight split shakes are used, the "froe-end" (the end from which the shakes have been split and which is smoother) should be laid uppermost (toward the ridge).

Finish at Ridge and Hips The most common type of finish is shown in Figure 67,A. Asphalt shingle squares (one-third of a strip) are used over the ridge or hip and blind-nailed. Each shingle is lapped to provide the same coverage as the roofing shingles. It is good practice to lay the ridge cap so as to provide the maximum protection from the prevailing wind.

In the case of wood shingles, 150 mm wide shingles are alternatively lapped and blind-nailed *(Fig. 67,B)*. Flashing is sometimes used under a wood-shingle ridge.

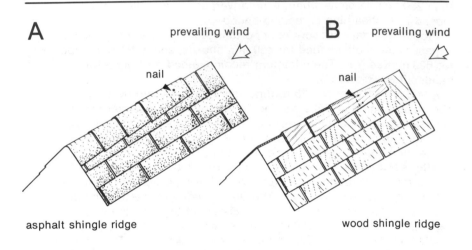

asphalt shingle ridge   wood shingle ridge

Figure 67. Finish at ridge and hips: A, asphalt shingles; B, wood shingles.

Built-Up Roofs Built-up roof coverings are installed by roofing firms that specialize in this work. Roofs of this type may have three or more layers of roofing felt. Each layer is mopped down with tar or asphalt, the final surface being coated with the same material. The surface is then covered with gravel (embedded in the asphalt or tar) or with a cap sheet. This covering provides ballast and protection from the sun's ultraviolet radiation. It is important to note that coal tar products and asphalt products are not compatible and must not be used together.

Material combinations for built-up roofs are shown in Table 32.

The eave line of projecting roofs is usually finished with metal edging or flashing. A gravel stop or cant strip is used in conjunction with the flashing at the eaves when the roof is covered with gravel *(Fig. 68,A)*. Where built-up roofing is finished against another wall (except a masonry-clad wall), the roofing is mopped to the cant strip and turned up the wall at least 150 mm. The wall-sheathing paper and siding is then applied over the roof membrane *(Fig. 68,B)*.

Where a built-up roof intersects a masonry-clad wall, the roof membrane is similarly returned up the face of the masonry. Counterflashing is then added. This counterflashing should be embedded into the mortar joints at least 25 mm, and extend down the wall about 150 mm, lapping over the flashing at least 100 mm.

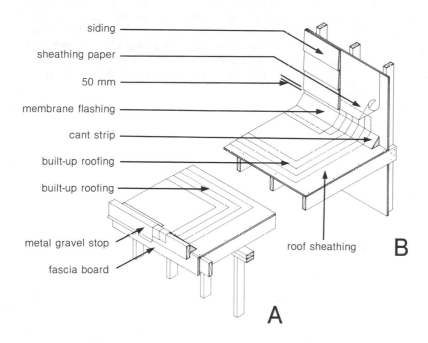

siding
sheathing paper
50 mm
membrane flashing
cant strip
built-up roofing
built-up roofing
metal gravel stop
fascia board
roof sheathing
B
A

Figure 68. Built-up roof: A, eave flashing and drip; B, junction of built-up roof and wall covered with siding.

Single-ply membranes can also be used for flat roofs. They consist of various synthetic materials that are resistant to freeze-then-thaw cycling, ozone attack and ultraviolet degradation. They are relatively simple to lay, but are not often used on the small roofs that are typically part of wood-frame construction.

Sheet Metal Roofing Sheet metal roofing is manufactured in 762 mm to 914 mm widths, depending on the profile of the corrugation, and in any lengths specified by the builder. It comes with the necessary accessories for treating the various details of the roof, such as hips, valleys, eave starters and edges *(Fig. 69)*. The usual method of fastening the metal roof sheets is to lay 19 × 89 mm wood nailing strips across the rafters at no more than 400 mm on centre. For more positive attachment and better nailing, 38 × 89 mm purlins can be used. There must be a nailing strip underneath each end joint *(Fig. 69)*. The choice of metal thickness, be it steel or aluminum, will depend on the local snow load, but it should not be less than 0.33 mm for galvanized steel and 0.48 mm for aluminum. The required thicknesses for specific snow loads are given in tables provided by the manufacturer.

Concrete and Clay Tile Roofing When considering the use of concrete or clay tile, it must be remembered that these materials are considerably heavier than other roofing systems, and thus the roof supporting structure of rafters or trusses must be designed to withstand the additional load. A professional engineer should be consulted to obtain a proper design. Simulated versions of tile roofing do not normally require a special structural design.

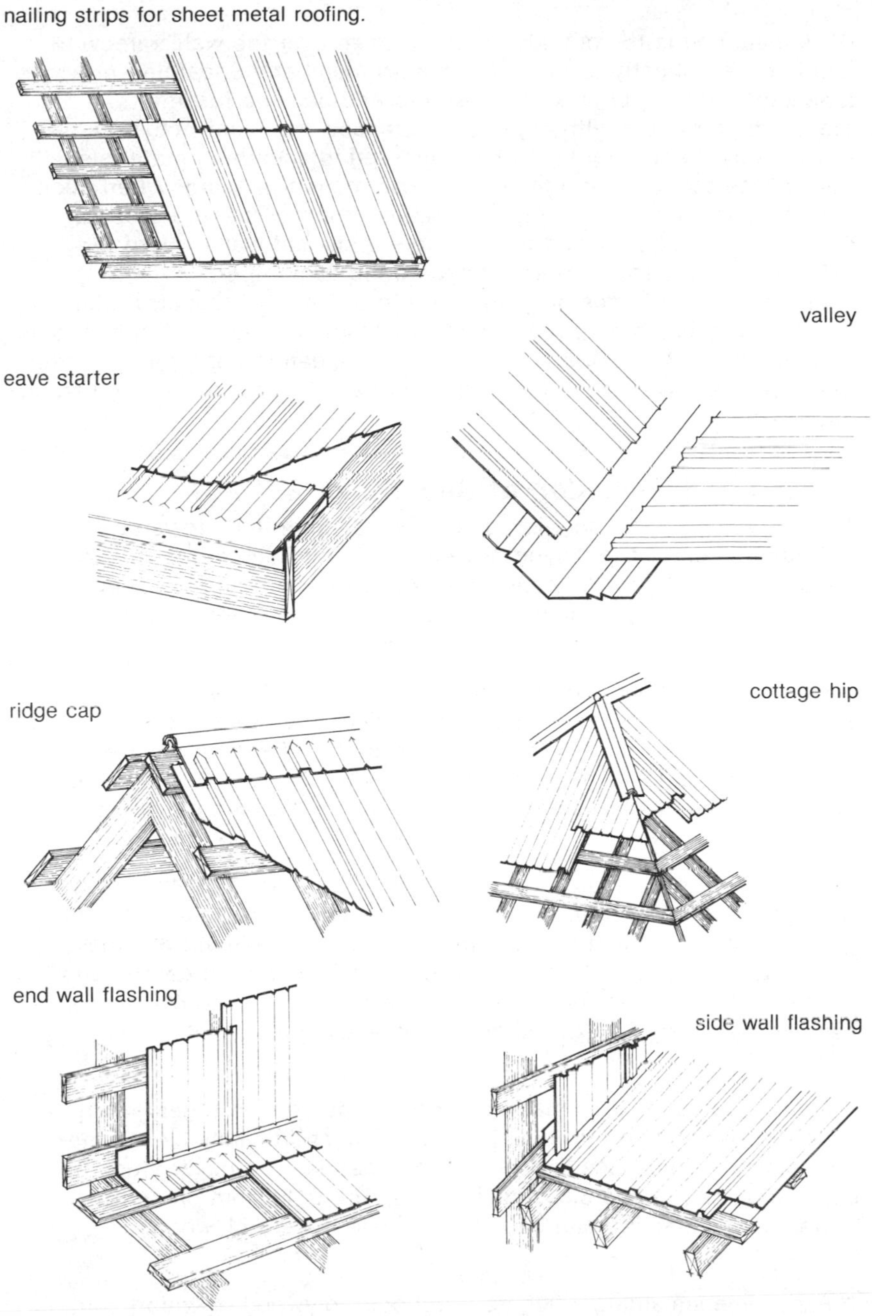

nailing strips for sheet metal roofing.

valley

eave starter

ridge cap

cottage hip

end wall flashing

side wall flashing

Figure 69. Details of sheet metal roofing.

Wall Sheathing and Exterior Finishes

Wall sheathing is the outside covering used over the wall framework and is nailed directly to the wall framing members. Sheathing provides a nailing base for some types of siding and backing for others. It also braces the structure, although in most cases sufficient bracing is provided by the interior wall finish. Insulating sheathing materials will not provide the required temporary or permanent bracing. When such sheathing is used, let-in corner braces of wood or metal are used. Sheathing must be applied to the gable ends and walls where the exterior cladding is a type that needs solid backing.

Several types of sheathing are used in present-day construction: fibreboard, gypsum board, plywood, waferboard, rigid insulation and lumber. Table 33 lists the various types of sheathing and the minimum thickness necessary to provide sufficient backing for exterior finishing materials.

Types and Installation of Sheathing

Fibreboard sheathing should be at least 11.1 mm thick for studs 600 mm on centre and 9.5 mm for studs 400 mm on centre. It is supplied in sheets 1.2 m wide and generally 2.4 m long and is usually impregnated with an asphalt material to increase water resistance.

Gypsum board sheathing consists of a gypsum filler faced on both sides with treated paper. It should be at least 12.7 mm thick for studs 600 mm on centre and 9.5 mm thick for studs 400 mm on centre. It is supplied in sheets 1.2 m wide and 2.4 m long. The sheets are applied horizontally across the studs and nailed to the framing members.

Plywood sheathing should be an exterior type, that is, laminated with a waterproof adhesive. The type most commonly used, called sheathing grade, is unsanded and may contain knots. The minimum thickness should be 7.5 mm sheathing grade for studs 600 mm on centre, and 7.5 mm sheathing or 6 mm sanded grade for studs up to 400 mm on centre. Sheets are 1.2 m wide and usually 2.4 m long.

Waferboard sheathing is made of wood chips bonded together with an adhesive and formed into sheets 1.2 m wide and usually 2.4 m long. The minimum thickness that should be used is 7.9 mm for studs up to 600 mm on centre and 6.35 mm for studs up to 400 mm on centre. Waferboard sheathing can be installed as if it were plywood.

Panel-type sheathing, such as fibreboard, plywood or waferboard, is generally applied vertically. The panels are nailed to the wall framework before the wall is raised to position. This sequence helps the wall maintain its squareness, avoids the need for scaffolding, and closes the house in as soon as the framing is completed. Often the window openings are covered by the sheathing panels and are not cut out until after the windows are delivered.

The sheathing panels can also be applied horizontally, in which case the vertical joints should be staggered wherever possible.

A space at least 2 to 3 mm wide should be left between the sheets to permit expansion without buckling. The panels are nailed to the framing at 150 mm on centre along the edges and 300 mm along the intermediate supports *(Fig. 70)*.

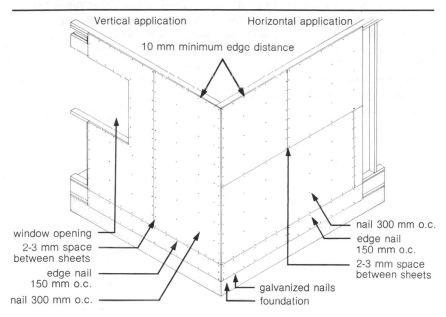

Figure 70. Vertical and horizontal application of panel-type sheathing.

Insulating sheathing is available in five types. The first is a semi-rigid glass fibre panel with an exterior vapour-permeable, waterproof membrane. The other four are rigid panels of either expanded polystrene, extruded polystrene, polyurethane or phenolic. They come in different thicknesses, and the insulating value per millimetre thickness varies.

They are installed on the wall like any other panel sheathing but with special large headed nails. A good reason for fastening this insulating sheathing before the wall is raised is its lightness and, for some types, its brittleness. Even a mild wind can make it difficult to install insulating sheathing on the vertical. The joints between rigid foam panels should not be sealed; however, the rigid glass fibre sheathing with the vapour-permeable membrane can become a good air barrier when the joints are sealed with a special tape.

There are two methods of installing sheathing down to the foundation sill. Either the panel extends beyond the bottom wall plate by the required length and the missing part at the top is filled in, or longer panels of 2.74 m length are used, where available, to cover the wall down to the sill area. It is advantageous to cover the header and sill with the same wall sheet because this increases the strength of the building and also reduces air infiltration.

Lumber sheathing, which should not be less than 17.5 mm thick, is used in boards 140 to 286 mm wide. It is milled in a shiplap, tongue-and-groove or square-edge pattern. The boards are nailed at each stud crossing with two nails for the 140 and 184 mm widths and three for the 235 and 286 mm widths. End joints in the board must be placed over the centre of the studs with the joints staggered on different studs. Lumber sheathing may be put on either horizontally or diagonally *(Fig. 71,A)* and is extended beyond the subfloor to cover the header joist and the sill plate *(Fig. 71,B)*. The angle cuts in the diagonal approach require more time and materials.

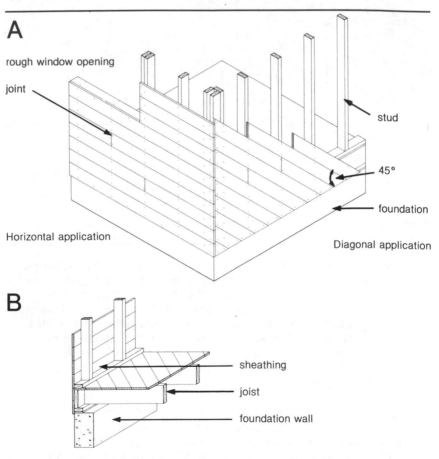

A

rough window opening

joint

stud

45°

foundation

Horizontal application

Diagonal application

B

sheathing

joist

foundation wall

Figure 71. Lumber sheathing application: A, horizontal and diagonal, B, started at foundation wall.

Wall Sheathing Paper

Sheathing paper should be water-resistant but vapour-permeable. Its function is to provide a second barrier to the entry of any wind and rain that might penetrate the cladding. It must be permeable enough, however, to permit the escape of any water vapour from the interior that may penetrate imperfections in the air and vapour barriers. One layer of sheathing paper is generally used over wall sheathing and may be applied horizontally or vertically with 100 mm laps at the joints. At horizontal flashings, the upper sheet should be lapped over the lower sheet to direct moisture outward.

Where wall sheathing is not used, two layers of sheathing paper are needed unless a large panel siding such as plywood is used. Both layers are applied vertically, with the joints lapped 100 mm at the studs. Both layers are stapled to the framing members, the top layer with staples spaced every 150 mm along the edges of the sheet to hold it securely in place.

Exterior Cladding

Because the type of exterior cladding used on the walls will greatly affect the appearance of the house and the cost of maintenance, it should be selected with care. Common types of cladding used are: board sidings made of metal, vinyl, hardboard or lumber; panel siding made of plywood or hardboard; wood shingles or shakes; stucco, and masonry cladding such as clay and concrete, brick, concrete block and stone.

Siding which may be affected by moisture, such as lumber, plywood, hardboard and stucco, should be kept 200 mm off the ground and 50 mm from an adjoining roof surface. Methods of flashing over window and door openings and between different types of wall covering are described in the chapter on Flashing.

Metal and Vinyl Sidings Metal and vinyl sidings are used extensively and are virtually maintenance-free since they come with factory-finished surfaces. They are produced in different shapes and patterns, some of which simulate the appearance of wood bevel siding and vertical board and batten. They come in configurations designed for continuous interlocking between boards so that only the upper side of the board is nailed while its bottom edge is locked to the upper part of the board below (Fig. 72,A). Interior and exterior corners, termination points of the soffit and gable ends as well as windows and doors are all treated with specially designed trim pieces. The installation follows the same simple steps that are generally applicable to any kind of siding of the small 150 to 200 mm width.

Horizontal Application. The wall is prepared by applying the sheathing paper as described. In wet and humid coastal climates, furring on the wall is recommended to provide a "rain screen" and a vented space to

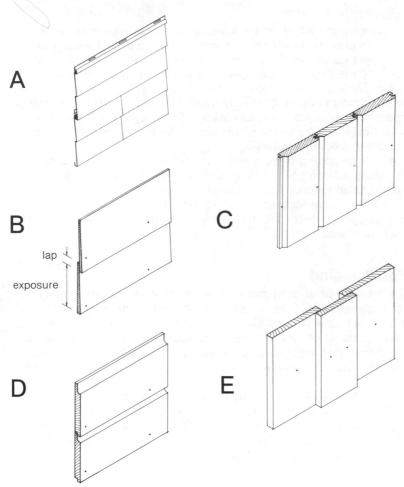

Figure 72. Types of siding; A, aluminum or vinyl; B, bevel or feather-edge; C, tongue-and-groove with V-joint; D, drop siding; E, board-on-board.

facilitate drying. A level line is established around the house for the starter strip that is normally placed a minimum of 150 to 200 mm above finished grade. All trim pieces for corners, windows, doors and openings and starter strips are fastened. The siding is then applied in successive courses to the underside of the soffit.

Laps of adjacent boards should be staggered more than 600 mm apart and should all face in the same direction away from the general viewing angle. The last horizontal board fits into the finish trim piece and is locked by special "ears" which are punched on the board at the site.

An important point that must be remembered in each step of the installation is the need to let the siding, especially vinyl siding, expand and contract with temperature changes. In the case of vinyl siding, the change in dimension could be from 6 to 12 mm; so if movement is restricted, buckling will occur. For this reason, the nails should be placed in the centre of the nail slot and not be hammered tight to the wall.

Vertical Application. The same general rules apply to vertical application as to the horizontal. Using the vertical method, the starting point is a corner of the building with the appropriate corner trim. All other trim pieces also precede the installation of the siding.

Hardboard Siding Hardboard horizontal siding comes with a primed or prefinished surface in a variety of colours. It often has plastic splines *(Fig. 73)* which function as the locking devices between panels. It is installed in a similar manner to metal and vinyl siding.

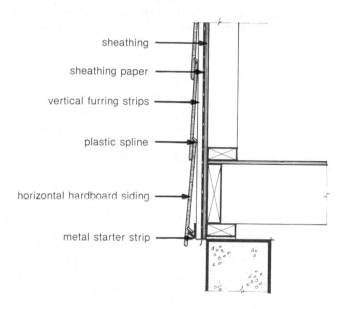

sheathing

sheathing paper

vertical furring strips

plastic spline

horizontal hardboard siding

metal starter strip

Figure 73. Horizontal hardboard siding.

Lumber Siding Lumber siding should be sound and free of knot holes, loose knots, checks or splits. Easy working qualities and freedom from warp are desirable features. The species most commonly used are the cedars, pines and redwood. It has also become more common to use pressure-treated lumber for siding. Pressure-treated siding may be pine or other species. The moisture content of the siding at the time of application should be the same as it will experience in service, that is, about 12 to 18 per cent, depending on the climate.

In wet, humid climates, such as the coastal regions of Canada, an air space is often formed behind the siding to prevent water penetration and vent moisture away from the wall. This is done by mounting the siding on furring strips nailed on top of the sheathing paper to the studs behind.

Horizontal Application. Bevel or feather-edge siding *(Fig. 72,B)* generally starts with the bottom course of boards blocked out as shown in Figure 74,B. A 6 mm thick furring strip is used for this purpose. Each succeeding course overlaps the upper edge of the lower course, the minimum lap being usually 25 mm. Spacing for the siding should be carefully laid out before the first board is applied. To determine the maximum board spacing (or exposure), the minimum lap should be deducted from the overall width of the siding. The number of board spaces between the soffit and the bottom of the first course at the foundation wall should be such that the maximum exposure will not be exceeded. This may mean that the boards will have less than the maximum exposure. Where possible, the bottom of the board that is placed over the top of the windows should coincide with the top of the window cap *(Fig. 74,A)*.

Bevel siding should have a butt thickness of at least 12 mm for 89, 114, 140 and 184 mm widths and 14.3 mm for 235 and 286 mm widths. The top edge should not be less than 5 mm thick.

Drop (or matched) siding should be at least 14.3 mm thick and 184 mm or less in width. It comes in a variety of patterns with matched or shiplap edges. Figure 72,D shows a common pattern for drop siding.

Where bevel or drop siding is used, the butt joints between boards in adjacent courses should be staggered as much as possible. Butt joints should be made on a stud. The siding should be carefully fitted and be in close contact with other members and adjacent pieces. Ends should be sealed. Loose-fitting joints allow water to get behind the siding which can cause paint deterioration around the joints and lead to decay at the ends of the boards. One method sometimes used to obtain a tight joint is to place a small bead of caulking compound or putty along the end of each board after it is nailed and press the next board into the compound. The excess compound is then struck off, leaving a smooth waterproof joint. Joints occurring elsewhere, such as at window or door trim, can be similarly treated.

Bevel and drop siding should be face-nailed to lumber sheathing or studs, the size of the nail depending on the thickness of the siding and the type of sheathing used. One method of nailing often used is to drive the nail through the siding just above the lap so that the nail misses the top edge of the piece of siding beneath. (See the nailing method detail in Figure 74.) This method permits each siding board to expand and contract as the moisture content changes. Thus, there is less tendency for the boards to split as may occur when both edges of the board are nailed. Since the amount of swelling or shrinking is proportional to the width of the wood siding, nailing above the lap is more important with wide boards than with narrow boards.

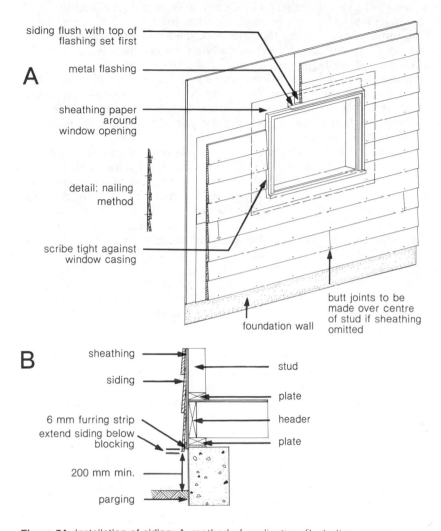

siding flush with top of
flashing set first

A   metal flashing

sheathing paper
around
window opening

detail: nailing
method

scribe tight against
window casing

butt joints to be
made over centre
of stud if sheathing
foundation wall   omitted

B   sheathing

siding   stud

plate

6 mm furring strip   header
extend siding below
blocking   plate

200 mm min.

parging

Figure 74. Installation of siding: A, method of application; B, starting course.

Vertical Application. Lumber siding that can be applied vertically
includes: plain matched boards; patterned matched boards; square-
edge boards covered at the joints with a batten strip, or square-edge
boards spaced apart and covered with another board. Vertical siding is
usually 14.3 mm thick. Boards should not be wider than 286 mm.
Vertical boards may be fastened to 14.3 mm lumber sheathing, 9.5 mm
plywood or 11.1 mm waferboard, 38 × 38 mm blocking fitted between
the studs at 600 mm on centre or to horizontal furring strips. The
furring may be 19 × 64 mm lumber where the framing is spaced not
more than 400 mm on centre or 19 × 89 mm lumber where the framing

is spaced not more than 600 mm on centre. Butt joints should be mitred to prevent the entry of water into the joint.

When the spaced method (sometimes called "board-on-board") is used *(Fig. 72,E)*, the boards next to the wall are normally wider than the top boards and are fastened with one row of nails near the centre of each board. The top board is then applied so that it laps the edges of the first board at least 25 mm. These top boards are fastened with two rows of nails driven slightly outside the edges of the boards underneath. This method of nailing permits the wider board to expand and contract without splitting.

The board and batten method uses square-edge boards which are ordinarily 184 mm or less in width. The boards are applied with the edges at least 6 mm apart and fastened with one row of nails near the centre of each board. To cover the joint, a narrow batten is used which laps the edges at least 12 mm. This batten is fastened with one row of nails driven in the joint between the two boards, so that the boards may swell or shrink without splitting either the boards or the batten strip. Since the batten also serves to prevent the board edges from curling outward, the nailing should be secure and closely spaced.

Tongue-and-groove matched siding *(Fig. 72,C)* is commonly 184 mm or less in width. The first board is face-nailed near the grooved edge and angle-nailed through the tongue. Each successive board is driven in closely and angle-nailed through the tongue. A nail set is used to finish off the nailing.

Nails cost little compared with the cost of the siding and labour, but the use of good nails is important. It is poor economy to buy siding that will last for years and then fasten it with nails that will rust badly within a short period. Corrosion-resistant nails, such as hot-dipped galvanized nails, will hold the siding permanently and will not disfigure the paint surface. Casing or siding nails are normally used for this purpose. Heads are driven flush with the face of the siding and later covered with paint. If finishing nails are used, the heads should be set below the surface and the hole filled with putty after the prime coat of paint is applied. The length of the nails depends on the thickness of the siding and the type of sheathing used. Nails should be long enough to penetrate at least 25 mm into the nailing support.

Plywood Panels Exterior type plywood is also used as a wall covering. The plywood sheets are made with a plain or grooved surface and are usually applied vertically. The joints may be V-grooved or flush or may be covered with batten. Plywood is available with a resin-impregnated kraft paper laminated to the face. This provides a smooth, moisture-resistant surface which resists checking or splitting after painting.

The minimum thickness of plywood applied to sheathing is 6 mm. It may also be applied directly to unsheathed wall framing, in which case the minimum thickness used (with the face grain parallel to supports) is 8 mm for stud spacings of 400 mm on centre and 11 mm for spacing of supports up to 600 mm on centre. If the face grain is at right angles to supports, the thickness is 6 mm for stud spacings of 400 mm on centre and 8 mm for spacing of supports up to 600 mm on centre.

After the plywood panels are cut and fitted, all edges should be protected with a suitable paint or sealer before installation. A 2 to 3 mm space between the sides and ends of the panels and butted ends of the strips will permit expansion without bulging. Vertical joints are filled with caulking or covered with a batten. Horizontal joints are flashed or lapped at least 25 mm.

The edges of plywood panels should be supported and fastened with corrosion-resistant nails which are usually 51 mm long. The nails are spaced 150 mm along the edges and 300 mm at intermediate supports.

Hardboard Panels Hardboard is also produced in sheets with a variety of finishes and may be applied over sheathing or to unsheathed walls. The minimum thickness of sheets should be at least 6 mm when applied over sheathing and 7.5 mm if applied without sheathing on supports that are not more than 400 mm on centre. It is fastened to the framing member or to lumber sheathing with corrosion-resistant nails at least 51 mm long. Nails are spaced 150 mm along the edges and 300 mm along intermediate supports. A gap at least 5 mm should be provided between sheets.

Corner Treatment for Siding The method of finishing siding at the corners may be influenced by the house design. Corner boards may be appropriate to some designs and mitred joints to others.

For lumber siding applied horizontally *(Fig. 75)*, mitred corners are most common, but metal corners or corner boards may also be used.

Mitred corners *(Fig. 75,B)* must fit tightly and smoothly for the full depth of the mitre. To maintain a tight fit at the mitre, it is important that the siding be properly seasoned before delivery and protected from rain when stored at the site. The ends are often set in caulking compound or putty when the siding is applied.

At interior corners, the siding is usually butted against a corner strip of 19 or 32 mm material, depending upon the thickness of the siding.

Metal corners *(Fig. 75,C)*, used as a substitute for mitred corners, are made of light-gauge metals such as aluminum or galvanized steel. The application of metal corners requires less skill than making good mitred corners or fitting siding to a corner board.

Corner boards *(Fig. 75,A and D)* are generally used with drop siding but may be used with other types of siding as well. The boards are made of 19 or 32 mm material, depending on the thickness of the siding. The corner boards are applied against the sheathing with the siding fitted tightly against the narrow edge of the corner boards. Joints between the siding and corner boards should be filled with caulking compound or putty when the siding is applied.

Plywood and hardboard are usually lapped at the corners or fitted to a corner board. Lumber siding applied vertically is lapped at the corners.

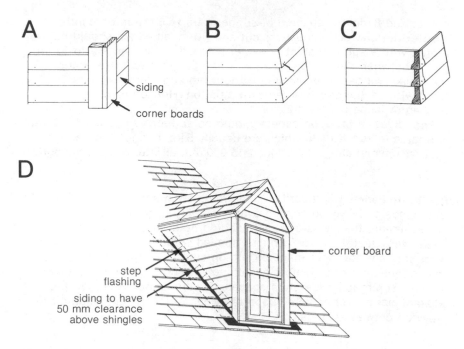

Figure 75. Corner treatment of siding: A, corner boards; B, mitred corner; C, metal corner; D, siding return on main roof, showing corner boards. Mitred or metal corners can also be used on the return, depending on the design.

Wood Shingles and Machine-Grooved Shakes Wood shingles or machine-grooved shakes are sometimes used for wall covering. A large selection is available, including special wall shingles in lengths of 400, 450 and 600 mm, factory-painted or stained.

Shingles are usually separated into three grades. The first grade is composed of clear shingles, all heartwood, all edge grain. The second grade consists of shingles with clear butts and admits defects in that part of the shingle which is normally covered in use. The third grade includes shingles that have defects other than those permitted in the second grade; these shingles may be used for undercoursing.

Shingles are made in random widths varying in the first grade from 65 to 350 mm; only a small proportion of the narrow width is permitted in the first grade. Shingles of a uniform width, known as dimension shingles, are also available. Widths of 100, 125 or 150 mm may be specified. Table 34 shows the commonly used exposure and thickness of wood shingles and machine-grooved shakes. Lumber, particleboard or plywood sheathing should be used under shingles or shakes.

When the single-course application is used, the joints in succeeding courses should be offset at least 40 mm and care taken that the joints in any two or three courses do not line up.

To obtain deep shadow lines, shingles can be laid in what is called double-coursing. This may be done by using a lower grade shingle under the shingle exposed to the weather. The exposed shingle butt extends about 12 mm below the butt of the undercourse. Where double-coursing is used, wider exposure to the weather is possible. Joints in the outer course should be offset from joints in the under-course by at least 40 mm.

Shingles should be fastened with corrosion-resistant nails. Shingles up to 200 mm wide require only two nails and those more than 200 mm wide require three. Nails should be driven about 20 mm from the edges and 25 mm above the exposure line for single-course application and 500 mm for double-coursing.

Stucco Side-Wall Finish Stucco generally consists of a mixture of port-land cement and well-graded sand, with hydrated lime added to make the mixture more plastic. An alternative stucco mixture calls for replac-ing the lime with masonry cement. Table 35 lists the proportions for the preparation of these two stucco mixes.

Applied in three coats (two base coats and one finish or "dash" coat), the stucco is held in place by stucco mesh or reinforcing. The finish coat may be left a natural cement colour or coloured by the addition of pigments. For what is called a "stone-dash finish," mineral chips are partially embedded into the second coat before it has set and no third coat is used in this case.

Stucco reinforcing of self-furring welded mesh, or fully primed or galvanized woven mesh, is stretched horizontally over sheathing paper, with the joints in the mesh lapped at least 50 mm. External corners are reinforced either by extending the mesh from one side 150 mm around the adjacent corner, or by vertical strips of reinforcing that extend 150 mm on either side of the corner. It is advisable to have stucco no closer than 200 mm from finished grade except where it is applied over concrete or masonry.

Galvanized steel fasteners should be used to hold the mesh in place. Suitable fasteners are 3.2 mm thick nails with 11.1 mm heads or 1.98 mm thick staples. Fasteners are spaced 150 mm vertically and 400 mm horizontally or 100 mm vertically and 600 mm horizontally. Other fastening patterns may be used, provided there are at least 20 fasteners per square metre of wall surface. Where the sheathing is other than lumber, waferboard or plywood, the fasteners should pene-trate the sheathing and go into the framing member (stud or plate) at least 25 mm.

Sheathing can be omitted from beneath stucco altogether when galvanized wire mesh, not lighter than 1.19 mm, is fastened horizontally to the framing at vertical intervals of 150 mm or less, or where accep-table paper-backed welded wire metal lath is used.

The first (or scratch) coat of stucco should be forced through the reinforcing, embedding the mesh completely and trowelled to a thick-ness of not less than 6 mm measured from the face of the mesh. The surface must then be scored to provide a bonding key for the second coat. In open-frame wood construction, the first coat must set for least 48 hours before the second (or brown) coat is applied.

Just before putting on the second coat, the base is dampened to ensure a good bond between the coats. The second coat is applied at least 6 mm thick and firmly trowelled into the scored surface of the base.

For a stone-dash finish, mineral chips are picked up in a hand scoop and "dashed" into the fresh mortar of the second coat. To ensure a good adhesion, this must be done while the mortar is still soft but firm enough to resist sagging.

For finish coats other than stone-dash, the second coat should be moist-cured for at least 48 hours and then left to dry for five days, preferably longer, before the finish coat is applied. The base should be dampened to ensure a good bond and the finish applied to a depth of at least 3 mm.

In dry warm weather, fresh stucco should be kept damp to ensure proper curing. In cold weather, each coat of stucco should be kept at a temperature of at least 10°C for 48 hours after application.

Masonry Veneer If masonry veneer is used for the exterior cladding of above-grade walls, the foundation must include a supporting ledge or offset wide enough to allow a space of about 25 mm between the masonry and the sheathing paper *(Fig. 76)*. A base flashing should

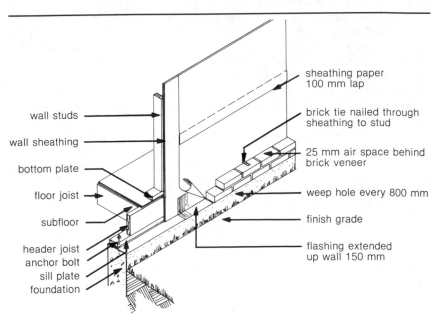

wall studs

wall sheathing

bottom plate

floor joist

subfloor

header joist
anchor bolt
sill plate
foundation

sheathing paper
100 mm lap

brick tie nailed through
sheathing to stud

25 mm air space behind
brick veneer

weep hole every 800 mm

finish grade

flashing extended
up wall 150 mm

Figure 76. Ledge in foundation wall for support of brick veneer or other masonry finish.

extend from the outside face of the wall over the top of the ledge and at least 150 mm up the wall behind the sheathing paper. Corrosion-resistant metal ties, nailed to the studs and embedded in the mortar joints between the masonry, should be used to tie the veneer to the framework. These are usually spaced 800 mm apart horizontally and 400 mm vertically; 600 mm horizontally and 500 mm vertically, or 400 mm horizontally and 600 mm vertically, depending on the stud spacing.

Weep holes serve both a venting and a drainage function. They should be placed about 800 mm apart in the bottom course of the veneer. This can be done by omitting the mortar from the vertical joints.

Masonry veneer should be at least 90 mm thick where there are raked joints and 75 mm thick where the joints are unraked.

If a brick veneer is used, the bricks selected should be hard, absorb little water and be manufactured for exposure to the weather. Stone veneers should be selected from materials known locally to be durable.

Brick or stone should be laid in a full bed of mortar. Care should be taken to avoid dropping mortar into the space between the veneer and sheathing paper, as this will block ventilation behind the veneer. Outside joints must be tooled to a smooth finish to provide maximum resistance to water penetration. Mortar mix proportions should conform to those shown in Table 5.

Masonry laid during cold weather should be protected from freezing until after the mortar has set. The temperature of the masonry and mortar should be maintained above 5°C for at least 24 hours after installation.

Exterior Trim and Millwork

Exterior trim (that part of the exterior finish other than the wall covering) includes such items as window and door trim, soffits, rake or gable trim and fascia. Much of this material is cut, fitted and nailed into place on the job. Other material or assemblies, such as louvres and shutters, are usually shop-manufactured.

The properties desired in materials used for trim are good painting and weathering characteristics, easy working qualities and maximum freedom from warp. Sealing the end joints or mitres of members exposed to moisture is recommended.

Fasteners used for trim, whether nails or screws, should be corrosion-resistant, that is, galvanized or aluminum. When finishing nails are used, they must be set and then puttied after the prime coat of paint. This method of fastening will generally prevent rust stains at nailheads. Fasteners must be compatible with the metal trim to avoid galvanic reaction between dissimilar metals, such as aluminum and steel.

Eave Projections

The eave overhang gives some protection to the side wall and forms a connection between the roof and wall. Soffits are usually closed in with pre-finished metal panels or 6 mm sanded plywood nailed at 150 mm on centre along the edges and 300 mm at intermediate supports. The exterior finish is then butted up to the underside of the soffit. A fascia board added as a finished covering for the rafter header usually extends about 12 mm below the soffit covering to form a drip edge. The three general types of eave construction are shown in Figure 77.

A narrow eave projection *Fig. 77,A)* is sometimes used with roofs having a steep slope. Here the rafters are projected a short distance over the wall plate, and the ends are cut to suit the angle required for the rafter header and soffit covering. The soffit covering is nailed to the angled surface of the rafter. Where the soffit covering is less than 140 mm wide, a 19 mm board is generally used for this purpose, as the board does not require support along its edges.

When wider eave projections are used with a horizontal soffit, blocking is installed to support the soffit covering *(Fig. 77,B)*. A 19 mm nailing strip is placed on top of the sheathing along the wall and nailed to the framing. This strip provides support for the inner ends of the blocking and edges of the soffit covering. The blocking, which may consist of 38 × 38 mm material, is usually spaced at 600 mm on centre. It is toenailed to the nailing strip and end-nailed to the rafter header. The soffit covering and fascia board are then nailed in place.

Where the blocking provides partial support for the roof overhang *(See Fig. 53)*, 38 × 89 mm material is used. The members are securely nailed to the side of each rafter and butted against a 38 × 89 mm nailing strip placed along the wall over the sheathing. This type of support is usually confined to overhangs of not more than 1.2 m.

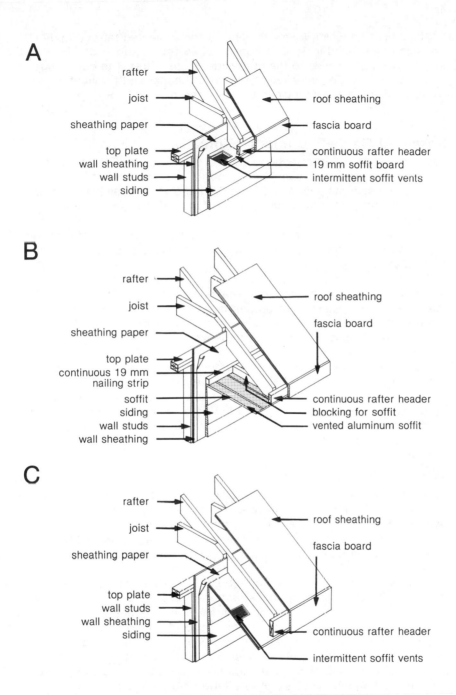

Figure 77. Roof projection at eaves: A, narrow eave projection; B, wide eave projection with horizontal soffit; C, wide eave projection with sloped soffit.

Sloped soffits which follow the line of the projected rafter (Fig. 77,C) are sometimes used instead of horizontal soffits. In this case, the soffit covering is nailed to the underside of the rafter. The outer edge of the soffit covering is nailed to the rafter header and the inner edge to 38 × 38 mm blocking placed between the rafters.

Eave and Gable-End Intersections

Eave and gable-end intersections depend largely on how the eave projection is finished. Figure 78 (A through C) shows three types of commonly used intersections. Figure 79,D shows an example of an aluminum soffit. Aluminum can be used for all three types of intersections shown.

Where a sloped soffit is used at the eave projection, the soffit of the gable-end projection is carried through on the same plane as the eave soffit (Fig. 78,B).

Where a horizontal soffit is used at the eave projection, the eave soffit may be carried through to the rake rafter (Fig. 78,C). In this case, the soffit of the gable-end projection is terminated at the side wall and returned down to intersect the eave soffit. The fascia board at the gable end is increased in width at the eave to close in the end of the eave soffit.

Another type of intersection sometimes used with a horizontal eave soffit has the eave soffit terminating at the side wall (Fig. 78,A). The gable-end sheathing and siding is continued out to the edge of the eaves and serves as a covering for the end of the soffit. The gable-end soffit is carried down beyond the side wall and terminates at the eave.

Window Frames and Sashes

Windows are used in a house principally to provide light and air, but they are also an important part of architectural design. Windows are available in many types, each having its own advantages. The principal opening types are vertical sliding, horizontal sliding, casement and awning. Window frames and sashes may be made of wood, metal or plastic.

All windows should shed water and snow and be easy to reglaze if damaged. Air infiltration and construction of sash and frame must normally meet recognized window standards. In living areas of the house, the glass area should be about 10 per cent of the floor area. In bedroom areas, this can be reduced to about 5 per cent, but at least one bedroom window should be openable and adequately sized for emergency exit. In kitchens and bathrooms, no windows are required if electric lighting and mechanical ventilation are provided.

Excessive areas of glazing should be avoided, as much more heat is lost through windows than through an equivalent area of insulated wall. Generally, a total glass area of about 12 per cent of the floor area of the house is adequate. On the other hand, double-glazed windows

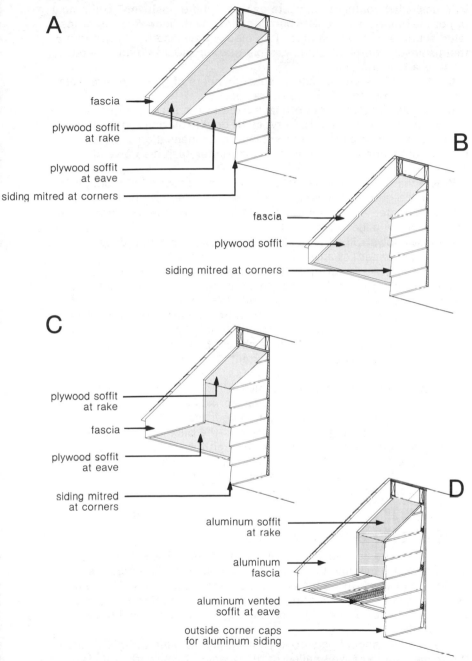

Figure 78. Eave and gable-end intersections: A, eave soffit is terminated at the wall line and gable-end soffit is continued to the fascia board at the eave; B, eave soffit is sloped on same plane as gable-end soffit; C, eave soffit carried out to rake rafter and gable-end soffit is returned down to meet the eave soffit; D, soffit and fascia detail using aluminum.

with unshaded southern exposure can contribute positively to the heating of the house, especially when combined with heavy drapes or insulated shutters that can be closed on cloudy days and at night. From a thermal insulation point of view, triple glazing should be considered for most locations in Canada.

Insulating glass units made of spaced sheets of glass are available for insertion in window sashes or frames.

Double-glazing (one sheet of glass fixed in the sash and one removable sheet) can also used. Both types of double-glazing insulate better than single-glazing and are less subject to condensation problems. Window units consisting of an inner and outer sash also give similar insulating values.

Where the total house air leakage has been reduced by good, airtight construction, interior humidity levels will be higher. Double glazing or storms in winter are a minimum requirement if excessive condensation on the window panes is to be avoided.

Good windows will be less effective if their installation does not produce a near-perfect air seal around the perimeter. Since it is not practical to obtain an airtight fit where the sash contacts the frame, weatherstripping is often used at these points to reduce air infiltration. Most manufacturers make complete window units with the sash fitted and glazed, with weatherstripping, operating balances and hardware installed. Units combining screens and storm sash are also available.

Wood window sashes and frames should be treated to resist decay or be made of a species that is resistant. This will ensure a longer life to the exposed parts and covered joints.

The exterior trim is usually attached to the window frame when the window is fabricated. To provide space for adjustment, the framework around the opening is usually slightly larger than the window. Wedges and shims are used to adjust the frame in the opening, and when in position the window frame is nailed through the wedges to the wall framing. The exterior trim is also nailed to the studs and lintel. The space around the window frame is later filled with insulation. Figure 79 shows a typical window frame installation.

Exterior Door Frames and Doors

Exterior door frames generally consist of 35 mm thick side and head jambs and a 44 mm sill. While a hardwood sill is more durable, a sill made of softwood with a metal threshold may also be used. Frames are rabbetted to form stops for the main door. Stops for a screen or combination door are provided by the edge of the jamb and the exterior trim.

The door sill should bear solidly on the floor framing *(Fig. 80)*, and the frame should be well nailed to the opening framework. This is usually done by adjusting the frame with wedges and then nailing through the trim and wedges into the studs. Exterior doors should be weatherstripped at the top, bottom and sides. For improved resistance to forced entry, the jamb of the door frame at the lock height should

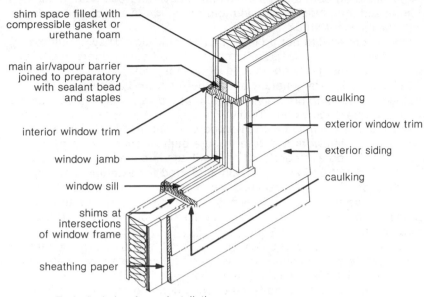

shim space filled with compressible gasket or urethane foam

main air/vapour barrier joined to preparatory with sealant bead and staples

interior window trim

window jamb

window sill

shims at intersections of window frame

sheathing paper

caulking

exterior window trim

exterior siding

caulking

Figure 79. Typical window frame installation.

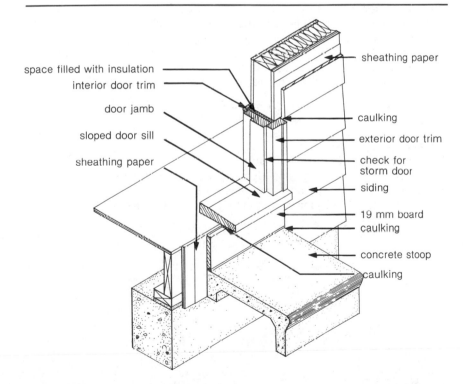

space filled with insulation
interior door trim

door jamb

sloped door sill

sheathing paper

sheathing paper

caulking

exterior door trim

check for storm door

siding

19 mm board

caulking

concrete stoop

caulking

Figure 80. Section through door frame at sill.

be shimmed on both sides immediately above and below the lock location. In addition, blocking should join the studs of the door opening with the adjacent studs.

Main doors should not be less than 44 mm thick. They should be at least 810 mm wide and 1.98 m in height. Wood storm doors should be 35 mm thick and metal doors at least 25 mm thick.

Exterior doors are generally either the flush or panel type. For methods of hanging doors and installing hardware, see the chapter on Interior Doors, Frames and Trim.

Flush doors are made with plywood or other suitable facings applied over a light framework and core. A core built of solid pieces of wood is called a solid core; a core built as a grillage is called a hollow core. Solid-core construction is generally preferred for exterior doors, particularly in cold climates, because this method of construction minimizes warping from differences in humidity or temperature on opposite sides of the door. Glazed panels may be inserted into solid-core doors.

Panel doors consist of stiles (solid vertical members), rails (solid cross members) and panels (thinner parts filling the spaces between stiles and rails). Many types with various wood or glass panels are available. Metal or plywood-faced doors whose cores are filled with rigid insulation are becoming more common; they should be used whenever a separate storm door is not provided.

Sliding doors, either fully or partially glazed, are sometimes used for access to patios or garden areas. All glazed areas in doors should be double-glazed and safety glass. Transparent glass in doors and sidelights which could be mistaken for unobstructed passageways should be of safety glass, such as tempered or wired glass.

Related Publications

Protecting Your Home Against Burglary
        Canada Mortgage and Housing Corporation NHA 5394
Trouble-Free Windows, Doors and Skylights
        Canada Mortgage and Housing Corporation NHA 5735

Framing Details for Plumbing, Heating and Wiring

One advantage of wood-frame construction is that the space between the framing members in wood-framed walls, floors and roofs provides a safe and economical location to conceal the greater part of the heating, plumbing and electrical distribution systems.

Most of the electrical wiring and many plumbing pipes and heating ducts run parallel to the joists and studs and can easily be concealed in the space between the members. Where it is necessary to run pipes or wires at right angles to the joists and studs, the wood members may be notched or drilled. Within certain limitations, the structural strength of a framing member is not seriously reduced by these notches or holes.

Cutting the Framing Members

Notching of Joists. Notches made in the top of the joists should be within one-half the joist depth from the edge of the bearing, and the depth of the notch should be no more than one-third of the joist depth *(Fig. 81,B).*

If notches are necessary elsewhere in the span *(Fig. 81,A),* this should be considered when deciding the size of joist to use, so that the size of joist can be increased by the depth of the notch. The bottom edge of joists should not be notched, since this may cause a joist to split when it deflects under load.

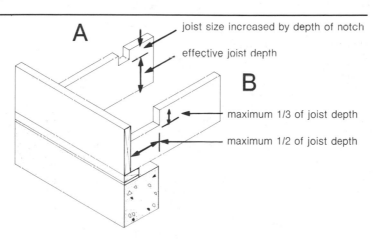

Figure 81. Example of notch limitations: A, notch located away from support; B, when applied to a 184 mm joist the depth of the notch at the support would be 61 mm maximum and the length of the notch would not extend more than 92 mm from the joist support.

Drilled Holes in Joists. Normally, holes drilled in joists should not be larger than one-quarter the joist depth or closer than 50 mm to either edge *(Fig. 82)*.

Notching and Drilling of Studs. Loadbearing wall studs that have been notched or drilled to more than one-third of their depth are usually reinforced with 38 mm lumber nailed to the side of the studs and extending about 600 mm each side of the notch or hole. Similar reinforcing is used when notched partition studs have less than 40 mm of solid wood remaining *(Fig. 83)*.

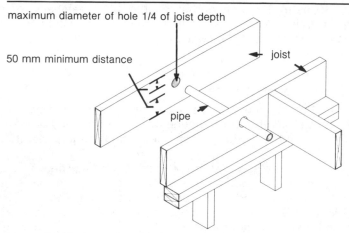

maximum diameter of hole 1/4 of joist depth

50 mm minimum distance

joist

pipe

Figure 82. Maximum size of holes drilled in joists.

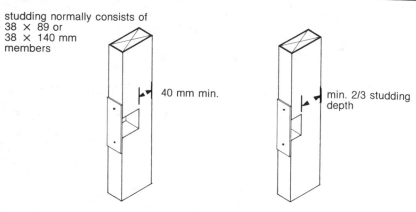

studding normally consists of
38 × 89 or
38 × 140 mm
members

40 mm min.

min. 2/3 studding depth

in partitions,
notched studding need not be
reinforced if remaining
portion is at least 40 mm

in loadbearing walls,
notched studding need not be
reinforced if remaining
portion is at least 2/3 the depth
of the studding

Figure 83. Notched studding for plumbing.

Notching and Drilling of Top Plates. In loadbearing walls, top plates are also reinforced with 38 mm lumber when the solid wood remaining in the plates is less than 50 mm in width. If the required reinforcing must be placed on the face of the plate or stud, sheet metal is normally used so that the wall finish may readily be applied over it.

Framing Details for Plumbing Systems

The installation of the plumbing system usually begins after the walls are framed. This initial work is called "roughing-in." It includes putting in the plumbing drains and all the hot and cold water piping which will be enclosed in the walls and ceilings and under the basement floor. Piping in outside walls should be insulated. Since the bathtub must be put in before the wall finish can be applied, the bathtub installation is usually included in roughing-in. Plumbing fixtures and accessories are not connected until after the installation of the interior finish has been completed. The design and installation of the entire plumbing system is usually regulated by provincial or municipal codes. (See Figures 84, 85 and 86 for details of plumbing system installation.)

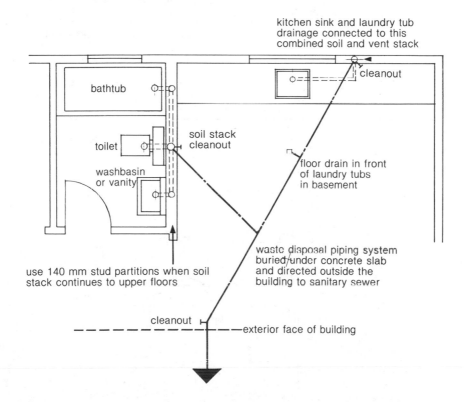

Figure 84. Kitchen and bathroom in proximity for minimum pipe length.

When 75 mm copper or plastic piping is used, the stack wall may be made of 38 × 89 mm material. Sealing the area around the pipe is necessary to prevent air leakage into the attic space *(Fig. 87)*.

Where soil stacks or large pipes must run horizontally at right angles to the joists, it will be necessary to frame out the joists. To do this, headers are installed between the joists *(Fig. 88)*.

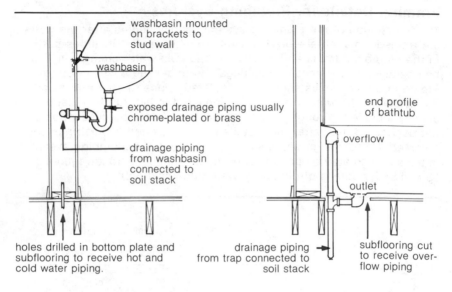

washbasin mounted on brackets to stud wall

washbasin

exposed drainage piping usually chrome-plated or brass

drainage piping from washbasin connected to soil stack

end profile of bathtub

overflow

outlet

holes drilled in bottom plate and subflooring to receive hot and cold water piping.

drainage piping from trap connected to soil stack

subflooring cut to receive over-flow piping

Figure 85. Washbasin and bathtub fixtures.

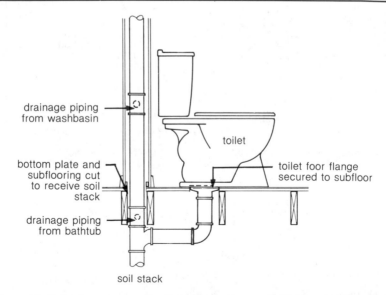

drainage piping from washbasin

bottom plate and subflooring cut to receive soil stack

drainage piping from bathtub

toilet

toilet foor flange secured to subfloor

soil stack

Figure 86. Toilet fixture.

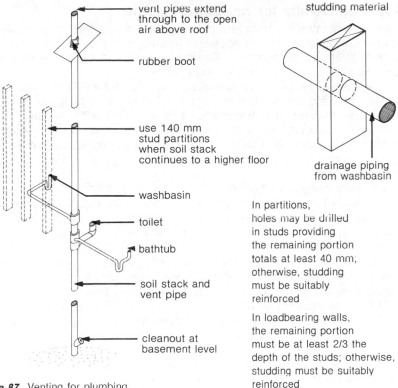

vent pipes extend
through to the open
air above roof

rubber boot

studding material

use 140 mm
stud partitions
when soil stack
continues to a higher floor

drainage piping
from washbasin

washbasin

toilet

bathtub

soil stack and
vent pipe

cleanout at
basement level

In partitions,
holes may be drilled
in studs providing
the remaining portion
totals at least 40 mm;
otherwise, studding
must be suitably
reinforced

In loadbearing walls,
the remaining portion
must be at least 2/3 the
depth of the studs; otherwise,
studding must be suitably
reinforced

Figure 87. Venting for plumbing.

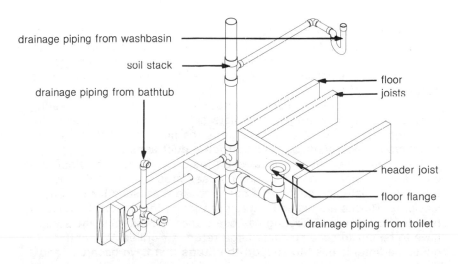

drainage piping from washbasin

soil stack

drainage piping from bathtub

floor

joists

header joist

floor flange

drainage piping from toilet

Figure 88. Framing for soil-stack pipes.

Framing Details for Heating Systems

There are many ways to heat a house. Heating systems range from the multi-controlled electric or hot-water heating systems to the relatively simple single space heater. In Canada, natural gas, oil and electricity are the most commonly used energy sources.

The three prevalent heating systems are: forced warm air, electric baseboards and forced flow hot-water heating. Other less frequently used systems are: air or water source heat pumps with electric resistance back-up, heat pumps with natural gas back-up and solid-fuel-burning (wood or coal) furnaces. Figure 89 illustrates a typical heating layout while Figure 90 shows an isometric view of a typical heating system.

All types of heating systems may be safely and easily installed in wood-frame houses. Certain clearances, however, must be maintained between parts of the system and combustible material. Installers of heating equipment should be aware of local regulations before starting work.

For a warm-air heating system, the ducts for supply and return air are usually located between studs in walls and between joists in floors. When planning the house, locating joists, beams and studs to suit the requirements of the duct system must be considered.

Provision should be made for controlled ventilation when planning the heat distribution system of the house. Assuming good airtight construction, the ventilation system should be designed to exhaust house air (primarily from bathrooms and kitchen but also from other rooms) and draw in outside air so that the air quality of the house is maintained. The ventilation system becomes even more necessary with combustion heating systems which need draft and combustion air for their proper functioning.

Warm-Air Systems Normally, wall studs and joists are located so that they do not have to be cut to install heating ducts. When ducts must pass up through a wall to heat the room above, the top and bottom plates must be removed at these points, and the ducts are then fitted between the studs.

When a partition is supported on doubled floor joists and a heating duct is to go in the partition, the joists are ordinarily spaced apart to allow room for the duct. This eliminates the need to cut framing members unnecessarily or to use intricate duct angles.

Return air grilles, usually located on inside walls near the floor level, can be connected to a duct or an enclosed stud space. At this point, the bottom plate and subfloor is cut to make a passage for the duct or air space. Blocks are nailed between the joists to support the ends of boards if diagonal subflooring has been used. Sometimes, the studs have to be cut to accommodate large return air grilles. Where this occurs, a lintel is used to support the studs that have been cut, and the opening is framed in the same way as the door opening shown in Figure 38. When enclosed, the space between floor joists may be used

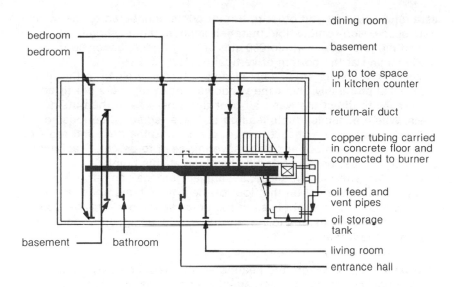

Figure 89. Basement plan showing typical heating layout.

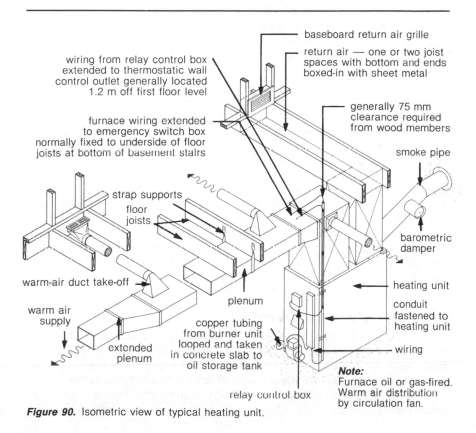

Figure 90. Isometric view of typical heating unit.

as a return air duct and other return air ducts connected to the same joist space. Non-combustible material, such as metal, should be used to line the joist space within 600 mm of the furnace, under floor registers and at the bottom of vertical ducts.

Warm-air registers are usually placed in the floor close to the outside walls, preferably under the windows. These registers are fitted with vanes to direct the warm air over the wide area of the outside walls. Where possible, ducts leading to these registers are located between joists with a shaped "boot" connecting the duct and register. Then, only the subfloor and floor covering need to be cut. Diagonal subflooring must be supported by blocking at this point.

In houses with a crawl space, a warm-air furnace can either be put in a special compartment on the floor of the house, hung under the floor or mounted on a concrete base in the crawl space beneath the house. In the first two cases, the joists will have to be designed to carry the weight of the furnace.

Hot-Water Systems Where the heating system requires only small pipes for a supply-and-return system, pre-planning of the structural framing layout to accommodate the pipes is not normally necessary.

Baseboard-type convectors are usually selected and located under windows along outside walls. In this manner, warm air rising through the convector blankets the outside walls. Virtually no cutting of the studs or joists is required with this type of installation as the baseboard type of convector is positioned on the surface of the wall.

Electric Baseboard Heating Systems Since it is easy to conceal wiring in walls and floors, the accommodation of electric heating systems requires little or no planning in the structural framing. As with hot-water and warm-air systems, electric heating units are usually located along outside walls, so that the air warmed by the heating elements blankets the walls. Because the heating elements are mounted on the surface of the wall, there is no need to cut the wall studs. Radiant heating with the heating elements located in the ceiling is also used.

With hot-water systems and electric systems which use baseboard radiators, it is important, especially in a well-constructed, well-sealed house, to provide for room-air replenishment and not rely entirely on natural convection and infiltration. If measures for air circulation are not implemented, humidity levels may rise to the point where condensation will occur.

Framing Details for Wiring

Wiring a house for electrical services is usually started after the house has been closed in, that is, after the exterior wall sheathing and roof have been completed. This initial phase of wiring, also termed roughing-in, includes the installation of wiring and the boxes for the switches, lights and outlets. Figure 91 presents some typical electrical equipment.

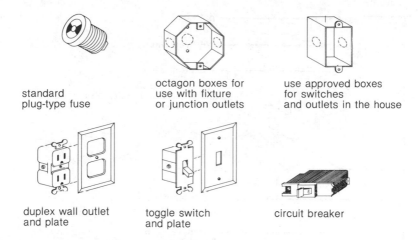

standard
plug-type fuse

octagon boxes for
use with fixture
or junction outlets

use approved boxes
for switches
and outlets in the house

duplex wall outlet
and plate

toggle switch
and plate

circuit breaker

Figure 91. Typical electrical equipment.

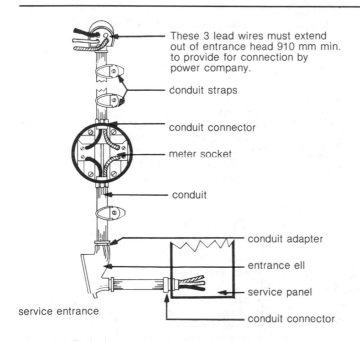

These 3 lead wires must extend
out of entrance head 910 mm min.
to provide for connection by
power company.

conduit straps

conduit connector

meter socket

conduit

conduit adapter

entrance ell

service panel

service entrance

conduit connector

Figure 92. Typical arrangement of service entrance.

Roughing-in is done before applying the inside finish and ordinarily before placing the insulation in walls or ceilings. Lighting fixtures, switches, outlets and cover plates are installed after the interior finish and painting operations.

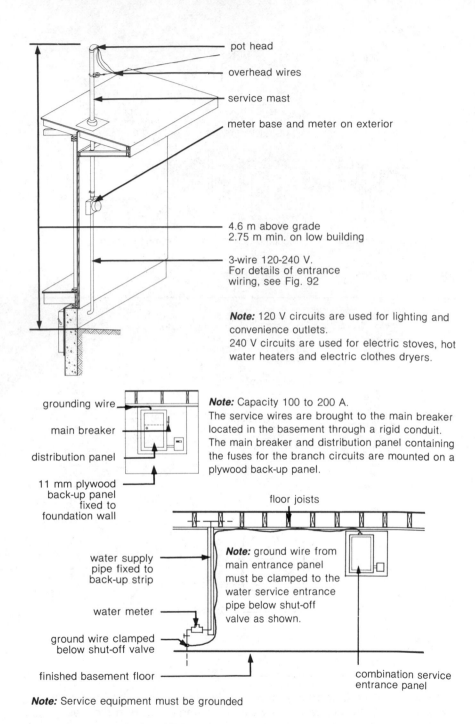

pot head

overhead wires

service mast

meter base and meter on exterior

4.6 m above grade
2.75 m min. on low building

3-wire 120-240 V.
For details of entrance
wiring, see Fig. 92

Note: 120 V circuits are used for lighting and
convenience outlets.
240 V circuits are used for electric stoves, hot
water heaters and electric clothes dryers.

grounding wire

main breaker

distribution panel

11 mm plywood
back-up panel
fixed to
foundation wall

Note: Capacity 100 to 200 A.
The service wires are brought to the main breaker
located in the basement through a rigid conduit.
The main breaker and distribution panel containing
the fuses for the branch circuits are mounted on a
plywood back-up panel.

floor joists

water supply
pipe fixed to
back-up strip

water meter

ground wire clamped
below shut-off valve

finished basement floor

Note: ground wire from
main entrance panel
must be clamped to the
water service entrance
pipe below shut-off
valve as shown.

combination service
entrance panel

Note: Service equipment must be grounded

Figure 93. Service entrance equipment.

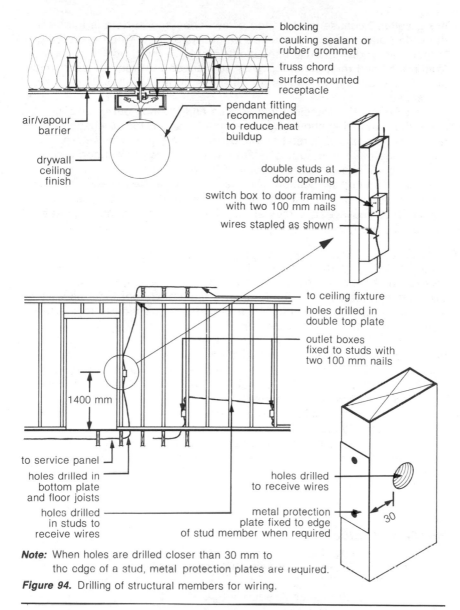

blocking
caulking sealant or
rubber grommet
truss chord
surface-mounted
receptacle
pendant fitting
recommended
to reduce heat
buildup
air/vapour
barrier
drywall
ceiling
finish
double studs at
door opening
switch box to door framing
with two 100 mm nails
wires stapled as shown
to ceiling fixture
holes drilled in
double top plate
outlet boxes
fixed to studs with
two 100 mm nails
1400 mm
to service panel
holes drilled in
bottom plate
and floor joists
holes drilled
in studs to
receive wires
holes drilled
to receive wires
metal protection
plate fixed to edge
of stud member when required
30

Note: When holes are drilled closer than 30 mm to
the edge of a stud, metal protection plates are required.

Figure 94. Drilling of structural members for wiring.

The design and installation of the entire wiring system is usually
regulated by a provincial electrical code. All provincial codes are
closely modelled on the Canadian Electrical Code published by the
Canadian Standards Association. The provincial codes usually require
installation by a licensed electrician. Owners are advised to check the
applicable code before doing any wiring.

Figures 92 and 93 show the typical arrangement of electrical service
entrance equipment. The details of drilling structural members for
wiring are shown in Figure 94.

Box Location Because the location of switches and outlets is important, the wiring plans should be studied carefully to ensure that everything is included. Today's house uses electricity for a multitude of purposes from radios and televisions to major appliances that require their own circuit. The location of outlets for all these purposes should be carefully planned.

The amperage of the electrical service and the number of circuits and outlets installed should also take into account future needs; after the house is finished, alterations and additions are expensive. To accommodate the multitude of electrical appliances in a modern house, electrical services are usually 200 amps.

When planning the location of outlets, it should be remembered that electrical boxes on insulated ceilings and exterior walls can be a major source of air leakage, and they should be kept to a minimum, unless they are carefully sealed.

Switches Switches are commonly located just inside the door of a room so that they may be easily reached upon opening the door. Switches may service a wall outlet for a table or a floor lamp as well as the usual ceiling or wall lights. It is common practice to locate the switch boxes about 1.4 m above the floor.

Multiple-control switches are convenient in many locations so that lights may be controlled from more than one switch. A living room light could have a switch near the outside entrance door and another at inner doors leading to the kitchen or to a bedroom hallway. In two-storey houses, three-way switches should be provided at the bottom and at the top of the stairway to control stairway lighting. Basement stair lights should also be controlled by three-way switches at the head and foot of the stairs, particularly if there is a garage or living accommodation in the basement or if there is an outside exit from the basement.

Related Publications
Canadian Plumbing Code
        National Research Council, NRC-23176, 1985
Electrical Code
        Canadian Standards Association, CAN3-C22.
CMHC Septic Tank Standards
        Canada Mortgage and Housing Corporation NHA 5213

Vapour and Air Barriers

Many normal activities which take place within a house, such as cooking, dishwashing, laundering and bathing, generate considerable amounts of water vapour which are absorbed by the air in the house, increasing its humidity. If, during cold weather, this water vapour is allowed to pass into the outer shell of the building, the low temperature within the thickness of the shell can cause the water vapour to condense back into liquid water or frost. Since wetting of the structure, cladding and insulation is obviously undesirable, some means must be used to contain the water vapour within the dwelling. This is the function of the building component which has traditionally been called the "vapour barrier."

There are two mechanisms that tend to drive the water vapour through the building shell: vapour pressure and air movement.

In the winter, there is more water vapour in the air inside the house than in the outside air. As a result, the difference in vapour pressure tends to force the water vapour to diffuse through the materials making up the shell. Most building materials are, to some degree, permeable to the passage of water vapour, but those classified as vapour barriers (such as polyethylene) have very low permeability and thus are very resistant to this diffusion mechanism.

The second mechanism by which water vapour is forced through the building shell is air movement. There are often differences in air pressure from inside to outside the house created by a stack effect, the operation of fans or the action of the wind. When the air pressure inside is greater than that outside, air will tend to flow outwards through any holes or cracks in the building envelope, carrying with it the water vapour it contains. It has been recognized that this air movement plays a much greater role in the transmission of water vapour than the diffusion mechanism. The most important aspect of an air barrier is continuity; an air barrier is only as good as it is continuous. Many materials, such as drywall, qualify as an air barrier even though they do not perform well as a vapour barrier.

Common practice uses polyethylene to perform both functions of an air and vapour barrier. This combination is workable, although it does not overcome easily the difficulty of creating a continuous air barrier. Certain spots on the envelope, such as headers, openings, services, vent stacks, chimneys, electric lines and unusual framing details, are hard to seal well.

However, once it is well understood that there should be no direct path from the house interior to the outside through the wall cavity, additional precautions and measures can supplement the function of the material chosen to be the air/vapour barrier. The air barrier must be able to resist wind pressures which occasionally become very strong. Vapour pressure, on the other hand, is not as forceful and can be easily resisted.

Placement

While the air barrier can be placed at any point on the building envelope, the vapour barrier must be placed on the warm side of the structure. When the air and vapour barriers are combined in the same material, the warm side is again the recommended location. A slight deviation from this rule is permitted with extra thick walls. In this case, one-third of the total thermal resistance or RSI value can be located in front of the air/vapour barrier.

The preferable method is to use polyethylene film. The film is available in large, room-height sheets which can be applied with a minimum of joints, thus reducing the chance of openings through which air can move. Any joints which do occur should be lapped over two adjacent framing members. While 0.05 mm polyethylene usually has low enough permeability to act as a good vapour barrier, it is easily torn and thus may not be a very good air barrier. A minimum of 0.15 mm thickness is, therefore, recommended (Fig. 95).

The ceiling vapour barrier should overlap on the wall vapour barrier, and both should be continuous over and around intersecting interior partitions. Since interior partitions are usually framed before the insulation and vapour barrier are installed, this latter condition is usually achieved by covering the top and ends of the interior partitions with

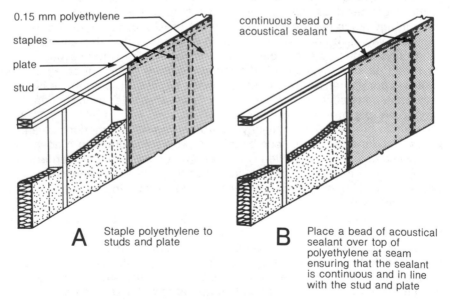

0.15 mm polyethylene		continuous bead of acoustical sealant
staples		
plate		
stud		

A Staple polyethylene to studs and plate

B Place a bead of acoustical sealant over top of polyethylene at seam ensuring that the sealant is continuous and in line with the stud and plate

Figure 95. Two methods of applying a vapour barrier.

strips of vapour barrier at least 450 mm wide which are subsequently
lapped onto the main vapour barrier. It is often necessary to use the
tops of interior partitions as a walking surface when installing roof
framing. In such cases, in order to avoid damage to the vapour barrier
strips and to provide better footing, they are installed between the two
top plates *(Fig. 96)*. In the case of non-loadbearing partitions, the upper
plate can consist of 19 mm lumber since its only function is to protect
the vapour barrier.

The vapour barrier should overlap and be stapled to door and
window framing and be taped to any wires or pipes which penetrate it.
It should also be continuous behind electrical boxes located in the
exterior walls. This can be achieved by wrapping the box with a piece
of 0.15 mm polyethylene and taping the polyethylene to the wires
entering the box. This piece of polyethylene can then be lapped onto
the surrounding vapour barrier when it is installed. The lap should be
at least 100 mm. Alternatively, special polyethylene box covers can be
used. Ideally, it is best to avoid locating electrical outlets on exterior
walls if at all possible.

It is also important to provide vapour barrier protection to insulation
installed between the ends of floor joists. It is usually very difficult to
achieve an effective air barrier at this location because the materials
must be cut and fitted between the joists *(Fig. 97)*. Extra care is, therefore, required especially on the higher floors where air exfiltration is
more likely to occur due to stack effect. When the exterior wall has
insulating sheathing, it is carried over the header. If additional insulation is placed on the inside, a vapour barrier will be necessary on the
inside face of the insulation to ensure that no moisture-laden air
reaches the header and condenses on it.

Caulking should be used around the fitted insulation to seal the
joints and prevent exfiltration. For this reason, a hard or semi-hard surface is preferred. Rigid board insulation is suitable for this purpose,

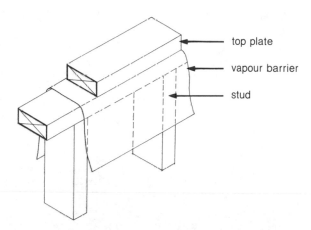

Figure 96. Installation of vapour barrier strips in interior wall framing.

but also some semi-rigid or soft insulation materials which come wit
a reinforced aluminum backing can be used effectively. Extra care in
ensuring continuity of the sheathing and sheathing paper at this poir
will also help to minimize air leakage.

A potential weak point in the air/vapour barrier is the attic access
hatch. This should be carefully weatherstripped or, preferably, locate
on an outside gable rather than in the ceiling.

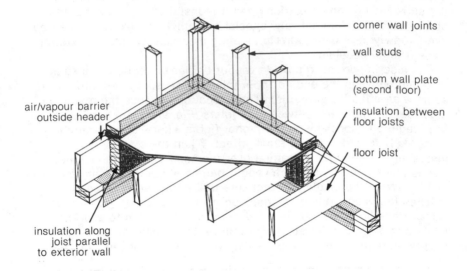

Figure 97. Placement of vapour barrier between ends of floor joists.

Thermal Insulation

The effectiveness of a building assembly such as a wall or ceiling in resisting the flow of heat is measured as its thermal resistance or RSI value. Although most materials have some resistance to the flow of heat, the materials used for structure, cladding and finish generally have relatively low resistance. Insulation is, therefore, added to reduce the loss of heat from the house. Wood-frame construction is quite easy to insulate since it incorporates many cavities which can be readily filled with relatively inexpensive types of insulation. The cavities or air spaces themselves have appreciable resistance to heat flow, but it is greatly increased by placing insulation in the space.

In the past, due to low energy prices, it was not common to completely fill wall stud spaces with insulation or to insulate attics to a depth greater than that of the truss bottom chords or ceiling joists. Nor was it common to insulate foundation walls. Now, however, higher energy prices and our increasing realization of the need for energy conservation make it apparent that insulation should at least fill all available cavities within the building shell and that perhaps the shell construction should be altered to accommodate even more insulation. It has also become more apparent that uninsulated foundation walls are a major source of heat loss.

Types of Insulation

Insulation is manufactured from a variety of materials and in a variety of forms. These forms can be grouped into four basic types as follows:

Batts. Batts consist of fibres of glass or steel mill slag spun together with a binding agent into a blanket-like strip of convenient length and width to fit standard framing spaces and in a range of thicknesses. This type is called "friction fit" because it is made slightly wider than the standard stud space so that it is held in place by friction.

It is often necessary to use insulation batts in cavities which are not as deep as the batts are thick. For example, 150 mm batts might be used in a wall built with 38 × 140 mm studs. The resulting compression reduces the thermal resistance of the batts, but the reduction in the RSI value is roughly proportional to the reduction in thickness.

Loose Fill. Many types of insulation are made in loose form for pouring or blowing into place. Materials include glass and slag fibre, cellulose fibre and expanded mica (vermiculite).

Rigid. Rigid insulation is manufactured in sheets or boards using materials such as wood fibre, foamed plastic and glass fibre.

Foamed-in-Place. Processes are available for spraying or injecting under pressure plastic resins such as polyurethane in a foamed liquid state. The foam sets into a rigid mass within minutes of installation. Because this foaming operation is, in effect, the last stage of manufacturing the product and it occurs at the building site, the installer must be highly skilled and very conscientious to provide a product of uniform quality and consistency.

Amount of Insulation

Table 36 shows the recommended minimum RSI values for various parts of houses and small buildings as called for in *Measures for Energy Conservation in New Buildings, 1983*. The amount of insulation is related to the severity of the climate as measured by the degree-day method. Degree-days are calculated for a given location by accumulating the differences between 18°C and the mean temperature for every day in the year when the mean temperature is below 18°C. Degree-day values for a number of locations in Canada are listed in the Supplement to the National Building Code of Canada or may be obtained from the local weather station or building department.

It should be recognized that the RSI values shown in Tables 36 are indeed minimums. In many cases, it is worth considering higher RSI values when building a new house. It is much easier to incorporate extra insulation when building than to add it afterwards.

All walls, floors and ceilings which separate heated space from unheated space or the outside air should be insulated. Foundation walls separating heated basements or crawl spaces from the outside air or soil should also be insulated to at least 600 mm below the exterior ground level or further. Methods of insulating these different areas are given in the following sections. The figures illustrate a number of possible methods of insulating building elements. It is not intended to imply that these are the only acceptable methods. Specific materials, thicknesses and spacings are shown in the illustrations in order to correlate with thermal resistance calculations. In most cases, the material, thickness or spacing illustrated is only one of a number of equally acceptable alternatives. The thermal resistance must be recalculated, however, if elements other than those illustrated are used.

Insulation of Foundations

Foundation walls enclosing heated space should be insulated from the underside of the subfloor to the top of the footing.

When insulation is applied on the outer surface of a wall or a slab perimeter, it should be of a type not susceptible to damage by water, such as expanded or extruded polystyrene or insulation capable of draining water, such as high density, rigid glass fibre insulation. In addition, the insulation should be protected above grade with 12 mm cement parging on wire lath applied to the exposed face and edge *(Fig. 98)*.

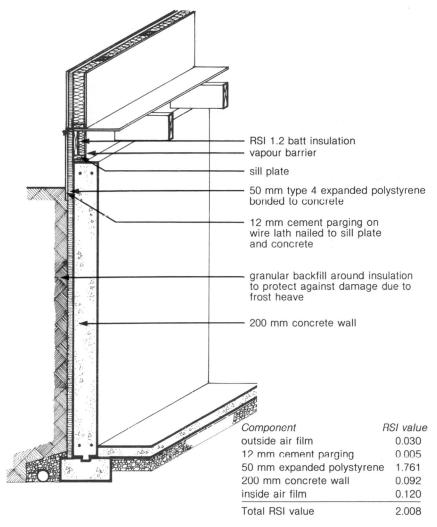

RSI 1.2 batt insulation
vapour barrier

sill plate

50 mm type 4 expanded polystyrene
bonded to concrete

12 mm cement parging on
wire lath nailed to sill plate
and concrete

granular backfill around insulation
to protect against damage due to
frost heave

200 mm concrete wall

Component	RSI value
outside air film	0.030
12 mm cement parging	0.005
50 mm expanded polystyrene	1.761
200 mm concrete wall	0.092
inside air film	0.120
Total RSI value	2.008

Figure 98. Concrete wall with rigid insulation on outer surface.

Where insulation is applied to the inner surface of foundation walls,
the below-grade portions of the insulation and any associated wood
strapping must be protected by dampproofing in the form of a 0.05 mm
polyethylene film or two coats of bitumen applied to the inner surface
of the wall. If the insulation is a type which will not readily absorb
water (for example, expanded polystyrene), no dampproofing is
required behind the insulation, but associated wood strapping should
be protected by, for instance, partial wrapping in 0.05 mm polyethylene.
However, in order to allow any moisture which does enter the wall to
escape, neither the inner nor the outer surface of the above-grade
portion of the wall should be dampproofed *(Fig. 99)*.

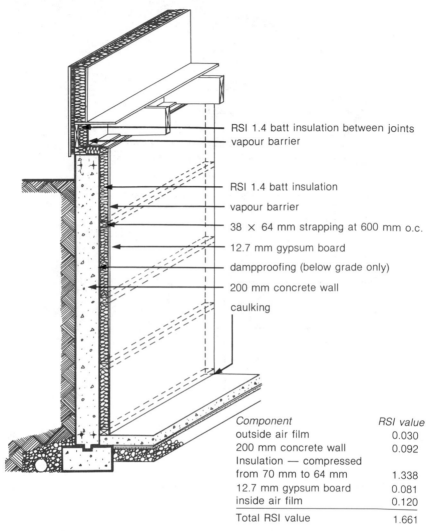

RSI 1.4 batt insulation between joints
vapour barrier

RSI 1.4 batt insulation

vapour barrier

38 × 64 mm strapping at 600 mm o.c.

12.7 mm gypsum board

dampproofing (below grade only)

200 mm concrete wall

caulking

Component	RSI value
outside air film	0.030
200 mm concrete wall	0.092
Insulation — compressed from 70 mm to 64 mm	1.338
12.7 mm gypsum board	0.081
inside air film	0.120
Total RSI value	1.661

Figure 99. Concrete wall insulated with batts — horizontal strapping.

Rigid board-type insulation should be bonded to the wall with cement grout or synthetic adhesive applied in bands forming a grid pattern. This pattern of bonding is recommended to limit warm moist air movement behind the insulation since this can cause water and ice build-up between the wall and the insulation. If a protein-based adhesive is used to bond the insulation to the wall, the adhesive should contain a preservative.

Due to its high potential for contributing to the rapid spread of fire, cellular plastic insulation applied to the inside of basement walls should not be left exposed but should be protected with an acceptable finish. Other types of insulation should also be covered to protect them from damage. Where fire protection covering is required, insulation should be held in place by mechanical fastening to framing members at least at the top and bottom of the insulation and around all openings.

Insulation can also be placed between the studs of preserved wood foundations. Preferably, the cavity should be filled above the normal requirements to prevent air pockets and convection loops from being set up within the cavity.

Normal weight concrete (that is, concrete with a density of about 2400 kg/m³) is indicated in the illustrations. Lightweight concrete may be used to achieve higher thermal resistance but should have a 28-day compressive strength of at least 15 MPa.

In the following illustrations, the insulation is shown extending the full height of the basement wall. With hollow core concrete block walls, convection currents may occur if the wall is not insulated over its full height. The bottom edge of the insulation should be sealed by caulking and, in the case of batt-type insulation, by solid blocking.

Insulation of Floors

Floors over unheated crawl spaces or over heated or unheated garages should be insulated.

Where there is no finished ceiling on the underside of the floor, some material must be added to support the insulation. For friction-fit type batts or for rigid insulation *(Fig. 100)*, wire lath or "chicken wire" tacked to the bottom of the joists may be the most economical method. For loose fill-type insulation *(Fig. 101)*, the support must be provided by a material which is solid (to prevent the insulation from falling through) but permeable (to avoid trapping water vapour which happens to penetrate the vapour barrier).

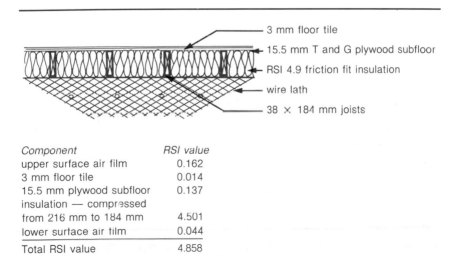

- 3 mm floor tile
- 15.5 mm T and G plywood subfloor
- RSI 4.9 friction fit insulation
- wire lath
- 38 × 184 mm joists

Component	RSI value
upper surface air film	0.162
3 mm floor tile	0.014
15.5 mm plywood subfloor	0.137
insulation — compressed from 216 mm to 184 mm	4.501
lower surface air film	0.044
Total RSI value	4.858

Figure 100. Floor over unheated crawl space insulated with friction fit batts.

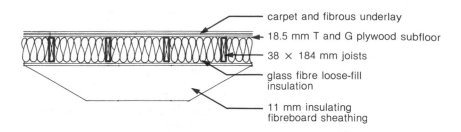

carpet and fibrous underlay

18.5 mm T and G plywood subfloor

38 × 184 mm joists

glass fibre loose-fill insulation

11 mm insulating fibreboard sheathing

Component	RSI value
upper surface air film	0.162
carpet and underlay	0.366
18.5 mm plywood subfloor	0.166
insulation	4.297
11 mm fibreboard sheathing	0.183
lower surface air film	0.044
Total RSI value	5.218

Figure 101. Floor over unheated crawl space insulated with loose fill insulation.

The vapour barrier must, of course, be installed on the upper or warm side of the insulation. No additional vapour barrier need be installed where a plywood subfloor with tight-fitting joints is used, as it is generally a good air barrier and a very good vapour barrier.

The insulation must be tightly fitted around cross bridging or blocking between joists. This requires particular care with batt and rigid insulation. It is also important not to omit insulation in small spaces such as between blocked double joists or between a wall and the first joist. In such cases, the insulation should be cut slightly oversize and carefully installed to avoid bunching and excessive compression.

When the insulation is installed only at the bottom of the joist space, the area at the ends of the joists must be carefully considered. The area of the joist header is, in effect, a wall and should be insulated accordingly. Also a well-sealed air barrier should be provided around the perimeter to minimize the possibility of cold air leaking into the joist space and "short-circuiting" the insulation.

Insulating a floor over unheated space reduces the heat loss through it but may not prevent it from feeling cold. Figure 102 illustrates a method which is recommended to avoid the "cold floor phenomenon."

Insulation of Walls

With normal 38 × 89 mm stud framing, the maximum thermal resistance that can be achieved by filling the cavity with batt-type insulation and using normal finishing, sheathing and cladding

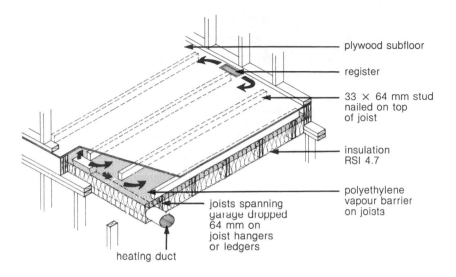

- plywood subfloor
- register
- 33 × 64 mm stud nailed on top of joist
- insulation RSI 4.7
- polyethylene vapour barrier on joists
- joists spanning garage dropped 64 mm on joist hangers or ledgers
- heating duct

Figure 102. Recommended method to avoid cold floor over garage.

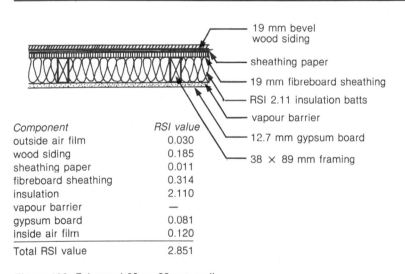

- 19 mm bevel wood siding
- sheathing paper
- 19 mm fibreboard sheathing
- RSI 2.11 insulation batts
- vapour barrier
- 12.7 mm gypsum board
- 38 × 89 mm framing

Component	RSI value
outside air film	0.030
wood siding	0.185
sheathing paper	0.011
fibreboard sheathing	0.314
insulation	2.110
vapour barrier	—
gypsum board	0.081
inside air film	0.120
Total RSI value	2.851

Figure 103. Enhanced 38 × 89 mm wall.

materials is about RSI 2.5. By careful selection of the sheathing and cladding, this can be extended to about RSI 2.8 *(Fig. 103)*. Going beyond this level requires special measures. One such approach is to use deeper studs, such as 38 × 140 mm, in order to accommodate thicker batt insulation *(Fig. 104)*. Another approach is to use 38 × 89 mm studs with the cavities filled with batt insulation, and rigid

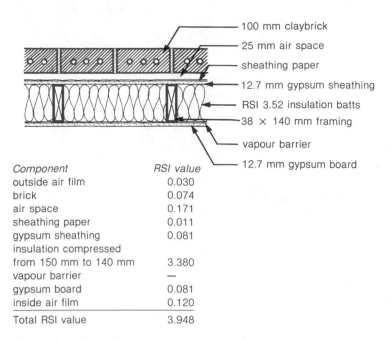

100 mm claybrick
25 mm air space
sheathing paper
12.7 mm gypsum sheathing
RSI 3.52 insulation batts
38 × 140 mm framing
vapour barrier
12.7 mm gypsum board

Component	RSI value
outside air film	0.030
brick	0.074
air space	0.171
sheathing paper	0.011
gypsum sheathing	0.081
insulation compressed from 150 mm to 140 mm	3.380
vapour barrier	—
gypsum board	0.081
inside air film	0.120
Total RSI value	3.948

Figure 104. 38 × 140 mm wall.

insulation applied to the outside either in place of or in addition to the normal sheathing *(Fig. 105)*. This latter method has the merit of providing a significant proportion of the wall's thermal resistance in a form which is continuous over the framing, thus reducing heat loss through the framing.

Some types of semi-rigid insulation come with a spunbonded polyolefin sheet attached to one surface. This material is vapour permeable but air impermeable and can constitute a good air barrier if the joints between the sheets are taped. Materials such as spunbonded polyolefin are available in 1.2 and 2.7 m rolls and can be applied to the exterior of any wall assembly to create an air barrier.

Other types of insulation, such as cellular plastics, have low water vapour permeance and are also air and water impermeable. If they are placed with the joints butted and caulked, they could also form a good air barrier, but their low vapour permeability requires that the joints not be sealed so that moisture in the wall cavity can be dissipated to the outside.

In every case, the use of sheathing paper on top of the insulating sheathing is recommended as a rain shedding device.

Loose fill insulation is not permitted for walls since the cavity must be closed in before the insulation is installed, and this makes it difficult to ensure complete filling of the cavity. In addition, loose fill insulation may settle and create a space at the top of the cavity when disturbed by vibration.

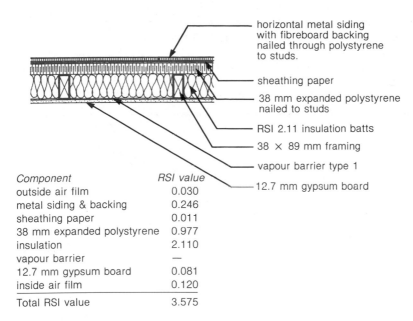

horizontal metal siding
with fibreboard backing
nailed through polystyrene
to studs.

sheathing paper

38 mm expanded polystyrene
nailed to studs

RSI 2.11 insulation batts

38 × 89 mm framing

vapour barrier type 1

12.7 mm gypsum board

Component	RSI value
outside air film	0.030
metal siding & backing	0.246
sheathing paper	0.011
38 mm expanded polystyrene	0.977
insulation	2.110
vapour barrier	—
12.7 mm gypsum board	0.081
inside air film	0.120
Total RSI value	3.575

Figure 105. Rigid insulation in place of sheathing.

Except where unavoidable, electrical and mechanical facilities such as boxes, pipes and ducts should not be installed in exterior walls. Where this cannot be avoided, insulation should be fitted tightly around the item in question and between the item and the outside surface in a manner which will minimize compression of the insulation.

Insulation for small spaces at intersections, corners and around openings should be cut only slightly oversize and carefully installed to avoid bunching and excessive compression.

Walls between dwelling units and garages should be insulated to the same degree as exterior walls whether the garage is heated or not, since garages are often left open for extended periods, and even where heating facilities are provided they are often not used.

Insulation of Truss or Rafter-Type Roof-Ceilings

The thicker batts now available for insulating roofs are made in widths equal to the full centre-to-centre distance of standard roof framing. The lower portion is slightly compressed when installed between the framing, but the upper portion retains its width and covers the tops of the framing, thus reducing heat loss through the framing.

Loose fill insulation can also be used to cover the framing and, unlike the standardized batts, offers the advantage that only the amount desired need be installed. On the other hand, care must be exercised to ensure it is installed at the correct density or settling may occur. Loose fill insulation must also be prevented from spilling onto eave vents and from being displaced by wind entering the vents. Baffles such as those shown in Figure 106 must be used to avoid blocking air circulation.

Batt and rigid type insulation should be installed so that it fits tightly against framing members, and care should be taken to ensure that air circulation to and from eave vents is not blocked.

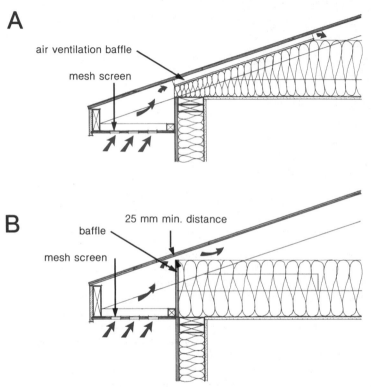

Figure 106. Eave details to avoid blocking ventilation: A, suggested detail with ordinary truss heel joint; B, alternative design with raised truss heel joint.

Insulation of Joist-Type Roof-Ceilings

When the ceiling finish is applied directly to its bottom surface, a roof framing member is called a joist rather than a rafter. This type of construction is found with flat roofs and "cathedral" or sloping ceilings. When such roofs are insulated between the ceiling and the sheathing, condensation problems can occur because the space between the insulation and the sheathing is divided into small compartments which are difficult to ventilate. Thus, any moisture which leaks through imperfections in the air/vapour barrier is not dissipated but accumulates and condenses. Measures to prevent this are shown in Figures 107 and 108.

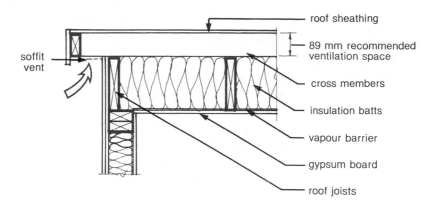

Figure 107. Insulating joist-type roof-ceiling between the ceiling and sheathing.

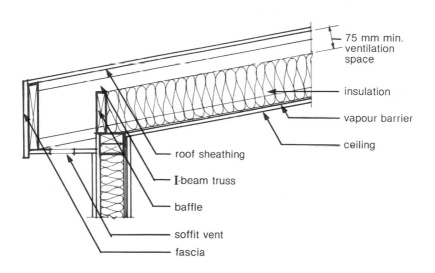

Figure 108. Alternative method of insulating joist-type roof-ceiling between the ceiling and sheathing. This method can be used where the slope is at least 1:6; the joists run in the same direction as the slope, and the ventilation space is continuous from eave to ridge and is vented in both directions.

Another approach to avoid condensation problems in joist-type roof-ceilings is to place the insulation above the sheathing, as is commonly done with flat roofs *(Fig. 109)*.

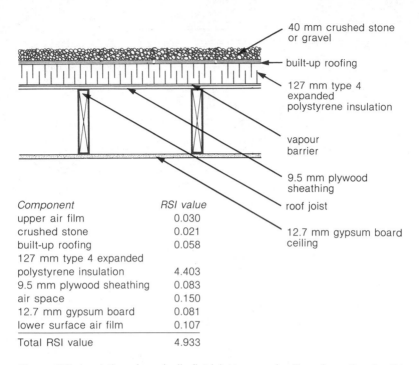

40 mm crushed stone or gravel

built-up roofing

127 mm type 4 expanded polystyrene insulation

vapour barrier

9.5 mm plywood sheathing

roof joist

12.7 mm gypsum board ceiling

Component	RSI value
upper air film	0.030
crushed stone	0.021
built-up roofing	0.058
127 mm type 4 expanded polystyrene insulation	4.403
9.5 mm plywood sheathing	0.083
air space	0.150
12.7 mm gypsum board	0.081
lower surface air film	0.107
Total RSI value	4.933

Figure 109. Insulation of nominally flat joist-type roof-ceiling above the sheathing.

Related Publications

Builder's Guide to Energy Efficiency in New Housing
        Canadian Home Builders Association, 1985
Energy-Efficient Housing Construction
        Canada Mortgage and Housing Corporation NHA 5488
Measures for Energy Conservation in New Buildings
        Associate Committee on the National Building Code, National
        Research Council of Canada, 1983

Fire and Sound Control

When a building is designed for multiple occupancy, as in the case of a duplex or semi-detached housing unit, there is a need for resistance to fire penetration and for sound transmission control between the units.

The sketches in Figure 110 show constructions which provide

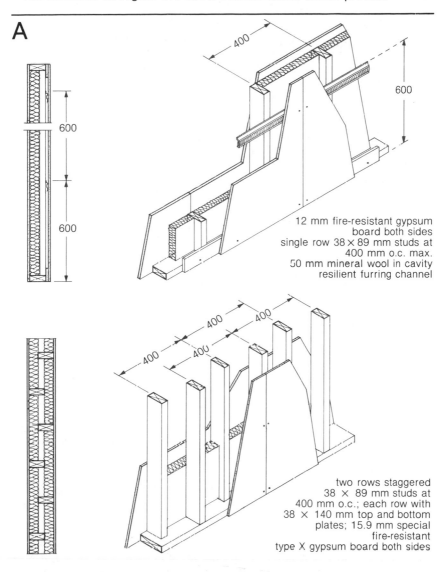

A

12 mm fire-resistant gypsum board both sides
single row 38 × 89 mm studs at 400 mm o.c. max.
50 mm mineral wool in cavity
resilient furring channel

two rows staggered 38 × 89 mm studs at 400 mm o.c.; each row with 38 × 140 mm top and bottom plates; 15.9 mm special fire-resistant type X gypsum board both sides

Figure 110. A, wood-frame walls providing an STC (sound transmission class) 45 or more; B, wood-frame floors providing an STC 45 or more; C, masonry walls providing an STC 45 or more. See overleaf for B and C.

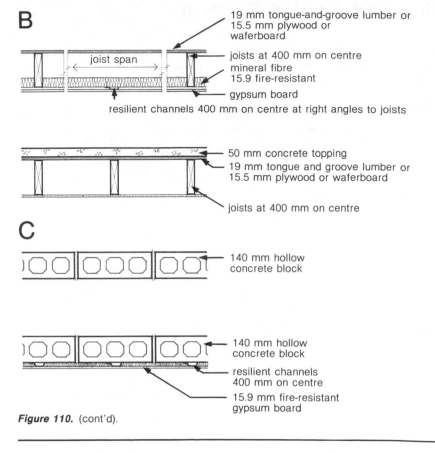

B

19 mm tongue-and-groove lumber or
15.5 mm plywood or
waferboard

joist span

joists at 400 mm on centre
mineral fibre
15.9 fire-resistant
gypsum board

resilient channels 400 mm on centre at right angles to joists

50 mm concrete topping
19 mm tongue and groove lumber or
15.5 mm plywood or waferboard

joists at 400 mm on centre

C

140 mm hollow
concrete block

140 mm hollow
concrete block
resilient channels
400 mm on centre
15.9 mm fire-resistant
gypsum board

Figure 110. (cont'd).

resistance to sound transmission in walls and floors to a degree that
meets normal requirements.

Resistance to the spread of fire can be provided when the interior
cladding meets the necessary flame spread rating. Various claddings
on the market offer ratings established by recognized testing agencies.

Smoke Alarms

The National Building Code and most local building codes require
early-warning, fire-detecting devices in dwellings, usually a self-
contained combined smoke detector and alarm that is wired into an
electrical system. The two basic types of smoke alarms are: ionization
(or "products-of-combustion") and photoelectric.

Location and Installation Where only one smoke alarm is provided, it
should be located between the sleeping area and the living area. Maximum protection is achieved, however, by providing a smoke alarm on
each storey and interconnecting their alarm functions. Smoke alarms

should be mounted on the ceiling or on a wall between 200 and 300 mm from the ceiling.

Building codes usually require smoke alarms to be permanently connected to an electrical circuit. There should be no disconnect switch between the smoke alarm and the dwelling's electrical service panel, and the circuit should not be connected to a wall outlet.

Where electrical power is not available, battery-powered smoke alarms may be used. These units are designed to operate for at least one year, followed by a seven-day trouble signal when the battery runs down.

Only "approved" or "listed" smoke alarms are certified as meeting building code requirements. Smoke alarms labelled by a recognized testing agency, such as the Underwriters' Laboratories of Canada, conform to acceptable standards.

Ventilation

Roof Space Ventilation

Even where air and vapour barriers are used, some moisture will leak around pipes and other openings and through the vapour barrier itself. If water vapour is allowed to accumulate in attic spaces and under flat roofs, during cold weather it is likely to condense in a cold spot in sufficient quantity to cause damage. Since most types of roof membranes are highly resistant to vapour transmission, the most practical way of removing vapour which enters the roof space is by ventilation.

During cold weather, heat loss through the ceiling insulation combined with exposure to sun may provide enough heat to melt the snow on the roof, but not on the eaves. Water from the melting snow can then freeze and form ice dams at the eaves trough and roof overhang. This may cause water to back up at the eaves, penetrate through the roof and leak into the walls and ceilings. Similar dams may form in roof valleys. A well-insulated ceiling and adequate ventilation will keep attic temperatures low and help prevent snow on the roof from melting.

A common method of providing ventilation is to install louvred openings or continuous screened slots in the eaves of gable and hip roofs *(Fig. 111)*. Air movement through such openings depends primarily on wind. These are most effective when combined with vents located high on the roof such as ridge vents *(Fig. 112,A)* or gable vents *(Fig. 112,B)*.

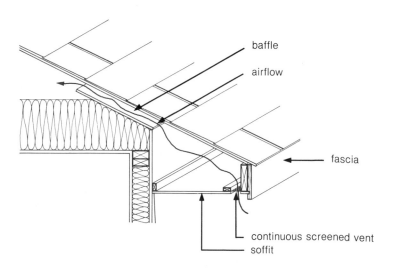

baffle

airflow

fascia

continuous screened vent
soffit

Figure 111. Soffit roof ventilators.

A

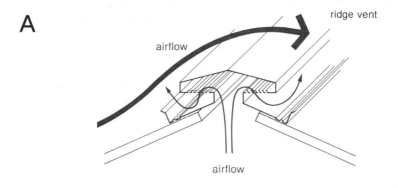

ridge vent

airflow

airflow

B

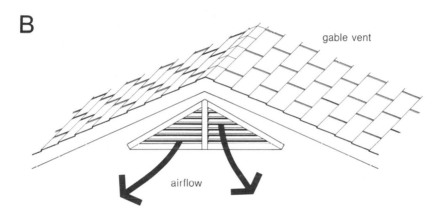

gable vent

airflow

Figure 112. High-level roof ventilators: A, ridge vent; B, gable vent.

Flat roofs insulated between the roof joists are difficult to ventilate unless there is clearance above the insulation, and the joist spaces are interconnected to permit free circulation of ventilating air (*Figs. 107 and 108*). These common techniques are not applicable where fine snow can be wind-driven through such vent openings and deposited on the roof insulation. In such situations, local building practices should be followed.

Size of Vents

The recommended minimum net area of ventilators for attic or roof spaces is one square metre for each 300 m² in net area. For example, a ceiling area of 100m² requires vents totalling at least 0.33m² in net area. The area provided should be increased to allow for restrictions such as louvres, wire cloth or screens. Corrosion-resistant metal or plastic materials should be used to screen ventilator openings.

Crawl Space Ventilation and Ground Cover

Unless it serves as a plenum for the heating system, the crawl space below the floor of a house should be ventilated through the outside walls. The net ventilating area should be at least 1/500 of the crawl space floor area. Where the crawl space serves as a plenum, the heating outlets in the floor will serve as ventilators as well.

Crawl spaces under the house or porch need to be ventilated during warm weather to remove moisture vapour rising from the soil through the ground cover. Otherwise, the vapour might condense on the wood below the floor and cause decay. Vents in outside walls should be screened and equipped with tight-fitting insulated covers to prevent air leakage in winter if the crawl space is heated *(Fig. 113)*.

Outside wall or floor ventilators are not usually necessary in a partial crawl space having one side open to the basement. The crawl space will be adequately ventilated through the open side into the basement, without any special provision being made.

The ground surface in all crawl spaces should be covered as described in the section on Footings and Foundations for Crawl Spaces.

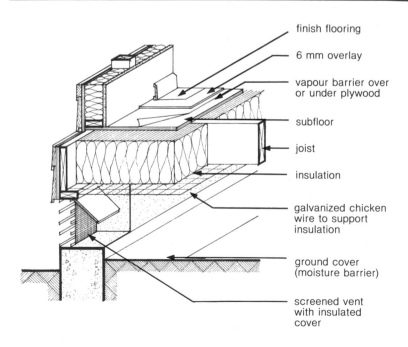

finish flooring

6 mm overlay

vapour barrier over or under plywood

subfloor

joist

insulation

galvanized chicken wire to support insulation

ground cover (moisture barrier)

screened vent with insulated cover

Figure 113. Crawl space vent and ground cover.

Interior Wall and Ceiling Finishes

Interior finish describes any material used to cover the interior wall and ceiling framing. The principal type of interior finish is gypsum board, although plywood, hardboard, simulated veneer hardboard and lumber can also be used.

Gypsum Board Finish

Gypsum board (sometimes referred to as "drywall") is the most widely-used interior finish because of its speed of installation, low cost and consistent result. In addition, gypsum board is manufactured in a variety of forms for different uses, such as fire-rated, foil-backed, water-resistant and prefinished. Various fasteners and glues, finishing accessories and wall systems or wall furring are also available. Thin sheet materials such as gypsum board require that studs and ceiling joists be well aligned. This is normally achieved by the use of good lumber, its proper placement (for example, crowns up for joists) and the use of additional bracing and blocking.

Gypsum board is a sheet material composed of a gypsum filler between two layers of paper. Sheets are 1.2 m wide and are supplied in various lengths, 2.4 m and longer. The edges along the length of the sheet are tapered on one face to receive joint compound and tape. Although gypsum board may be used in 9.5 mm thickness on support spacings up to 400 mm on centre, a 12.7 mm board is more commonly used for its extra strength. Where supports are spaced at 600 mm on centre, the minimum thickness should be 12.7 mm.

Gypsum wallboard is usually applied in single sheets directly on the framing members. On ceilings, the board is generally applied with the long dimension at right angles to the joists. On walls, it is more common to apply the sheets horizontally rather than vertically as it reduces the amount of nailing and the length of the joints. Horizontal joints at 1.2 m above the floor are below eye level, making them less conspicuous. Horizontal joints are also easier to tape than vertical joints, as they are continuous and at a convenient height. Ends of sheets, which are not recessed, should terminate at a corner and always on a support. This method provides a secure attachment and eliminates nail-popping.

Gypsum board panels are applied and attached with a minimum number of supplementary fasteners. Gypsum board can be attached to wood members by single nailing, double nailing, glue and nailing or screwing. In the glue and nail-on application, a continuous bead of adhesive is applied to the face of the wood framing.

Nails used to fasten gypsum board should be ringed, with 2.3 mm shanks and 5.5 mm diameter heads. The nails should be long enough to penetrate the support 20 mm. Where fire-resistant ceilings are required, greater penetration may be necessary. By using special hammers, the nail heads can be set slightly below the surface without damaging the paper. A slight dimple is thus formed in the face of the board *(Fig. 114,A)*. The nails at the recessed edge of the sheet may be driven with the heads flush since they will be covered with tape and joint cement.

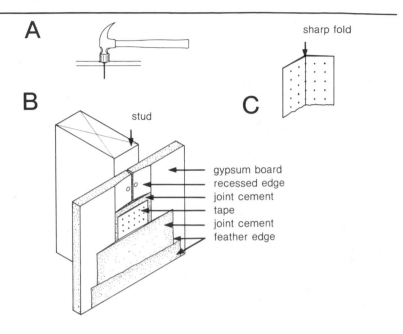

Figure 114. Finishing of gypsum board: A, nail set with crowned hammer; B, cementing and taping of joint; C, taping at inside corners.

Gypsum board may be "double-nailed," that is, nails are driven in pairs about 50 mm apart at intervals of 300 mm along the supports *(Fig. 115,B)* or the nails may be driven in a single pattern, spaced 120 to 180 mm along the supports on ceilings and 150 to 200 mm on the walls *(Fig. 115,A)*. The double-nailing method is more commonly used, as nail-popping is less likely to occur.

With special power-operated screwdrivers, screws can be used to fasten gypsum board. Screws are usually spaced 300 mm on centre at both the edge and intermediate supports. This distance can be increased to 400 mm on walls when the supports are not more than 400 mm on centre. The screws should be long enough to penetrate the support at least 15 mm.

If two layers of gypsum board are needed, the boards can be fastened in the usual manner with nails or screws or by using joint cement to fasten the second layer onto the first.

Before the joints are taped, all loose paper must be removed and the joints cleaned. All joints wider than 3 mm are then filled with joint cement and allowed to dry. External corners are protected with corrosion-resistant corner beads or wood mouldings, and at interior corners the tape is folded as shown in Figure 114,C.

Joint compound is supplied premixed or in powder form which is mixed with water to a soft putty consistency. Joint compound may be applied with hand tools, but mechanical applicators are now commonly used for both taping and filling.

The first layer of joint compound is applied in a band 125 mm wide along the joint. The tape is then applied and pressed into the fresh cement with a trowel or wide blade putty knife. Care should be taken to remove the excess cement, smooth the tape and feather the compound band to zero thickness at its outer edges *(Fig. 114B)*.

After the first layer has set, a second layer is applied in a band

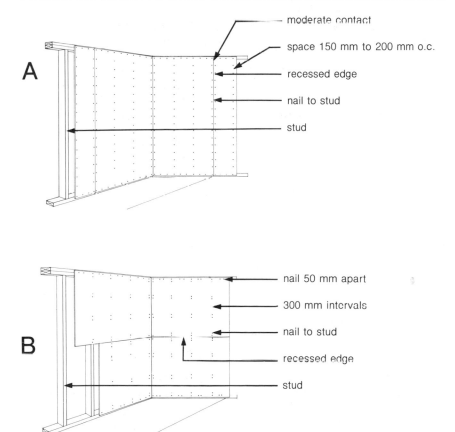

Figure 115. Application of drywall finish: A, vertical application of gypsum board showing single nailing method; B, horizontal application of gypsum board showing double nailing method. Where the ceiling sheets are supported by the wall sheets around the perimeter of the ceiling, the nails along the upper edge of the gypsum board may be omitted, with the uppermost wall nails being not more than 200 mm below the ceiling.

200 mm wide on recessed joints and 250 mm wide where the edges of the board are not recessed. Once again, the edges are feathered.

A third layer is applied and feathered to a band 250 to 300 mm wide on recessed joints and 400 mm on joints that are not recessed. Special care should be taken with this final layer so that the joint surface is smooth, and it does not form a noticeable bulge in the wall. When the third layer has set, the feathered edges should be sanded lightly with fine sand paper, care being taken to avoid damaging the paper surface of the gypsum board.

Nail heads and indentations in the centre of the board are filled with two layers of joint compound. Taping and finishing of gypsum board should be done at a temperature of 10°C or more.

Other Finishes

Other products used for finishing walls and ceilings are plywood, hardboard, simulated veneer hardboard and lumber.

Plywood is usually installed vertically in panels or in strips. The minimum thickness should be 4.7 mm for support at 400 mm centres and 8 mm for 600 mm centres. Where blocking is provided at mid-height in the walls, however, 4.7 mm thickness is used at 600 mm centres or less. When grooved plywood panels are used to simulate boards with the grooves parallel to the supporting framing, the grooves must not extend deeper than the face ply unless the grooves are located over the framing, or the plywood thickness exceeds the minimum by at least the depth of the grooves. Panels or strips are nailed on all edges with 38 mm finishing nails, spaced 150 mm along the edges and 300 mm at intermediate supports. Panels are available unfinished or with a factory-applied finish. Joints may have a V-edge, or a moulding may be used to cover the joints. For a panelled effect, plywood may be installed in strips, with a 20 mm space between strips, and supported on a backing course nailed to the framing members.

Hardboard finish is supplied in panels and is usually installed vertically. Thin sheets 3.2 mm thick need continuous backing. Sheets may be nailed directly to the studs, provided 6 mm thick sheets are used for supports up to 400 mm centres and 9 mm sheets on supports up to 600 mm centres. Hardboard should be supported on all edges and nailed as recommended for plywood. Both finished and unfinished panels are available.

Hardboard is also supplied in tile form and used principally on ceilings. Tile size may vary from about 300 mm square to 400 × 800 mm. The tile is tongue-and-grooved and is supported by concealed nails, clips or stapes. It should be 12.7 mm thick when supported not more than 400 mm on centres.

Lumber is sometimes used as a decorative finish to walls and ceilings. Lumber is supplied in tongue-and-groove boards of about 100 to 200 mm in width and 15 to 20 mm in thickness. Softwood species include cedar, pine or hemlock; hardwoods include maple, birch or cherry. Some of these species are supplied in plywood form as well.

Floor Coverings

Any material used as the final wearing surface on a floor is called finish flooring. There are many such materials on the market, each with specific advantages for a particular use. Two essential properties of any kind of finish flooring are durability and ease of cleaning.

Hardwoods such as birch, maple, beech and oak are used in a variety of widths and thicknesses as strip flooring; some species are also available in parquet form. Vertical grain strips of soft woods such as fir or hemlock are sometimes used. Wood finish flooring is widely used in living and dining rooms, bedrooms, corridors and general-purpose rooms such as family rooms and dens.

Other materials suitable for finish flooring include resilient flooring (in tile or sheet form) and ceramic tile. These materials provide water resistance and are used in bathrooms, kitchens, public entrance halls and general storage areas. Carpets, of course, may also be used as a finish flooring, except where water resistance is required.

Wood Strip Flooring

Wood strip flooring is manufactured in various widths and thicknesses and is available in several grades. The strips come in random lengths in separate bundles, the number of short pieces depending on the grade chosen. The thickness of wood-strip flooring required for various support conditions is shown in Table 37.

To link the wood strips together, one edge of each strip has a tongue and the other a groove. Wood flooring is generally hollow-backed, and the top face is slightly wider than the bottom so that when the strips are driven together the upper edges touch, but the lower edges are slightly apart. The tongue must fit snugly, as a loose fit may cause the floor to squeak.

The flooring should not be laid until gypsum board taping and other interior wall and ceiling finishes are completed. All windows and exterior doors should also be in place. This precaution prevents damage to the wood flooring either through wetting or other construction activities.

Strip flooring presents a better appearance when laid lengthwise in a rectangular room. Lumber subflooring is usually laid diagonally under wood strip flooring so that the strips can be laid either parallel or at right angles to the joists. Where it is necessary to place the wood strips parallel to the lumber subflooring, an underlay as described in Underlay for Resilient Flooring should be used to provide a level base for the narrow strips.

Hardwood flooring should not be brought into the house until the basement floor slab has been placed and gypsum board taping is completed. Moisture given off during these operations can be absorbed by the flooring and make the wood swell; then, after being put into place, the wood strips will shrink and open the joints. The flooring should be stored in the warmest and driest place available in the house until it is installed.

Various types of nails, including annular and spiral-grooved types, are used for nailing the flooring. Minimum nail lengths and nail spacing are listed in Table 38.

To nail the wood strips in place, many workers use a mallet-driven nailing tool which drives the nail in the proper location, at the correct angle, and sets the head to the proper depth. Others drive the nails using a carpenter's hammer.

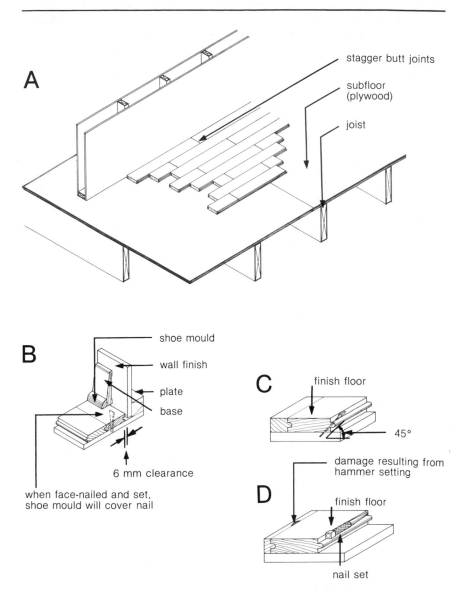

Figure 116. Application of strip flooring: A, general application; B, laying first strip; C, nailing method; D, suggested method for setting nails.

Figure 116,B shows the method of nailing the first strip of flooring with the nail driven down through the board at the grooved edge. The nails should be driven into the subfloor or joist and near enough to the edge so that the base or shoe moulding will cover the nail heads. The first strip of flooring should also be nailed through the tongue.

Succeeding strips of flooring can be fastened (using a carpenter's hammer) by driving nails into each strip at a 45° angle at the spot where the tongue adjoins the shoulder (Fig. 116,C). Nails should not be driven home with the hammer as the wood may be struck and easily damaged (Fig. 116,D). Instead, to finish the driving, a nail set positioned as shown in Figure 116,D is used. To avoid splitting, it is sometimes necessary to pre-drill the nail holes through the tongue. For all courses of flooring after the first, the pieces should be selected by length so that the butt joints are well separated from those in the previous course (Fig. 116,A). By using a piece of scrap flooring as a driving block, each board can be driven up tightly against the previous course with no danger of damaging the wood with the hammer.

Wood Tile Flooring

Flooring manufacturers have developed a wide variety of special patterns of flooring which are sometimes called floor tile and sometimes referred to as parquet flooring. One type is a block about 230 mm^2, available in various thicknesses and made up of several individual strips of flooring, with two edges tongued and the opposing edges grooved. In laying, the direction of the strips is alternated to create a checkerboard effect. Manufacturers provide specific directions for laying their own type of tile, and these directions should be followed carefully.

Underlay for Resilient Flooring

When the subfloor is not constructed as a combination subfloor and underlay type as described in the chapter on Floor Framing, an underlay should be installed under resilient flooring or carpets.

Plywood panels 6 mm thick are commonly used, although particleboard in the same thickness is also used. The panels are attached to the subfloor with annular grooved nails spaced 150 mm apart along the edges and at 200 mm on centre both ways over the rest of the panel. Nails should be at least 19 mm long for 6 mm panels and 22 mm for 7.9 mm panels. Staples may also be used. (See Table 29.)

Joints between panels and any defects in their surface should be filled with a non-shrinking filler compound that will bond to the underlay. The filler should be sanded smooth after it has set.

Installation of Resilient Floor Covering

Resilient flooring is usually installed after other trades have finished their work. The more common types of resilient floor covering used are solid vinyl and rubber; both types are available in tile and sheet form.

Resilient flooring is cemented to the underlay with a special adhesive. Waterproof adhesives are preferable to the non-waterproof types, especially in kitchens, bathrooms, entranceways and laundry rooms. Both tile and sheet material should be installed in accordance with the manufacturer's recommendations. Immediately after the flooring is laid, it should be rolled in both directions, the surface cleaned and then, if necessary, sealed with the type of floor wax recommended for the material used.

Resilient flooring for concrete slabs supported on the ground must be of a type recommended by the manufacturer for this particular use. A waterproof adhesive should be used in its application.

Seamless Resin Constituent Resilient Flooring

Resilient flooring can also be applied as a fluid with plastic chips or other decorative particles and fillers to form a resilient seamless wearing surface. Such flooring must be quality controlled as to components, application conditions and finished thickness in conformity with specifications from a recognized authority and the manufacturer's procedures.

Carpeting

Carpeting is normally used in living rooms, bedrooms, family rooms and occasionally in dining rooms. In rooms such as kitchens, laundry rooms or other areas where water damage or staining is likely to occur, carpeting should be avoided. When carpet is desired in such areas, a synthetic-fibre type should be used. For hygienic reasons, carpet is not recommended for use in rooms containing a toilet.

Carpeting should be installed over a panel-type subfloor or an underlay. Except for cushion-backed carpeting, felt or polymeric carpet underlay should be used.

Ceramic Tile

Ceramic tile can be obtained in different colours and with a glazed or unglazed surface. Since this tile has a hard impervious surface, it is often used as a floor covering in bathrooms and vestibules as well as for fireplace hearths.

Ceramic tile may be installed on a concrete slab floor, applied to a mortar base supported on the subfloor, or attached by a special adhesive to panel-type underlay such as plywood or hardboard.

When a mortar base is used, an asphalt sheathing paper is placed over the subfloor. The base should be at least 30 mm thick and reinforced with wire mesh. The mortar may consist of 1 part portland cement, $1/4$ part lime and 3 to 5 parts coarse sand. The tiles are pressed into the fresh mortar. To ensure a good bond between the joint material and base, the joints between the tiles should be filled the same day the tile is installed. To provide sufficient depth for the mortar bed, it is often desirable to drop the wood subfloor between the joists so

that the finish floor will be level with floors in adjoining rooms
(Fig. 117). Where the tops of the joists have to be cut out for this purpose, the span of the joists should be calculated on the basis of the
reduced depth.

When an adhesive is used to fasten the tiles to an underlay or
concrete floor, the base must be smooth and free from surface
irregularities. The adhesive is applied to both the tile and the base, and
each tile is then pressed firmly in place. After the adhesive is well set,
the joints between the tiles are filled with the material recommended
by the tile manufacturer for this purpose.

Ceramic tiles in shower bases may be laid on a lead or plastic liner
which is connected to the shower drain. This will prevent water
damage to the ceiling below should the tile and its concrete base
develop a crack.

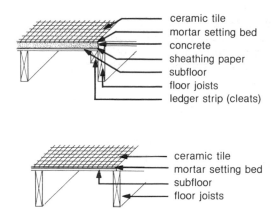

Figure 117. Installation of ceramic tile floor.

Interior Doors, Frames and Trim

Interior doors, door frames and interior trim are usually installed after the hardwood flooring is in place, but before it is sanded and before the resilient flooring is laid. Kitchen cabinets and other millwork are usually installed at the same time. The decorative treatment for interior doors and trim may be paint or natural finish using stain, filler and varnish or other selected materials. The finish selected for the woodwork in various rooms may determine the type or species of wood to be used.

Wood trim should be smooth, clean, sound stock suitable for finishing. Some of the commonly used species are pine, fir and basswood. The moisture content of the wood trim at the time of installation should not be more than 12 per cent.

Door frames are made up of two jambs and a head, together with separate mouldings called doorstops. Stock jambs are made of 19 mm lumber and in widths to suit the thickness of the finished wall. Jambs are often dadoed at the mill, with doorstops and head cut to size *(Fig. 118)*. Frames may also be rabbetted to form the stop, in which case the thickness of the frame is usually increased to 32 mm. If frames are unassembled when delivered, they should be securely nailed together at each corner.

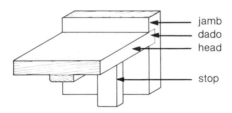

Figure 118. Interior door frame showing typical connection between jamb and head.

Casing is the framing or edging trim used around door openings. Many standard patterns in various widths and thicknesses are obtainable. Those with moulded forms require mitre joints.

There are two general types of interior doors: flush and panel. The standard thickness of interior doors is 35 mm, and they may be obtained in various widths and heights.

The flush door is made up with facings of plywood or other sheet material glued to a light framework. For natural or varnished finish, the face plies are selected for quality and colour. For a painted finish, the face plies may be the less expensive or non-select grades.

The panel door consists of solid stiles and rails with panel fillers of various materials.

Special doors are also obtainable with various kinds of closing hardware. Sliding doors and folding doors are popular for clothes closets. Sliding doors made of single sheets of plywood should be used in small sizes only since larger sheets will have a greater tendency to warp.

Doors should be hinged so that they open in the direction of natural entry. Doors should also swing against a blank wall wherever possible and not be obstructed by other swinging doors.

Interior doors are usually 760 mm wide and 1.98 m high. These sizes will generally allow easy passage of furniture.

Setting the interior door frame is done by means of wedges that are used between the jamb and rough-opening studs *(Fig. 119)*. Shingles may be used for this purpose. Frames are set plumb and square; wedges are fitted snugly, and the jambs are then securely nailed to the studs through the wedges. After nailing, the wedges are sawed flush with the face of the wall. Nails should be driven in pairs as shown in Figure 119.

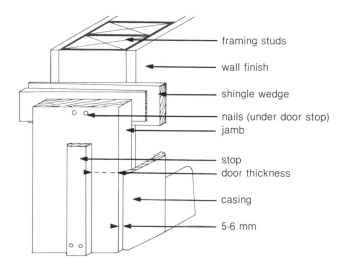

framing studs
wall finish
shingle wedge
nails (under door stop)
jamb
stop
door thickness
casing
5-6 mm

Figure 119. Door frame and trim showing frame blind-nailed under doorstop.

Casings are nailed to both the framing studs and the jambs with finishing nails. Nails should be spaced about 400 mm apart and the heads countersunk and filled. The casing is placed 5 to 6 mm from the inner edge of the jamb.

Stops are usually 10 × 32 mm and are nailed to the jamb with finishing nails after the door is hung.

Casing joints at the head of the frame are usually mitred. Careful cutting and fitting is required to ensure a tight joint. Mitred joints are sometimes glued because a glued joint is less likely to open when slight shrinkage occurs.

Standard clearances and the location of door hardware are shown in Figure 120. The clearances may vary slightly, but those shown are widely used. Hinges are shown as 175 mm from the top and 275 mm from the bottom, but these distances may also vary slightly, especially in panel doors. Where three hinges are used, the centre one is spaced midway between the top and bottom hinges. Standard knob height is 860 to 960 mm from the floor, and locks or latches should be installed accordingly.

Clearance around the door should be 2 to 3 mm on the latch side and 1 mm on the hinge side. A clearance of 2 mm at the top and 19 mm at the bottom is usual, but if the door is to open over heavy carpeting, the bottom clearance should be greater to permit air movement either into or out of the room.

Some manufacturers supply pre-fitted frames and doors, with the hinge slots already grooved for installation. Also on the market are sheet-metal door frames with formed stops and casings. Hinge slots and strike plates are integral with these units.

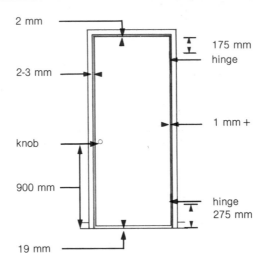

Figure 120. Suggested door clearance and location of hardware.

Installation of Door Hardware

Hinges should be of the proper size for the door they support. For 35 mm thick interior doors, two 76 × 76 mm butt hinges are used. The door is first fitted to the framed opening to ensure it has the proper clearances; then the door is removed, and the hinges are fitted to it. The door edge is routed to take the two half hinges. The edge of each hinge should be at least 3 mm back from the face of the door. When the hinge halves are screwed in place, they must be flush with the surface and square.

The door is now placed in the opening and blocked up at the bottom to provide the proper clearance. The jamb is marked at the hinge locations and routed to take the other two hinge halves which are then fastened in place. The door may now be placed in the opening, and the hinge pins inserted.

There are several types of door locks which vary both in cost and in method of installation. Lock sets are supplied with installation instructions that should be followed.

The location of the latch is marked on the jamb, and the strike plate located in this way. The marked outline is routed out to take the strike plate; the recess for the latch is also routed out *(Fig. 121,A)*. The strike plate is then fixed in place and should be flush with or slightly below the face of the jamb. When the door is latched, the face of the door should be flush with the edge of the jamb.

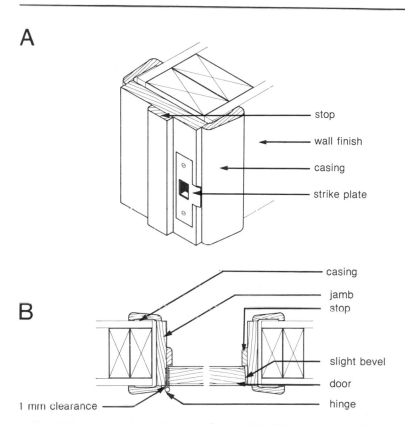

A

stop

wall finish

casing

strike plate

B

casing

jamb

stop

slight bevel

door

1 mm clearance

hinge

Figure 121. Installation of: A, typical strike plate; B, stops.

Doorstops may have been set temporarily during the installation of the hardware, but now is the time to nail them permanently in place. The stop at the jamb on the latch side is nailed first *(Fig. 121,B)* and should be set up tight against the door face when the door is latched. The stop on the hinge side is nailed next and should be given a 1 mm clearance from the door face to prevent scraping as the door is opened. Finally, the head stop is nailed in place. Finishing nails should be used and heads countersunk and filled. When door and trim are painted, some of the clearances allowed will be taken up.

Window Trim Installation

Casing for window trim is usually the same pattern as that selected for the doors. Finishing nails are applied to casing on all four sides of the window, except where a sill is used. In this instance, the casing terminates on top of the sill, and an apron is added as a finish member below the sill.

Base Mouldings

Base moulding serves as a finish between the walls and floor. It may vary in size and form but must be of sufficient thickness at the bottom to cover the flooring joint. A two-piece base moulding consists of a baseboard fitted with a shoe mould at the bottom *(Fig. 122,A)*. A one-piece base is milled with a thickened edge at the bottom to cover the flooring joint *(Fig. 122,B)*.

When a two-piece base is used, the baseboard is nailed through to the wall plate and studs, high enough so that the lower edge clears the finish floor. The shoe mould is later nailed to the subfloor using a long thin nail driven at an angle which holds the shoe mould tightly against both the baseboard and the finish floor. A one-piece base is fitted tightly to the finish floor and nailed to the wall plate or studs. The one-piece base or the shoe mould is installed after the resilient floor has been laid or after hardwood flooring has been sanded.

Joints at interior corners may either be mitred or butted and coped. Butted and coped corners are made by butting the first piece of trim against the corner; the second piece is then mitred or coped to correspond to the moulded face of the first. Exterior corners are mitred. All nails used should be finishing nails with heads countersunk and filled.

Millwork

Kitchen cabinets, shelving, mantels and other items of millwork are installed at the same time as the interior trim. This work is ordinarily carried out before the hardwood floors are sanded or the resilient flooring laid.

Cabinets and similar units may be either built in place or shop-built. The cabinets, shelving and other items can be made from a variety of

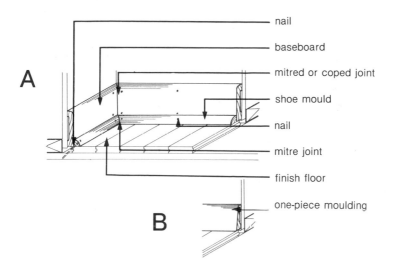

A

B

Figure 122. Base moulding: A, two-piece; B, one-piece.

lumber or other wood products.

Factory-made cabinets of steel or other materials are also available and can be obtained in various sizes.

Kitchen Cabinets

The kitchen deserves special attention, since it is a focal point of household activity. An efficient arrangement of kitchen cabinets, refrigerator, sink and range reduces work and saves steps.

Base units of kitchen cabinets are approximately 900 mm high with the counter top 600 mm deep. Various combinations of drawers and doors may be included in the base. Some cabinet arrangements include a corner cabinet equipped with revolving shelves. The counter top and backsplash (added along the wall above the counter top) are faced with plastic laminate or other impervious covering.

To provide work space, wall units are set about 400 mm above the counter. This distance should be increased to at least 600 mm for wall units over the range. The shelves, which can be adjustable, are usually 275 to 300 mm deep. The ceiling may be dropped over the cabinets as shown in Figure 123.

Closets

Although many variations are possible, clothes closets are commonly provided with shelves and a closet rod or metal track. A standard interior door can be installed *(Fig. 124,A)*; however, sliding doors in

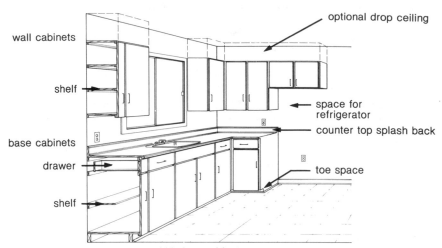

wall cabinets

shelf

base cabinets

drawer

shelf

optional drop ceiling

space for refrigerator

counter top splash back

toe space

Figure 123. An arrangement of kitchen cabinets.

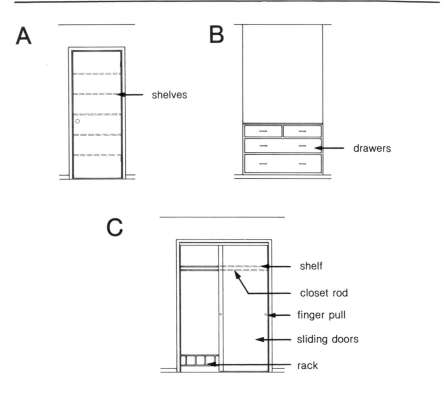

A

shelves

B

drawers

C

shelf

closet rod

finger pull

sliding doors

rack

Figure 124. Storage closets: A, linen closet with shelves; B, built-in cabinet in bedroom; C, clothes closet.

pairs or other multiple combinations are often used. Sliding doors are hung on a track with rollers fastened to the doors *(Fig. 124,C)*. Bifold doors consisting of narrow wood or metal panels, or accordion-type doors consisting of a metal frame covered with a vinyl fabric, are also used.

Built-in cabinets may also be used in bedrooms. Although this type of unit costs more than a standard opening, the inclusion of dressers and chests of drawers eliminates the need for much of the bedroom furniture *(Fig. 124,B)*.

Stairs

Stairways should be designed, arranged and installed to afford safety, adequate headroom and space for the passage of furniture. In general, there are two types of stairs in a house, those between finished areas usually referred to as main stairs and those which lead to areas used only for storage, laundry and heating equipment, such as unfinished basements or attics. The main stairs are built to provide ease and comfort and are often a feature of design, while stairs to unfinished basements and attics are usually somewhat steeper and narrower and are built of less expensive materials. If the basement or attic is to be used as a living space, however, the stair dimensions should be similar to those of the main stairs. Stairs may be built in place or built as units in the shop and set in place.

Stair Design Terminology

The terms generally used in stair design (*and shown in Figs. 125-28*) are defined as follows:

Baluster: Vertical member in a guard placed between the handrail and the tread in the open portion of a stairway, landing or balcony *(Fig. 125,D)*.

Effective Depth: The portion remaining after the stringer has been cut out or ploughed to fit the treads and risers *(Fig. 126)*.

Guard: Protective barrier, with or without openings, placed alongside the open portion of a stairway, landing or balcony.

Handrail: A rail running parallel to and on at least one side of the stairs, to be grasped when ascending or descending.

Headroom: The vertical distance from the outer edge of the nosing to the underside of the ceiling above *(Fig. 126)*.

Landing: A flat platform incorporated in a stairway, at least as wide and as long as the width of the stairs. Normally used to change direction of the stairs at right angles and to avoid the use of winders.

Newel: The main post for the handrail at the start and finish of the stairs, and the stiffening post at changes of direction and landings.

Nosing: The projection of the tread beyond the face of the riser *(Fig. 126)*.

Rise: The vertical height of a step *(Fig. 126)*.

Riser: *Closed*. The vertical board under a tread.
Open. The vertical board under the tread is omitted and the tread is supported on the stringers only.

Run: The net width of the tread measured from riser to riser *(Fig. 126)*.

Stringer: The member supporting the treads and risers.
Cut-out (Open). A stringer cut out to fit the treads and risers *(Figs. 127,B and C)*.
Ploughed (Housed). A stringer grooved to receive the exact profile of the treads and risers *(Fig. 125,C)*.

Tread: The horizontal plane of a step.

Winder: A radiating or wedge-shaped tread converging on a centre point at an angle of 30°.

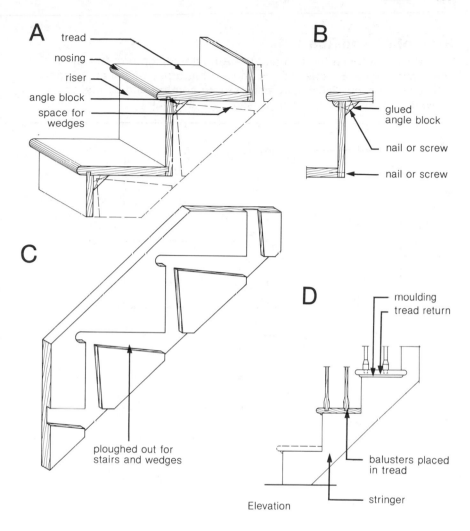

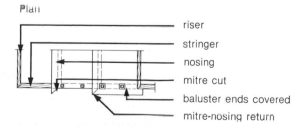

Figure 125. Parts of stairs: A, risers and treads tongued and grooved together; B, risers and treads connected with angle blocks; C, housed stringers; D, cut-out stringer (open) showing balusters and mitre-nosing return.

Ratio of Rise-to-Run

The relation between the rise and the run should conform to well-established rules. Experience has shown that a rise of 180 to 190 mm with a run of about 250 mm combines both comfort and safety, and these dimensions are commonly used for main stairs.

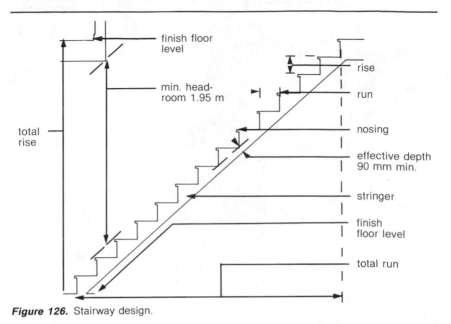

finish floor level

min. head-room 1.95 m

total rise

rise

run

nosing

effective depth 90 mm min.

stringer

finish floor level

total run

Figure 126. Stairway design.

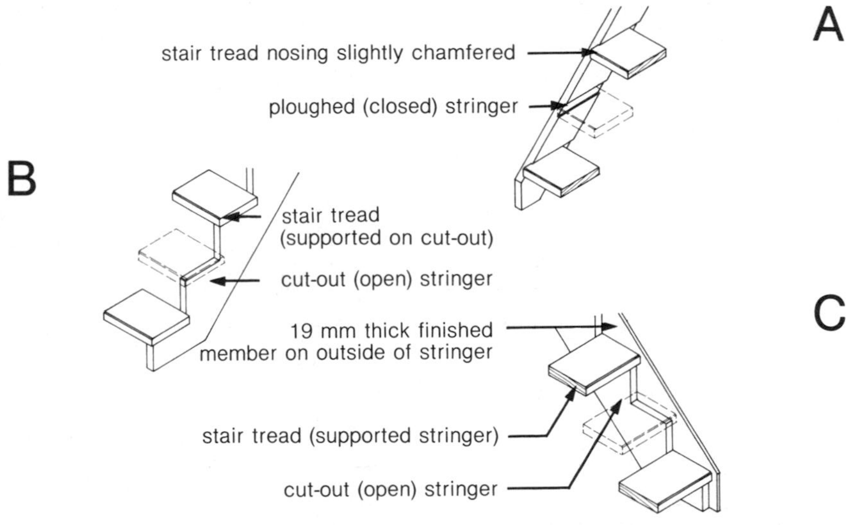

A

stair tread nosing slightly chamfered

ploughed (closed) stringer

B

stair tread (supported on cut-out)

cut-out (open) stringer

19 mm thick finished member on outside of stringer

C

stair tread (supported stringer)

cut-out (open) stringer

Figure 127. Basement stairs: A, ploughed stringers; B, cut-out stringers; C, cut-out stringers with finish member nailed to the outside of the stringer.

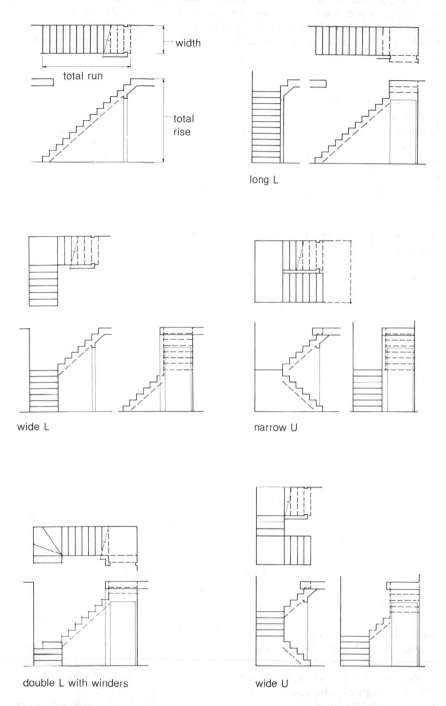

Figure 128. Types of stair designs.

Although the dimensions presented above may be considered desirable, space does not always permit their use. If such is the case, the following limitations should be observed: all stairs should have a maximum rise of 200 mm, a minimum run of 210 mm and a minimum tread width of 235 mm.

Stairway Design

Stairways may have a straight, continuous run without an intermediate landing, or they may consist of two or more runs with changes in direction. In the best and safest practice, a landing is introduced at any change in direction, but the turn may be made with radiating risers called winders. The length or width of any landing should not be less than the width of the stairs. Stairs should be at least 860 mm wide measured face to face of wall.

The diagrams in Figure 128 show different types of stairway designs. If winders are necessary because of cramped space, they must form an angle of 30°, so that three treads would be necessary for the maximum 90° turn permitted. Only one set of such winders is permitted between floor levels.

Once the location and the width of a stairway and landing, if any, have been determined, the next step is to fix the rise and the run. Once a suitable rise is chosen, the exact distance between the finish floors of the two storeys under consideration is divided by the rise. If the answer is an even number, the number of risers is thereby determined. It usually happens, however, that the result is uneven, in which case the storey height is divided by the next higher or lower whole number, and this will give the actual rise. The run is then established by dividing the number of treads into the total run of the stairs.

It is important to remember that the minimum headroom for a stairway should be 1.95 m *(Fig. 126)*.

Stringers

The treads and risers are supported on stringers which must always be solidly supported, firmly fixed, and truly positioned. The stringers may be either cut out *Figs. 125,D and 127,B and C)* or ploughed *(Fig. 125,C)* to fit the outline of the treads and risers.

Stringers should not be less than 25 mm thick when they are supported along their length or 38 mm when supported only at the top and bottom. The overall depth should be at least 235 mm, and when the stringer is cut out to fit the treads and risers, the portion remaining should not be less than 90 mm deep. A third stringer should be used when the width of the stairs is more than 900 mm. This may be increased to 1.2 m where risers support the front of the treads. Treads should be at least 38 mm thick when used with open risers. This thickness can be reduced to 25 mm where the stringers are not more than 750 mm apart or where the tread is supported by a closed riser attached to the treads.

The wall stringer may be ploughed out to the exact profile of the tread and riser with sufficient space at the back to take wedges *(Fig. 125,C)*. The top of the riser may be connected to the bottom of the tread by angle-blocks glued to both surfaces, screws being added to reinforce the joint. The bottom of the riser is attached to the back of the tread with screws *(Fig. 125,B)*. Another method is to tongue the top of the riser into the front of the tread and the back of the tread into the bottom of the next riser *(Fig. 125,A)*. The wall stringer is nailed to the wall, the nails being located behind the treads and risers. The treads and risers are fitted together and forced into the wall-stringer nosing, where they are set tight by driving and glueing wood wedges behind them. The wall stringer thus shows above the profiles of the treads and risers as a finish against the wall and is often made continuous with the baseboard of the upper and lower floors.

If the outside stringer is an open stringer, it may be cut out to fit the risers and treads. The edges of the risers are mitred with the corresponding edges of the stringer, and the nosing of the tread may be returned on its outside edge along the face of the stringer *(Fig. 125,D)*.

Newels, Handrails and Guards

Handrails run parallel to stairs and are designed to be grasped when ascending or descending, while guards surround openings to protect against falling over the edge. All stairways of three or more risers should have a handrail from floor to floor, and on both sides if the stair is 1.1 m or wider. For stairways that rise between enclosing walls, the rail is attached to the wall with brackets; for stairs that are open on one or both sides, handrails are supported by balusters and end against newel posts. Handrails should be set between 800 and 920 mm above the tread at the nosing, with at least 40 mm clearance from the wall, and be built so that there is no obstruction that could break a handhold.

Guards should be placed around openings such as landings and balconies that are more than 600 mm above the adjacent level, and alongside the open portions of stairways. They should be at least 1.07 m high around openings and 800 to 900 mm above the stair nosings along the open sides of stairways. Where one or both sides of a stairway are open, the guard is also the handrail.

Basement Stairs

Ploughed stringers *(Fig. 127,A)* are probably the most widely used supports for treads on basement stairs, but the tread may be supported on cut-out stringers *(Fig. 127,B)*. Another method sometimes used is cut-out stringers nailed to a finish member as shown in Figure *127,C*.

Exterior Steps and Stoops

Proportioning of risers and treads in laying out porch steps or approaches to terraces should be as carefully considered as in the design of interior stairways. The riser-to-tread ratio should not exceed those for main stairs referred to previously.

Outside steps and stoops need good support. If they are supported independently, their foundation should extend below the frost penetration line and be carried down to undisturbed ground. Outside steps and stoops leading to entranceways usually consist of precast units which are designed to be highly resistant to moisture, frost and impact damage. If the steps and stoops need to be made on site, the concrete should be air-entrained and have a minimum of 30 MPa compressive strength.

Flashing

Flashing is provided, where necessary, to prevent the entry of water through joints between materials. Proper installation of flashing is important, as is the selection of the most suitable materials for each specific location.

The minimum recommended weights and types of materials for flashing are as follows:

Exposed flashing: 1.73 mm sheet lead, 0.33 mm galvanized steel, 0.36 mm copper, 0.46 mm zinc, or 0.48 mm aluminum.

Concealed flashing: 1.73 mm sheet lead, 0.33 mm galvanized steel, 0.36 mm copper, 0.46 mm zinc, Type S roll roofing, 0.15 mm polyethylene and 0.05 mm cooper or aluminum laminated to felt or kraft paper.

Aluminum flashing should be isolated from masonry or concrete or coated with an impervious membrane to reduce the possibility of corrosion.

Flashing should be used at the junction of roofs and walls, roofs and chimneys, over window and door openings, in roof valleys and in other critical areas.

A typical example of construction requiring flashing is at the intersection of two types of materials, as shown in *Figure 129*. The stucco is separated from the wood siding below by a wood drip cap. To prevent the water from entering the wall, formed flashing is installed over the drip cap so as to form a drip at the outside edge. The flashing should extend at least 75 mm above this drip cap and under the sheathing paper. This type of flashing is also used over the heads of windows and doors unless they are well protected by a roof overhang. Where the vertical distance between the top of the trim and the underside of the overhang is more than one-quarter of its horizontal projection, flashing should always be used.

The heads and sills of openings in masonry-veneered, wood-frame walls should be flashed. Head flashing should extend from the front edge of the lintel, up and over the lintel and on up under the sheathing paper. Where a jointed masonry sill is used, the flashing should extend from the outer edge under the masonry sill up to the underside of the wood sill.

Flashing should also be used at the junction of roof surfaces and walls. If built-up roofing is used, a cant strip should be provided to avoid a right-angle bend in the membrane and consequent puncturing. The built-up roofing is carried at least 150 mm up the wall of the house over the cant strip and sheathing. The sheathing paper is then lapped 100 mm over the edge of the roofing. When the siding is placed on the wall, a clearance of at least 50 mm should be allowed between the siding and the roof to keep the siding well clear of drainage water *(Fig. 130)*.

Where stack-vents penetrate the roof, they should be flashed to

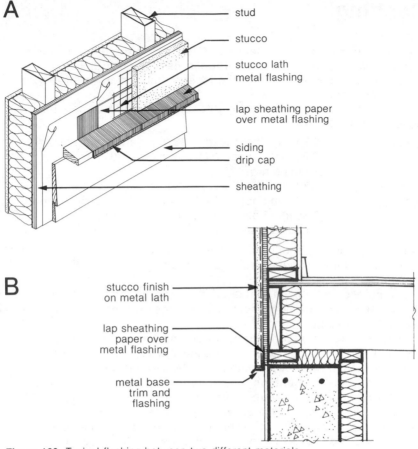

A

- stud
- stucco
- stucco lath
- metal flashing
- lap sheathing paper over metal flashing
- siding
- drip cap
- sheathing

B

- stucco finish on metal lath
- lap sheathing paper over metal flashing
- metal base trim and flashing

Figure 129. Typical flashing between two different materials.

prevent moisture entry. Sheet lead or neoprene is generally used for this purpose.

Flashing should be used where two roof lines intersect to form a valley. Depending on the shingling method used, valleys are referred to as open or closed. Open valleys usually are flashed with one layer of sheet metal at least 600 mm wide or with two layers of roll roofing. When roll roofing is used, the bottom layer may be Type S or Type M mineral surface material (mineral surface down) and at least 457 mm wide. This layer is centred on the valley and fastened along the edges with nails spaced 400 to 450 mm apart. A 100 mm band of cement is then applied along the edges of the bottom layer, and a strip of Type M mineral surface roll roofing approximately 914 mm wide is placed over the first layer. The top layer is fastened along the edges with only enough nails to hold it in place until the shingles are applied. The roof shingles are stopped on a line 100 to 150 mm from the centre of the valley, this distance being greater at the eaves than at the ridge *(Fig. 130,A).*

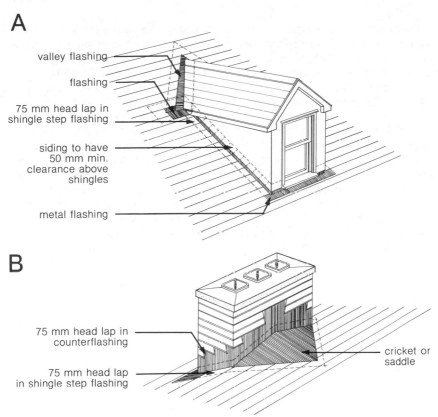

A

valley flashing

flashing

75 mm head lap in
shingle step flashing

siding to have
50 mm min.
clearance above
shingles

metal flashing

B

75 mm head lap in
counterflashing

75 mm head lap
in shingle step flashing

cricket or
saddle

Figure 130. A, open valley and shingle flashing at side wall; B, cricket flashing used with chimney that is more than 750 mm wide.

Closed valleys are flashed with one layer of sheet metal, 0.15 mm polyethylene or Type S roll roofing at least 600 mm wide. Each course of asphalt shingles is continued across the valley, ensuring that shingle nails are not placed within 75 mm of the valley centre line at the ridge or 125 mm at the eaves. Where rigid shingles are used, they are cut to fit the centre line of the valley, but these should not be used with the closed valley method of roofs that slope less than 1:1.2.

Flashing squares (sometimes called "step-flashing" or "shingle flashing") should be used at the intersections of shingled roofs with walls or chimneys. This type of flashing is installed at the time the shingles are applied, with one square being used at each course and being bent up along the wall under the sheathing paper *(Fig. 130,A)*. The siding will cover the flashing along the wall, except for the clearance allowed. These squares should be large enough to give a good lap at the roof and wall line, and the head lap should be no less than 75 mm. On roof slopes behind a chimney, the flashing should extend both up the roof slope and up the chimney to a point equal in height to the counterflashing of the chimney, but in any case not less than 1¹/₂ times the shingle exposure.

Counterflashing is used at the intersection of a roof with a masonry wall or chimney. This counterflashing should extend at least 150 mm up the side of the chimney or masonry veneer and be embedded at least 25 mm into the mortar joint. The counterflashing is fitted tightly against the masonry and lapped over the shingle flashing at least 100 mm. Counterflashing is applied to all sides of the chimney.

If the upper side of a chimney is more than 750 mm wide, a cricket or saddle should be installed (Fig. 130,B). These are often made of sheet metal and should be placed over a wood-framing support constructed during roof-framing operations. The saddle should be suitably flashed at the roof and counterflashed at the chimney. Open joints and laps should be soldered or sealed, or a locked joint used. A saddle is not required, however, if the metal flashing is carried up both the roof and the chimney to a height at least equal to $\frac{1}{6}$ the chimney width. This shingle flashing should never be less than $1\frac{1}{2}$ times the shingle exposure and the chimney flashing never less than 150 mm.

Eaves Troughs and Downspouts

The use of eaves troughs and downspouts in Canadian housing has become so common that many people regard them as mandatory. They are not required, however, by most building codes. Eaves troughs and downspouts reduce groundwater adjacent to the foundation and thus provide extra insurance against foundation leakage. They may, however, contribute to ice-damming problems. (See Figure 63 in the chapter on Roof Sheathing and Covering).

Formed metal eaves troughs are available in several different lengths. Fittings such as inside and outside corners, downspout connectors and elbows are available in sizes and angles to suit installation requirements. Plastic materials are also used for eaves troughs and downspouts.

Eaves troughs are installed after the exterior finish is in place. They are mounted on the fascia board as close as possible to the shingle overhang, with a slight slope toward the downspouts. Eaves troughs are fastened with 150 mm corrosion-resistant spikes spaced about 750 mm apart. A sheet metal spacer tube or ferrule is placed between the interior surfaces of the eaves trough, and the spike is driven through the eaves trough and the ferrule into the fascia board and rafter header. Joints in the eaves trough are soldered or otherwise sealed.

Downspouts may be rectangular or round, and those made from metal are usually corrugated for added strength. The corrugated patterns are also less likely to burst when plugged with ice. Goosenecks, made up from elbows and short sections of downspout piping, are used to bring the downspout in line with the wall.

Downspouts are fastened to the wall by means of straps or hooks. At least two hooks or straps should be used with each 3 m length of downspout.

Where the downspouts are not connected to a storm sewer, an elbow with an extension, or a splash block, is used to direct the water away from the foundation wall to avoid erosion. The final grading of the lot should be such as to ensure positive drainage away from the building and off the lot.

Garages and Carports

Garages can be classified as attached, detached or built-in; the type used is sometimes determined by the nature and size of the lot. Where space is not a limitation, the attached garage has many points in its favour. It is warmer during cold weather and, when equipped with an connecting door to the house, provides covered protection between car and house.

Built-in garages with living accommodation over the garage area are sometimes used in two-storey houses. A built-in garage may also be incorporated in the basement where reasonable access from the street can be provided. However, considering the snow and ice conditions in some regions, the slope of the driveway to the garage door should be gentle and a grated trough and drain should be installed in front of the garage door.

It is a mistake to make the garage too small for convenient use. Motor vehicles vary in size, and the garage should be long and wide enough to take any model and still leave space to walk all around the vehicle. This requires a minimum of 6.1 m between the inside face of the front and rear walls. If a work bench or storage space is to be located on the rear wall, the length of the garage must be increased accordingly. A width of 3.05 m clear should be a minimum, but 3.5 m or more is better so that doors on either side of the vehicle can be opened freely. A two-car garage should be at least 5.55 m wide. Since garage space is valuable for storage of garden tools, bicycles, screens, storm windows and other articles, additional space should be considered for this purpose.

Footings and foundations for garages are discussed in the chapter on Footings, Foundations and Slabs.

The framing and exterior finish of the side walls and roof of a garage are similar to that of the house. Interior finish is largely a matter of choice. Protection against fumes is required, but protection against fire is not required in the case of an attached garage serving only one single-family house. When the garage is to be heated, insulation and a vapour barrier should be included and covered with a wall finish to protect them from damage. The door between the garage and house should be fitted with weatherstripping and a self-closing device to prevent gas and exhaust fumes from entering the house.

There are many types of doors for garages, each with different advantages. The two most commonly used are the swing-up door *(Fig. 131,A)* and the sectional overhead door *(Fig. 131,B)*. Hinged doors are sometimes used. The one-piece swing-up door operates on a pivot principle with the track mounted on the ceiling and rollers located at the centre and top of the door. Counterbalance springs are mounted on the door, one at each side to make operation easier. The sectional overhead door has rollers at each section fitted into a track up each side of the door and along the ceiling. These doors are occasionally fitted with automatic openers.

Carports are generally attached to the house with all or most of the other three sides open. Carport roofs are usually supported by posts located on top of concrete piers. Piers should be at least 190 × 190 mm in size. Round piers formed in paper cylinders available for this purpose are often used. The base of the pier should be sufficiently large to ensure that the safe bearing pressure for the soil is not exceeded and far enough below grade to prevent frost heaving. Where wood posts are used, piers should extend at least 150 mm above the ground to protect the posts from ground moisture. Posts must be securely anchored to both piers and roof framing to resist wind uplift.

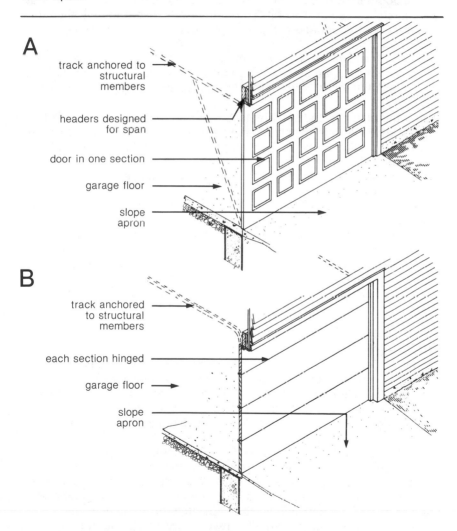

A

track anchored to structural members

headers designed for span

door in one section

garage floor

slope apron

B

track anchored to structural members

each section hinged

garage floor

slope apron

Figure 131. Types of garage doors: A, overhead swing; B, overhead sectional.

Chimneys and Fireplaces

Chimneys and fireplaces are usually of masonry construction supported on a suitable foundation. Lightweight, factory-built chimneys and fireplaces requiring no foundation may also be used. A chimney must be capable of producing sufficient draft to maintain the fire and carry off the products of combustion.

Since an ordinary fireplace has a very low heating efficiency, its chief value is decorative. Its efficiency can be increased, however, by use of a factory-made metal unit incorporated in the fireplace structure. In addition to direct heat from the fire, the room is also heated by air circulating through the unit. To be most effective, the unit should have draft-tight doors and a separate air supply directly from the exterior for combustion.

The inefficiencies of wood burning and the air leakage characteristics of fireplaces are somewhat offset when wood stoves are used. The fire safety requirements for wood stoves are similar to those for fireplaces.

Both the chimney and the fireplace must be carefully built to be free of fire hazards. Where possible, chimneys and fireplaces should not be located on outside walls. When located entirely within the house, they offer substantial advantages:
- heat that would otherwise be lost up the chimney and outdoors stays in the house;
- there will be less deterioration of the masonry from condensation of flue gases;
- if located near south-facing windows and of masonry construction, they will contribute to the thermal inertia of the house by storing solar energy gained during the day, and releasing it to the house during the night, and
- due to its warmer temperature, the chimney will have a better draft and thus exhaust flue gases more efficiently.

Chimneys

Masonry chimneys must be built on a concrete footing, properly proportioned to support the load. Because a chimney may contain more than one flue, the minimum dimensions depend on the number of flues and their arrangement and size. The wall thickness of a masonry chimney should not be less than 75 mm of solid masonry units.

The flue is a vertical shaft through which smoke and gases are carried to open air. A single flue may serve one or more appliances, for example, a furnace and water heater. In this case, both connections to the flue should be located one above the other to ensure a good draft. The size of the flue depends on the capacities of the appliances connected to it. A fireplace should always have a separate flue.

The flue lining usually consists of rectangular glazed clay pipe in sections, which are about 600 mm long and installed when the surrounding masonry is being placed. Care should be taken to set the linings close and flush on top of each other with full mortar beds. If more than one flue is used in a chimney, flues should be separated from each other by at least 75 mm of solid masonry or concrete, or 90 mm of fire brick where fire-brick liners are used *(Fig. 132)*. The linings usually start about 200 mm below the flue pipe connection and extend 50 to 100 mm above the chimney cap.

75 mm min. solid masonry between linings

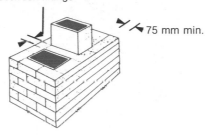

75 mm min.

Figure 132. Installation of flue linings.

Most factory-built metal chimneys are fabricated in sections and connected during installation. They are comparatively light in weight and can be supported by special anchors that are attached to the floor joists when the chimney is erected. Two precautions to be observed in the use of a factory-built chimney are:
- make sure the model has been tested and approved by the Underwriters' Laboratories of Canada, and
- ensure that it is installed in strict accordance with both the manufacturer's instructions and the conditions of approval set out by the Underwriters' Laboratories of Canada.

The chimney should be carried high enough above the roof to avoid downdrafts caused by wind turbulence. The height should never be less than 900 mm above the highest point where the chimney inter-sects the roof and should extend at least 600 mm above the ridge or any other obstruction within 3 m of the chimney *(Fig. 133)*.

The top of masonry chimneys should be capped to keep water away from masonry joints. Concrete is generally used for this purpose. The top of the cap should be sloped away from the flue lining and extend beyond the chimney wall at least 25 mm to form a drip edge.

A metal cleanout opening and door should be provided near the bottom of the flue so that soot can easily be removed from the chimney.

Chimneys may be used to vent gas-burning equipment; alternatively, the equipment may be vented through special gas vents approved for this purpose.

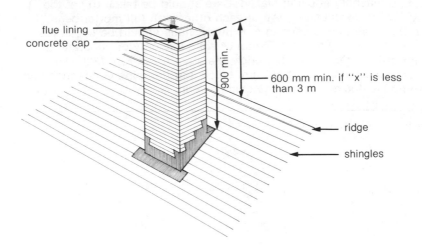

Figure 133. Chimney height above ridge.

Fireplaces

A fireplace that draws properly can be assured by applying proper principles of design. Fireplaces should have an external air supply to improve combustion. The fireplace flue should be lined. Its size depends on the size of the fireplace opening. One rule commonly used is to take one-tenth of the area of the fireplace opening to find the minimum size of the flue; however, the outside dimension of the flue liner should never be less than 200 × 300 mm. The terminology and locations of the various parts of a fireplace are illustrated in Figure 134.

Other design principles commonly used in the construction of a fireplace with a single face are:
- the front of the fireplace should be wider than the back and the upper part of the back should tilt forward to meet the throat for better burning performance.
- the back, which should rise one-half the height of the opening before sloping forward, is usually about two-thirds of the opening in width.
- a smoke shelf, to reduce back drafts, is formed by projecting the throat forward as much as possible. The throat should be as wide and shallow as possible, but in total area it must equal the area of the flue.
- the sides of the fireplace above the throat are drawn together to form the flue, which usually starts over the centre of the width of the fireplace; this slope, however, should not exceed 45° to the vertical.

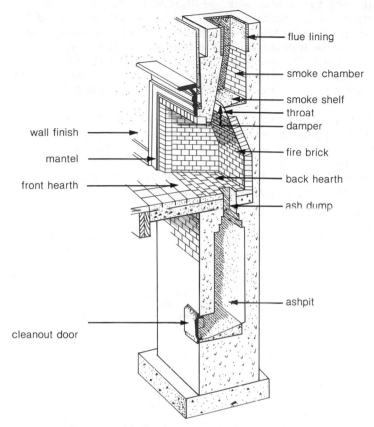

Figure 134. Terms used in fireplace construction.

The lining of the fire box must be built with materials having a high resistance to heat. A steel liner designed for this purpose or 50 mm of fire brick meet this requirement. When fire brick is used, it should be laid with fire-clay mortar or high-temperature cement.

If a 50 mm fire-brick liner is used, the back and sides of the fireplace should be at least 190 mm thick including the thickness of the masonry liner. Portions of the back exposed to the outside may be 140 mm thick. Where a steel fireplace liner with a air circulating chamber surrounding the fire box is used, the back and side may be solid masonry units 90 mm thick or 190 mm hollow units.

The damper is a large valve set in the throat of the fireplace which can be adjusted from the front to regulate the draft. Many types of damper units are available. By choosing one with a correctly proportioned throat passage, the risk of failure in the function of the fireplace is reduced. The damper should be capable of being fully closed and should be as tight-fitting as possible in the closed position to minimize heat losses up the chimney when the fireplace is not in use.

The hearth may be set even with the floor, or raised above floor level. It consists of two parts: the front or finish hearth and the back hearth under the fire. Because the back hearth must withstand more heat, it is usually built of fire brick. The front hearth is simply a precaution against flying sparks and is usually built of 100 mm reinforced concrete finished with ceramic tile. The front hearth should extend at least 400 mm in front of the fireplace opening and 200 mm on each side.

At the back of the fireplace, it is customary, but not essential, to have an ash dump through which ashes can be dropped into an ash pit. A cleanout door to the ash pit is provided in the basement for periodic removal of ashes.

If a factory-built fireplace is used *(Fig. 135)*, the same precautions should be observed as indicated for the use of factory-built chimneys.

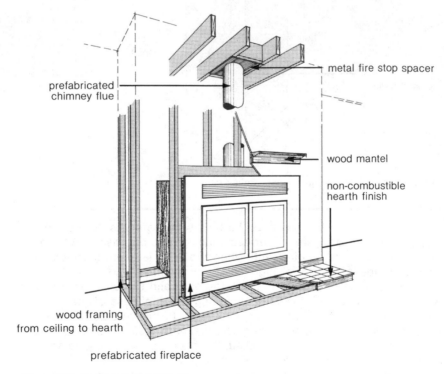

prefabricated chimney flue

metal fire stop spacer

wood mantel

non-combustible hearth finish

wood framing from ceiling to hearth

prefabricated fireplace

Figure 135. Factory-built fireplace.

Surface Drainage, Driveways and Walkways

For a successful landscape plan, it is necessary to assess the needs for surface drainage, driveways and walkways. Driveways and walkways should be made of materials in character with the house and yard.

Surface Drainage

A surface drainage pattern should be established which will drain the entire lot and direct water away from the house. Driveways and walkways should be set low enough to avoid interference with the drainage pattern. If a well is used to supply water for the house, all surface drainage must be directed away from the well to avoid contamination of water supply.

Driveways

A safe driveway should not slope too steeply to the street and should be graded so that water will not accumulate on the surface. The drainage slope, which may be across the driveway or along its length, should be not less than 1:60.

The commonly used materials for driveways are concrete, asphalt and crushed stone. A full-width driveway is preferable, although a satisfactory driveway may be made of two ribbons at least 600 mm wide, spaced about 1.5 m apart centre-to-centre. The ribbon type is more economical than full-width pavement. It is not, however, suitable for use where curves and turnout areas are required.

The full-width driveway is easier to drive over; in addition, by increasing its width, the full-width driveway may also serve as a walkway. A driveway should be at least 2.5 m wide, and increased to 3 m when it serves as a walkway.

In the construction of driveways, the area to be paved should be graded to a uniform smooth surface and be well compacted. All soft material as well as loose rocks or boulders must be removed to a depth of approximately 100 mm and the holes filled and well tamped with hard material. If the ground has recently been filled, it should be well compacted as any settlement in the subsoil is likely to cause cracking in the finished driveway. A well-compacted base of gravel or crushed stone, at least 100 mm thick, is necessary if the driveway is to be surfaced with asphalt. Asphalt is usually about 40 mm thick. Concrete 120 mm thick may be used without a base, but this thickness can be reduced to 75 mm when put down over a 120 mm gravel base.

Concrete placing, finishing and curing should be carried out as described under "Basement Floor Slabs" in the chapter on Footings, Foundations and Slabs. Overworking the surface during bull floating operations, that is, bringing up too much paste and bleed water, will result in a less durable finish. Control joints in driveways should be placed from 3 to 3.5 m apart. The resulting panels should be as nearly square as possible. Isolation joints, consisting of premoulded joint filler or sheathing paper, should be used to isolate the driveway from the curb, garage slab and house foundation wall. Control joints should be made as described under "Basement Floor Slabs." Premoulded joint filler in isolating joints should extend to the full depth of the driveway slab and be 6 to 12 mm thick.

Walkways

Cast-in-place concrete or precast slabs are commonly used for walkways. Other types of material such as asphalt, clay or concrete brick, fine gravel or crushed stone may also be used.

Walkways should be built on a well-compacted base, with a slight slope to drain the water off the surface. A base course is not normally used under concrete walks but must be used under asphalt surfaces. Concrete walks should be at least 100 mm thick and asphalt about 40 mm thick. Control joints are included in concrete walks for the same reason as described for driveways. These joints are usually spaced apart about one-and-a-half times the walkway width. Precast slabs are generally laid in a levelling bed of sand.

Protection Against Decay and Termites

Wood used under conditions where it will always be dry or even where it is subject to short periods of intermittent wetting followed by rapid drying will not decay. However, all wood and wood products used in construction are subject to decay if allowed to remain wet for long periods. Most of the wood used in a house is not subject to this condition, provided suitable precautions are taken. Protection is accomplished by methods of design and construction, by use of suitable materials and in some cases by treating the materials.

The building site should be well drained and untreated wood should not come in contact with the soil. Foundation walls should extend at least 150 mm above the ground and where wood siding or wood-base sidings are used, they should be kept at least 200 mm from the ground. The ground level in a crawl space should be at least 300 mm below joists and beams, and it should be increased to 450 mm where termites are a problem.

Surfaces like steps, porches, and door and window sills should be sloped to promote water run-off. Flashing should be used over doors and windows and other projections where water is likely to seep into the structure. (See the chapter on Flashing). The use of roofs with considerable overhang gives added protection to the siding and other parts of the houses. Similarly, covered entranceways protect the doors.

Exterior wood steps, rails and porch floors exposed to rain and snow have a high decay potential. Unless they are pressure-treated, wood members in such applications should not be in direct contact with the ground. It is important to protect the end grain of wood at the joints since end grain absorbs water easily. If pressure-treated lumber must be cut on the job site, the cut ends should be soaked in preservative until they have absorbed as much preservative as possible. The ends and joints in siding may be treated during erection or filled later to prevent the entry of water. A good quality caulking compound should be used around the window frames, door frames, siding that comes in contact with masonry veneer, under door sills that are not fully protected from rain and at other similar locations to prevent the entry of water into the structure.

If a moisture barrier is not used on the ground surface, crawl spaces are apt to become very humid and expose the framing members to conditions that are conducive to decay. The ground cover, which prevents moisture in the ground from entering the space, should be installed as described in the chapter on Ventilation. The crawl space should also be ventilated in the summer.

Wood is subject to attack by termites. In regions where termites are known to occur, precautions should be taken to safeguard the structure against damage. The best time to provide protection is during the planning and construction of the house. Provincial or municipal building codes which outline necessary methods of protection should be followed.

Painting

The primary purposes of exterior painting are to protect surfaces from the weather and to enhance appearance. As well as for appearance, interior surfaces are painted to protect them from damage by moisture which is prevalent in the kitchen, bathroom and laundry room. Painted surfaces are also easier to clean.

A wide variety of paints, stains and other coatings are available for exterior and interior use. Good quality materials should be selected and applied in accordance with the manufacturers' recommendations. Since the cost of the materials is nearly always a small proportion of the total cost of painting, it is false economy to use poor quality materials. Good quality house paint properly applied will usually last for four or five years.

Surfaces to be painted should be clean and free from substances that will interfere with the adhesion of the paint. After the prime coat is applied, nail holes, cracks and other defects should be filled with putty or a suitable filler. Painting should not be carried out in temperatures below 5°C. The surface to be painted should be dry.

Clear coatings that provide a protective film over the surface of wood are adversely affected by direct sunlight and have a short life expectancy, perhaps one or two years, on surfaces exposed to the sun's rays. Direct sunlight causes the film to disintegrate and fall off in patches leaving parts of the wood exposed. Since the parts of the film that remain are hard and brittle, preparation of the surface for re-coating becomes difficult. Coloured stains soak into the wood leaving no visible film on the surface and protect all sides of the house much longer — perhaps four years or more. Re-coating is also much easier as it can be done with a minor amount of surface preparation.

Maintenance

A house that is well built using suitable materials, with adequate attention being paid to construction details as described in this publication, will require far less maintenance than a house that is not well constructed and uses poor quality materials. Yet, while sound construction methods and suitable materials in the initial construction will greatly reduce the cost of maintenance, they will not result in a "maintenance-free" house, and some maintenance can be expected even during the first year of occupancy.

In a newly-built house, it is quite common, for example, for the interior wall finish to develop some minor cracks and for some of the doors to stick. These flaws usually show up during or after the first heating season when the wood-frame members may shrink slightly due to changes in moisture content or after the bearing members have settled to their final position under loading.

Quite frequently, the backfill material around the house foundation will settle which can cause the surface water to pond against the basement or foundation wall. This should be corrected by filling up any settled areas to their proper level as soon as settling has taken place.

Prudent homeowners develop a well-planned program of care and maintenance which they continue throughout the years. Just as maintenance costs are greatly reduced by adequate attention to the methods and materials used in construction, it is equally true that a continuing program of maintenance will further reduce the cost of upkeep, enhance the value of the property and greatly increase the useful life of a wood-frame house.

Related Design Publications

Internal Spaces for the Dwelling
Canada Mortgage and Housing Corporation NHA 5791
Landscape Architectural Design and Maintenance
Canada Mortgage and Housing Corporation NHA 5476

Appendix A
Tables

Table 1
Minimum Thickness of Foundation Walls

Type of Foundation Wall	Minimum Wall Thickness, mm	Maximum Height of Finish Grade Above Basement Floor or Inside Grade	
		Foundation Wall Laterally Unsupported At the Top,[1] to [4] m	Foundation Wall Laterally Supported At the Top,[1] to [4] m
Solid concrete (15 MPa min. strength)	150	0.70	1.52
	200	1.22	2.13
	250	1.37	2.29
	300	1.52	2.29
Solid concrete (20 MPa min. strength)	150	0.76	1.83
	200	1.22	2.29
	250	1.37	2.29
	300	1.52	2.29
Concrete block	140	0.61	0.61
	190	0.91	1.22
	240	1.22	1.83
	290	1.37	2.13

Notes to Table 1.

[1] Foundation walls are considered laterally supported at the top if the floor joists are embedded in the top of the foundation walls, or if the floor system is anchored to the top of the foundation walls with anchor bolts, in which case the joists may run either parallel or perpendicular to the foundation wall.

[2] When a foundation wall contains an opening more than 1.2 m in length or openings in more than 25 per cent of its length, that portion of the wall beneath such openings is considered laterally unsupported unless the wall around the opening is reinforced to withstand the earth pressure.

[3] When the length of solid wall between windows is less than the average length of the windows, the combined length of such windows is considered as a single opening.

[4] When foundation walls support solid masonry walls, the foundation wall is considered to be laterally supported by the first floor.

Table 2
Concrete Mixes (by Volume)

Concrete Strength	Cement (part)	Sand (parts)	Coarse Aggregate
15 MPa	1	2	4 parts up to 50 mm in size
	1	—	6 parts pit run gravel
20 MPa	1	1 3/4	3 parts up to 40 mm in size
	1	—	4 3/4 parts pit run gravel

Table 3
Minimum Depths of Foundations

Type of soil	Foundations containing Heated Basements or Crawl Space		Foundations containing No Heated Space	
	Good Soil Drainage to at Least the Depth of Frost Penetration	Poor Soil Drainage	Good Soil Drainage to at Least the Depth of Frost Penetration	Poor Soil Drainage
Clay or soils not clearly defined	1.2 m	1.2 m	1.2 m but not less than the depth of frost penetration	1.2 m but not less than the depth of frost penetration
Silt	No limit	No limit	Below the depth of frost penetration	Below the depth of frost penetration
Coarse grained soils	No limit	No limit	No limit	Below the depth of frost penetration
Rock	No limit	No limit	No limit	No limit

Table 4
Minimum Footing Sizes
(Length of Supported Joists 4.9 m or less. Design Floor Load 2.4 kN/m² Maximum)

No. of Floors Supported	Minimum Widths of Strip Footings, mm		Minimum Area of Column[1] Footings, m²
	Supporting Exterior Walls	Supporting Interior Walls	
1	250[2]	200[3]	0.4
2	350[2]	350[3]	0.75
3	450[2]	500[3]	1.0

Notes to Table 4.
[1] Sizes are based on columns spaced 3 m (on centre). For other column spacings, footing areas must be adjusted in proportion to the distance between columns.
[2] For each storey of masonry veneer over wood-frame construction, footing widths must be increased by 65 mm. For each storey of masonry construction other than foundation walls, the footing width must be increased by 130 mm.
[3] For each storey of masonry supported by the footing, the footing width must be increased by 100 mm.

Table 5
Mortar Mix Proportions (by volume)

Permissible Use of Mortar	Portland Cement	Masonry Cement (Type H)	Lime	Aggregate
All locations[1]	$1/2$ to 1	1	—	
	1	—	$1/4$ to $1/2$	
All locations,[1] except: foundation walls and piers	—	1	—	Not less than $2 1/4$ and not more than 3 times the sum of the volumes of the cement and lime
	1	—	$1/2$ to $1 1/4$	
All locations, except loadbearing walls of hollow units	1	—	$1 1/4$ to $2 1/2$	
All non-loadbearing partitions and all load-bearing walls of solid units except foundation walls	1	—	$2 1/4$ to 4	
	—	—	1	

Note to Table 5.
[1] Must not be used for sand-lime brick or concrete brick.

Table 6
Dimension Lumber — Grades and Uses

Sizes (mm)	Grades	Common Grade mix[1]	Principal uses	Grade Category
38 to 89 mm thick, 38 to 89 mm wide	Select structural No. 1 No. 2	No. 2 and Better (No. 2 & Btr.)	Most common; used in most construction. Shows high strength, stiffness and good appearance. Preferred for trusses, rafters and roof joists.	Structural Light Framing
	No. 3[3]	—	Used in construction where high strength and appearance are not important, such as studs in non-loadbearing walls.	
	Construction[3] Standard[3]	Standard and Better (Std. & Btr.)	Most common, used in general framing work. Has less strength and smaller spans than No. 2 & Btr. structural light framing, but is stronger and allows longer spans than No. 3.	Light Framing
	Utility[2]	—	Used most economically where high strength is not important, such as studs and plates in partition walls, blocking and bracing.	

Table 6 (Cont'd)
Dimension Lumber — Grades and Uses

Sizes (mm)	Grades	Common Grade mix[1]	Principal uses	Grade Category
	Economy[2]	—	Used in temporary or low cost construction where strength and appearance are not important.	
38 to 89 mm thick, 114 mm and wider	Select structural No. 1 No. 2	No. 2 & Btr.	Most common; used in most construction where high strength and stiffness are desired, such as floor joists, roof joists and rafters.	Structural Joists and Planks
	No. 3[3]	—	Used in general construction where strength is not important.	
	Economy[2]	—	Used in temporary or low cost construction where strength and appearance are not important.	
38 × 38, 38 × 64, 38 × 89, 38 × 140, 64 × 64, 64 × 89, 89 × 89	Stud[3]	—	Most common; special purpose grade intended for all stud uses.	Stud
	Economy Stud[2]	—	Used in temporary or low cost construction where strength and appearance are not important.	

Notes to Table 6.
[1] For ease in grade sorting at the mill, the higher grades are combined and sold as a grade mix. Pieces of lumber in the grade mix are still individually grade stamped.
[2] Except for the utility and economy grades, all grades are stress graded which means specified strengths have been assigned and span tables calculated.
[3] Construction, Standard, Stud and No. 3 Grades should not be used in designs that are not composed of 3 or more essentially parallel members spaced on 610 mm centres or less, so arranged or connected to mutually support loading.

Table 7
Facsimiles of Grade Marks Used by Canadian Lumber
Manufacturing Associations and Agencies Authorized
to Grade Mark Lumber in Canada

Facsimile of Grade Mark	Association or Agency
A.F.P.A.® 00 S—P—F S-DRY STAND	Alberta Forest Products Association 204—11710 Kingsway Avenue Edmonton, Alberta T5G 0X5
C L A S-P-F **100** No. 1 S-GRN.	Canadian Lumbermen's Association 27 Goulburn Avenue Ottawa, Ontario K1N 8C7
 1 S-GRN 1 1 D FIR-N	Cariboo Lumber Manufacturers Association 301—197 Second Avenue North Williams Lake, B.C. V2G 1Z5
CFPA® 00 S-P-F S-DRY CONST	Central Forest Products Association P.O. Box 1169 Hudson Bay, Sask. S0E 0Y0 and Saskatchewan Forest Products Corporation 550 First Avenue East Prince Albert, Sask. S6V 2A5
⌂⌂⌂® W.CEDAR S-GRN.-(N) **100** N̲o 3	Council of Forest Industries of British Columbia 1500—1055 West Hastings Street Vancouver, B.C. V6E 2H1 and Council of Forest Industries of British Columbia Northern Interior Lumber Sector 803—299 Victoria Street Prince George, B.C. V2L 2J5

Table 7 (Cont'd)
Facsimiles of Grade Marks Used by Canadian Lumber
Manufacturing Associations and Agencies Authorized
to Grade Mark Lumber in Canada

Facsimile of Grade Mark	Association or Agency
	Interior Lumber Manufacturers Association 203—2350 Hunter Road Kelowna, B.C. V1X 6C1
	Maritime Lumber Bureau P.O. Box 459 Amherst, Nova Scotia B4H 4A1
	Ontario Lumber Manufacturers Association 1312—55 York Street Toronto, Ontario M5J 1R7
	Quebec Lumber Manufacturers Association 200—3555 Boulevard Hamel W. Québec, P.Q. G2E 2G6
	MacDonald Inspection 125 School House Street Coquitlam, B.C. V3K 4X9

Table 7 (Cont'd)
Facsimiles of Grade Marks Used by Canadian Lumber
Manufacturing Associations and Agencies Authorized
to Grade Mark Lumber in Canada

Facsimile of Grade Mark	Association or Agency
IO CONST S·P·F S–GRN	N.W.T. Grade Stamping Agency P.O. Box 346 Sardis, B.C. V2R 1A7
PLIB NLGA RULE No 1 00 S · GR N HEM-FIR-N	Pacific Lumber Inspection Bureau 1460—1055 West Hastings Street Vancouver, B.C. V6E 2G8

Table 8
Grade Mark Facsimiles for MSR Lumber

Facsimile of Grade Mark	Association or Agency
(Company Name) **A.F.P.A.®31 S-P-F** MACHINE RATED S-DRY **2100f 1.8E**	Alberta Forest Products Assoc. 204—11710 Kingsway Avenue Edmonton, Alberta T5G 0X5
ILMA® S—P—F S·DRY **15** MACHINE RATED **2400f 2.0E**	Interior Lumber Manufacturers Association 295—333 Martin Street Penticton, B.C. V2A 5K7

Table 9
Commercial Species of Lumber

Commercial Species Group Designation	Grade Stamp Identification	Species in Combination	Wood Characteristics
Spruce-Pine-Fir	S-P-F	Spruce (all species except Coast sitka spruce) Lodgepole pine Jack pine Alpine fir Balsam fir	Woods of similar characteristics. They work easily, take paint easily and hold nails well. Generally white to pale yellow in colour.
Douglas fir-Larch (North)[1]	D Fir-L (N)	Douglas fir Western larch	High degree of hardness and good resistance to decay. Good nail holding, gluing and painting qualities. Colour ranges from reddish-brown to yellowish-white.
Hem-Fir (North)[1]	Hem-Fir (N)	Western hemlock Amabilis fir	They work easily, take paint well and hold nails well. Good gluing characteristics. Colour range pale yellow-brown to white.
Eastern hemlock-Tamarack (North)[1]	Hem-Tam (N)	Eastern hemlock Tamarack	Mostly used for general construction. Fairly hard and durable. Colour range yellowish-brown to whitish.
Coast species	Coast Species, or often marked individually as: D Fir (N) Larch (N) W Hem (N) Am Fir (N) G Fir (N)	Douglas fir Western larch Western hemlock Amabilis fir Grand fir	See characteristics in previous groups.
	C Sitka	Coast sitka spruce	A light, resilient wood that works and takes paint easily, and holds nails well. Creamy white to light pink in colour with large proportion of clear wood.
Western cedars (North)[1]	W Cedar (N)	Western red cedar Pacific coast yellow cedar	Woods with exceptional resistance to decay. Relatively weak in strength. High in appearance qualities, they work easily and take fine finishes. Each species has distinct and easily recognizable colourations: red cedar varies from reddish-brown heartwood to light sapwood, and yellow cedar has a uniform warm yellow colour.

Most common

Less common

Table 9 (Cont'd)
Commercial Species of Lumber

Less common

Commercial Species Group Designation	Grade Stamp Identification	Species in Combination	Wood Characteristics
Northern species	North Species, or often marked individually as:	All species above plus:	See characteristics in previous groups.
	R Pine (N) P Pine	Red pine Ponderosa pine	A fairly strong and easy to work wood that takes a good finish and holds nails and screws well. Moderately durable; it seasons with little checking or cupping. Sapwood is a pale yellow colour; heartwood pale brown to reddish tinge.
	W W Pine	Western white pine	Softest of the Canadian pines, it works and finishes exceptionally well. Not as strong as most pines but does not tend to split or splinter. Good nail holding properties. Low shrinkage, better than all other Canadian species except the cedars. Takes stains, paints and varnishes well. Colour of sapwood almost white; heartwood creamy white to light straw brown.
	East White Pine (E W Pine) (N)	Eastern white pine	
Northern aspen[2]	N Aspen	Trembling aspen Largetooth aspen Balsam poplar	Light woods of moderate strength, they work easily, finish well and hold nails well. Generally light in colour, varying from almost white to greyish-white.
Black cottonwood[2,3]	B Cot	Black cottonwood	Characteristics similar to those of northern aspen group, but it is lower in strength and stiffness. No specified strength provided for black cottonwood.

Notes to Table 9.
[1] Designation "North" or "N" in the grade mark provides regional identification for lumber exported to U.S.
[2] Northern aspen species group and black cottonwood are technically hardwoods, but are graded and marketed under softwood standards.
[3] Normally not marketed in Canada.

Table 10
Metric Sizes for Dimension Lumber and Boards

Nominal Sizes (Inches)		Actual Sizes (Inches)		Metric Equivalents (mm)		Metric Nomenclature (mm)
		Dry	Green	Dry	Green	
	2 × 2	$1^1/_2 \times 1^1/_2$	$1^9/_{16} \times 1^9/_{16}$	38.10 × 38.10	39.69 × 39.69	38 × 38
	3	$2^1/_2$	$2^9/_{16}$	63.50	65.09	64
	4	$3^1/_2$	$3^9/_{16}$	88.90	90.49	89
	5	$4^1/_2$	$4^5/_8$	114.30	117.47	114
Dimen-	6	$5^1/_2$	$5^5/_8$	139.70	142.87	140
sion	8	$7^1/_4$	$7^1/_2$	184.15	190.50	184
Lumber	10	$9^1/_4$	$9^1/_2$	234.95	241.30	235
	12	$11^1/_4$	$11^1/_2$	285.75	292.10	286
	14	$13^1/_4$	$13^1/_2$	336.55	342.90	337
	16	$15^1/_4$	$15^1/_2$	387.35	393.70	387
	3 × 4 etc.	$2^1/_2 \times 3^1/_2$	$2^9/_{16} \times 3^9/_{16}$	63.50 × 88.90	65.09 × 90.49	64 × 89
	4 × 4 etc.	$3^1/_2 \times 3^1/_2$	$3^9/_{16} \times 3^9/_{16}$	88.90 × 88.90	90.49 × 90.49	89 × 89
	1 × 2	$3/_4 \times 1^1/_2$	$1^3/_{16} \times 1^9/_{16}$	19.00 × 38.10	20.64 × 39.69	19 × 38
	3	$2^1/_2$	$2^9/_{16}$	63.50	65.09	64
	4	$3^1/_2$	$3^9/_{16}$	88.90	90.49	89
	5	$4^1/_2$	$4^5/_8$	114.30	117.47	114
	6	$5^1/_2$	$5^5/_8$	139.70	142.87	140
Boards	8	$7^1/_4$	$7^1/_2$	184.15	190.50	184
	10	$9^1/_4$	$9^1/_2$	234.95	241.30	235
	12	$11^1/_4$	$11^1/_2$	285.75	292.10	286
	14	$13^1/_4$	$13^1/_2$	336.55	342.90	337
	16	$15^1/_4$	$15^1/_2$	387.35	393.70	387
	$1^1/_4 \times 2$ etc.	$1 \times 1^1/_2$	$1^1/_{32} \times 1^9/_{16}$	25.40 × 38.10	26.19 × 39.69	25 × 38
	$1^1/_2 \times 2$ etc.	$1^1/_4 \times 1^1/_2$	$1^9/_{32} \times 1^9/_{16}$	31.75 × 38.10	32.54 × 39.69	32 × 38

Note: Tables 11 to 17 include only the most common grades of lumber —
No. 1, No. 2, and No. 3. For Select Structural, Construction Standard, and
Utility grades, refer to the National Building Code, Part 9.

Table 11
Ceiling Joist Spans — Attic Not Accessible by a Stairway

Grade		No. 1			No. 2			No 3		
Joist Spacing (mm)		300	400	600	300	400	600	300	400	600
SPECIES	Size, mm	ALLOWABLE SPANS IN METRES								
Douglas Fir Larch	38 × 89	3.40	3.09	2.69	3.28	2.98	2.60	3.15	2.82	2.31
(includes Douglas	140	5.34	4.85	4.24	5.16	4.69	4.10	4.81	4.16	3.40
Fir and Western	184	7.04	6.40	5.59	6.81	6.18	5.40	6.34	5.49	4.48
Larch)	235	8.98	8.16	7.13	8.68	7.89	6.89	8.09	7.01	5.72
	286	10.93	9.93	8.67	10.56	9.60	8.38	9.84	8.52	6.96
Hem Fir	38 × 89	3.27	2.97	2.60	3.16	2.87	2.51	2.81	2.43	1.98
(includes Western	140	5.15	4.67	4.08	4.97	4.51	3.87	4.15	3.59	2.93
Hemlock and	184	6.78	6.16	5.38	6.55	5.95	5.10	5.47	4.74	3.87
Amabilis Fir)	235	8.66	7.87	6.87	8.36	7.60	6.51	6.98	6.05	4.94
	286	10.53	9.57	8.36	10.17	9.24	7.92	8.49	7.36	6.01
Eastern Hemlock	38 × 89	3.12	2.83	2.47	3.01	2.73	2.38	2.90	2.63	2.22
Tamarack	140	4.90	4.45	3.89	4.73	4.29	3.75	4.55	4.00	3.26
(includes Eastern	184	6.46	5.87	5.13	6.23	5.66	4.94	6.01	5.27	4.30
Hemlock and	235	8.25	7.49	6.55	7.95	7.22	6.31	7.66	6.73	5.49
Tamarack)	286	10.03	9.12	7.96	9.67	8.79	7.68	9.32	8.18	6.68
Coast Species	38 × 89	3.27	2.97	2.60	3.16	2.87	2.51	2.78	2.40	1.96
(includes Douglas	140	5.15	4.67	4.08	4.97	4.51	3.81	4.10	3.55	2.89
Fir, Western Larch,	184	6.78	6.16	5.38	6.55	5.95	5.02	5.40	4.68	3.82
Western Hemlock,	235	8.66	7.87	6.87	8.36	7.60	6.41	6.89	5.97	4.87
Amabilis Fir and	286	10.53	9.57	8.36	10.17	9.24	7.79	8.38	7.26	5.93
Coast Sitka Spruce)										
Spruce Pine Fir	38 × 89	3.09	2.80	2.45	2.98	2.71	2.37	2.74	2.37	1.94
(includes Spruce — all	140	4.85	4.41	3.85	4.69	4.26	3.72	4.04	3.50	2.85
species except Coast	184	6.40	5.81	5.08	6.18	5.62	4.91	5.33	4.61	3.76
Sitka Spruce — Jack	235	8.16	7.41	6.48	7.89	7.17	6.26	6.80	5.89	4.80
Pine, Lodgepole Pine,	286	9.93	9.02	7.88	9.60	8.72	7.62	8.27	7.16	5.84
Balsam Fir and										
Alpine Fir)										
Western Cedars	38 × 89	2.97	2.70	2.36	2.87	2.61	2.28	2.74	2.37	1.94
(includes Western	140	4.67	4.24	3.71	4.51	4.10	3.58	4.04	3.50	2.85
Red Cedar and Pacific	184	6.16	5.59	4.89	5.95	5.41	4.72	5.33	4.61	3.76
Coast Yellow Cedar)	235	7.86	7.14	6.24	7.60	6.90	6.03	6.80	5.89	4.80
	286	9.56	8.68	7.58	9.24	8.39	7.33	8.27	7.16	5.84
Northern Species	38 × 89	2.97	2.70	2.36	2.87	2.61	2.28	2.64	2.29	1.86
(includes all softwood	140	4.67	4.24	3.71	4.51	4.10	3.58	3.87	3.35	2.73
species covered by	184	6.16	5.59	4.89	5.95	5.41	4.72	5.10	4.42	3.60
NLGA Standard	235	7.86	7.14	6.24	7.60	6.90	6.03	6.51	5.64	4.60
Grading Rules)	286	9.56	8.68	7.58	9.24	8.39	7.33	7.92	6.85	5.60
Northern Aspen	38 × 89	3.02	2.74	2.39	2.91	2.64	2.31	2.74	2.37	1.94
(includes Aspen Poplar,	140	4.74	4.31	3.76	4.57	4.16	3.63	4.04	3.50	2.85
Large Tooth Aspen	184	6.26	5.68	4.96	6.03	5.48	4.79	5.33	4.61	3.76
and Balsam Poplar)	235	7.98	7.25	6.33	7.70	6.99	6.11	6.80	5.89	4.80
	286	9.71	8.82	7.70	9.36	8.51	7.43	8.27	7.16	5.84

Table 12
Floor Joist Spans — Living Quarters
(Live Load 1.9 kN/m^2)

SPECIES	Size, mm	Grade* No. 1 300	400	600	No. 2 300	400	600	No 3 300	400	600
	Joist Spacing (mm)	300	400	600	300	400	600	300	400	600
		ALLOWABLE SPANS IN METRES								
Douglas Fir Larch	38 × 89	2.17	1.98	1.72	2.10	1.91	1.67	1.88	1.63	1.33
(includes Douglas	140	3.42	3.11	2.71	3.31	3.00	2.59	2.77	2.40	1.96
Fir and Western	184	4.51	4.10	3.58	4.36	3.96	3.42	3.66	3.17	2.59
Larch)	235	5.76	5.23	4.57	5.56	5.05	4.36	4.67	4.04	3.30
	286	7.00	6.36	5.56	6.77	6.15	5.31	5.68	4.92	4.01
Hem Fir	38 × 89	2.10	1.90	1.66	2.02	1.84	1.54	1.62	1.40	1.14
(includes Western	140	3.30	2.99	2.49	3.16	2.73	2.23	2.39	2.07	1.69
Hemlock and	184	4.35	3.95	3.28	4.16	3.60	2.94	3.16	2.73	2.23
Amabilis Fir)	235	5.55	5.04	4.19	5.31	4.60	3.76	4.03	3.49	2.85
	286	6.75	6.13	5.09	6.46	5.60	4.57	4.90	4.24	3.46
Eastern Hemlock	38 × 89	2.00	1.81	1.58	1.92	1.75	1.53	1.81	1.57	1.28
Tamarack	140	3.14	2.85	2.49	3.03	2.75	2.40	2.66	2.31	1.88
(includes Eastern	184	4.14	3.76	3.29	3.99	3.63	3.17	3.51	3.04	2.48
Hemlock and	235	5.28	4.80	4.19	5.09	4.63	4.04	4.48	3.88	3.17
Tamarack)	286	6.43	5.84	5.10	6.20	5.63	4.92	5.45	4.72	3.85
Coast Species	38 × 89	2.10	1.90	1.66	2.02	1.84	1.52	1.60	1.39	1.13
(includes Douglas	140	3.30	2.99	2.46	3.11	2.69	2.20	2.36	2.05	1.67
Fir, Western Larch,	184	4.35	3.95	3.24	4.10	3.55	2.90	3.12	2.70	2.20
Western Hemlock,	235	5.55	5.04	4.13	5.23	4.53	3.70	3.98	3.44	2.81
Amabilis Fir and	286	6.75	6.13	5.03	6.36	5.51	4.50	4.84	4.19	3.42
Coast Sitka Spruce)										
Spruce Pine Fir	38 × 89	1.98	1.79	1.57	1.91	1.73	1.49	1.58	1.37	1.12
(includes Spruce — all	140	3.11	2.82	2.41	3.00	2.65	2.16	2.33	2.02	1.65
species except Coast	184	4.10	3.72	3.18	3.96	3.49	2.85	3.07	2.66	2.17
Sitka Spruce — Jack	235	5.23	4.75	4.06	5.05	4.46	3.64	3.92	3.40	2.77
Pine, Lodgepole Pine,	286	6.36	5.78	4.93	6.15	5.42	4.43	4.77	4.13	3.37
Balsam Fir and										
Alpine Fir)										
Western Cedars	38 × 89	1.90	1.73	1.51	1.84	1.67	1.46	1.58	1.37	1.12
(includes Western	140	2.99	2.72	2.37	2.89	2.63	2.18	2.33	2.02	1.65
Red Cedar and Pacific	184	3.94	3.58	3.13	3.81	3.46	2.87	3.07	2.66	2.17
Coast Yellow Cedar)	235	5.03	4.57	3.99	4.87	4.42	3.67	3.92	3.40	2.77
	286	6.12	5.56	4.86	5.92	5.38	4.46	4.77	4.13	3.37
Northern Species	38 × 89	1.90	1.73	1.51	1.84	1.67	1.45	1.52	1.32	1.07
(includes all softwood	140	2.99	2.72	2.33	2.89	2.56	2.09	2.23	1.93	1.58
species covered by	184	3.94	3.58	3.07	3.81	3.38	2.76	2.94	2.55	2.08
NLGA Standard	235	5.03	4.57	3.92	4.87	4.31	3.52	3.76	3.25	2.65
Grading Rules)	286	6.12	5.56	4.77	5.92	5.25	4.28	4.57	3.96	3.23
Northern Aspen	38 × 89	1.93	1.75	1.53	1.86	1.69	1.48	1.58	1.37	1.12
(includes Aspen Poplar,	140	3.04	2.76	2.41	2.93	2.65	2.16	2.33	2.02	1.65
Large Tooth Aspen	184	4.01	3.64	3.18	3.86	3.49	2.85	3.07	2.66	2.17
and Balsam Poplar)	235	5.11	4.65	4.06	4.93	4.46	3.64	3.92	3.40	2.77
	286	6.22	5.65	4.93	6.00	5.42	4.43	4.77	4.13	3.37

*See Note preceding Table 11.

Table 13
Floor Joist Spans — Bedrooms and Attics accessible by a Stairway
(Live Load 1.4 kN/m²)

SPECIES	Size, mm	No. 1 300	No. 1 400	No. 1 600	No. 2 300	No. 2 400	No. 2 600	No 3 300	No 3 400	No 3 600
Douglas Fir Larch	38 × 89	2.41	2.19	1.91	2.33	2.11	1.85	2.14	1.86	1.51
(includes Douglas	140	3.79	3.44	3.00	3.66	3.33	2.90	3.16	2.74	2.23
Fir and Western	184	4.99	4.54	3.96	4.83	4.38	3.83	4.17	3.61	2.95
Larch)	235	6.37	5.79	5.06	6.16	5.60	4.89	5.32	4.61	3.76
	286	7.75	7.04	6.15	7.49	6.81	5.95	6.47	5.60	4.57
Hem Fir	38 × 89	2.32	2.11	1.84	2.24	2.04	1.76	1.84	1.60	1.30
(includes Western	140	3.65	3.32	2.83	3.52	3.11	2.54	2.73	2.36	1.93
Hemlock and	184	4.81	4.37	3.74	4.65	4.11	3.35	3.60	3.11	2.54
Amabilis Fir)	235	6.14	5.58	4.77	5.93	5.24	4.28	4.59	3.97	3.24
	286	7.47	6.70	5.00	7.21	6.37	5.20	5.58	4.84	3.95
Eastern Hemlock	38 × 89	2.21	2.01	1.75	2.13	1.94	1.69	2.05	1.79	1.46
Tamarack	140	3.48	3.16	2.76	3.35	3.04	2.66	3.03	2.63	2.14
(includes Eastern	184	4.58	4.16	3.64	4.42	4.01	3.51	4.00	3.46	2.83
Hemlock and	235	5.85	5.32	4.64	5.64	5.12	4.48	5.11	4.42	3.61
Tamarack)	286	7.12	6.47	5.65	6.86	6.23	5.44	6.21	5.38	4.39
Coast Species	38 × 89	2.32	2.11	1.84	2.24	2.04	1.73	1.82	1.58	1.29
(includes Douglas	140	3.65	3.32	2.80	3.52	3.07	2.50	2.69	2.33	1.90
Fir, Western Larch,	184	4.81	4.37	3.69	4.65	4.04	3.30	3.55	3.07	2.51
Western Hemlock,	235	6.14	5.58	4.71	5.93	5.16	4.21	4.53	3.92	3.20
Amabilis Fir and	286	7.47	6.79	5.73	7.21	6.28	5.12	5.51	4.77	3.89
Coast Sitka Spruce)										
Spruce Pine Fir	38 × 89	2.19	1.99	1.74	2.11	1.92	1.68	1.80	1.56	1.27
(includes Spruce — all	140	3.44	3.13	2.73	3.33	3.02	2.46	2.65	2.30	1.88
species except Coast	184	4.54	4.12	3.60	4.38	3.98	3.25	3.50	3.03	2.47
Sitka Spruce — Jack	235	5.79	5.26	4.59	5.60	5.08	4.15	4.47	3.87	3.16
Pine, Lodgepole Pine,	286	7.04	6.40	5.59	6.81	6.18	5.04	5.44	4.71	3.84
Balsam Fir and										
Alpine Fir)										
Western Cedars	38 × 89	2.11	1.91	1.67	2.04	1.85	1.61	1.80	1.56	1.27
(includes Western	140	3.31	3.01	2.63	3.20	2.91	2.48	2.65	2.30	1.88
Red Cedar and Pacific	184	4.37	3.97	3.47	4.22	3.84	3.27	3.50	3.03	2.47
Coast Yellow Cedar)	235	5.57	5.06	4.42	5.39	4.90	4.18	4.47	3.87	3.16
	286	6.78	6.16	5.38	6.55	5.95	5.08	5.44	4.71	3.84
Northern Species	38 × 89	2.11	1.91	1.67	2.04	1.85	1.61	1.73	1.50	1.22
(includes all softwood	140	3.31	3.01	2.63	3.20	2.91	2.38	2.54	2.20	1.80
species covered by	184	4.37	3.97	3.47	4.22	3.84	3.14	3.35	2.90	2.37
NLGA Standard	235	5.57	5.06	4.42	5.39	4.90	4.01	4.28	3.70	3.02
Grading Rules)	286	6.78	6.16	5.38	6.55	5.95	4.88	5.20	4.51	3.68
Northern Aspen	38 × 89	2.14	1.94	1.70	2.06	1.87	1.64	1.80	1.56	1.27
(includes Aspen Poplar,	140	3.36	3.06	2.67	3.24	2.95	2.46	2.65	2.30	1.88
Large Tooth Aspen	184	4.44	4.03	3.52	4.28	3.89	3.25	3.50	3.03	2.47
and Balsam Poplar)	235	5.66	5.14	4.49	5.46	4.96	4.15	4.47	3.87	3.16
	286	6.89	6.26	5.47	6.64	6.03	5.04	5.44	4.71	3.84

Grade* / Joist Spacing (mm) / ALLOWABLE SPANS IN METRES

*See Note preceding Table 11.

Table 14
Roof Joist Spans — Supporting Ceiling
(Live Load 2.5 kN/m²)

SPECIES	Size, mm	No. 1			No. 2			No 3		
Joist Spacing (mm)		300	400	600	300	400	600	300	400	600
		ALLOWABLE SPANS IN METRES								
Douglas Fir Larch	38 × 89	1.98	1.80	1.57	1.92	1.74	1.52	1.80	1.56	1.27
(includes Douglas	140	3.12	2.83	2.48	3.02	2.74	2.39	2.66	2.30	1.88
Fir and Western	184	4.11	3.74	3.27	3.98	3.61	3.16	3.51	3.04	2.48
Larch)	235	5.25	4.77	4.17	5.08	4.61	4.03	4.48	3.88	3.17
	286	6.39	5.80	5.07	6.17	5.61	4.90	5.45	4.72	3.85
Hem Fir	38 × 89	1.91	1.74	1.52	1.85	1.68	1.46	1.55	1.34	1.10
(includes Western	140	3.01	2.73	2.39	2.90	2.62	2.14	2.30	1.99	1.62
Hemlock and	184	3.97	3.60	3.15	3.83	3.46	2.82	3.03	2.62	2.14
Amabilis Fir)	235	5.06	4.60	4.01	4.89	4.41	3.60	3.87	3.35	2.73
	286	6.16	5.59	4.88	5.95	5.37	4.38	4.70	4.07	3.32
Eastern Hemlock	38 × 89	1.82	1.65	1.44	1.76	1.59	1.39	1.69	1.51	1.23
Tamarack	140	2.86	2.60	2.27	2.76	2.51	2.19	2.55	2.21	1.80
(includes Eastern	184	3.78	3.43	3.00	3.64	3.31	2.89	3.37	2.92	2.38
Hemlock and	235	4.82	4.38	3.83	4.65	4.22	3.69	4.30	3.72	3.04
Tamarack)	286	5.87	5.33	4.65	5.65	5.14	4.49	5.23	4.53	3.70
Coast Species	38 × 89	1.91	1.74	1.52	1.85	1.68	1.46	1.53	1.33	1.08
(includes Douglas	140	3.01	2.73	2.36	2.90	2.58	2.11	2.27	1.96	1.60
Fir, Western Larch,	184	3.97	3.60	3.11	3.83	3.40	2.78	2.99	2.59	2.11
Western Hemlock,	235	5.06	4.60	3.97	4.89	4.34	3.55	3.81	3.30	2.70
Amabilis Fir and	286	6.16	5.59	4.82	5.95	5.29	4.31	4.64	4.02	3.28
Coast Sitka Spruce)										
Spruce Pine Fir	38 × 89	1.80	1.64	1.43	1.74	1.58	1.38	1.52	1.31	1.07
(includes Spruce — all	140	2.83	2.58	2.25	2.74	2.49	2.07	2.23	1.93	1.58
species except Coast	184	3.74	3.40	2.97	3.61	3.28	2.73	2.95	2.55	2.08
Sitka Spruce — Jack	235	4.77	4.33	3.79	4.61	4.19	3.49	3.76	3.26	2.66
Pine, Lodgepole Pine,	286	5.80	5.27	4.61	5.61	5.10	4.25	4.58	3.96	3.23
Balsam Fir and										
Alpine Fir)										
Western Cedars	38 × 89	1.73	1.58	1.38	1.68	1.52	1.33	1.52	1.31	1.07
(includes Western	140	2.73	2.48	2.16	2.64	2.40	2.09	2.23	1.93	1.58
Red Cedar and Pacific	184	3.60	3.27	2.86	3.48	3.16	2.76	2.95	2.55	2.08
Coast Yellow Cedar)	235	4.59	4.17	3.64	4.44	4.03	3.52	3.76	3.26	2.66
	286	5.59	5.08	4.43	5.40	4.91	4.28	4.58	3.96	3.23
Northern Species	38 × 89	1.73	1.58	1.38	1.68	1.52	1.33	1.46	1.26	1.03
(includes all softwood	140	2.73	2.48	2.16	2.64	2.40	2.01	2.14	1.85	1.51
species covered by	184	3.60	3.27	2.86	3.48	3.16	2.64	2.82	2.44	1.99
NLGA Standard	235	4.59	4.17	3.64	4.44	4.03	3.38	3.60	3.12	2.55
Grading Rules)	286	5.59	5.08	4.43	5.40	4.91	4.11	4.38	3.79	3.10
Northern Aspen	38 × 89	1.76	1.60	1.40	1.70	1.54	1.35	1.52	1.31	1.07
(includes Aspen Poplar,	140	2.77	2.52	2.20	2.67	2.43	2.07	2.23	1.93	1.58
Large Tooth Aspen	184	3.66	3.32	2.90	3.53	3.20	2.73	2.95	2.55	2.08
and Balsam Poplar)	235	4.67	4.24	3.70	4.50	4.09	3.49	3.76	3.26	2.66
	286	5.68	5.16	4.50	5.47	4.97	4.25	4.58	3.96	3.23

*See Note preceding Table 11.

Table 15
Roof Joist Spans — Supporting Ceiling
(Live Load 2.0 kN/m²)

Grade*		No. 1			No. 2			No 3		
Joist Spacing (mm)		300	400	600	300	400	600	300	400	600
SPECIES	Size, mm	ALLOWABLE SPANS IN METRES								
Douglas Fir Larch	38 × 89	2.14	1.94	1.70	2.07	1.88	1.64	1.98	1.71	1.40
(includes Douglas	140	3.36	3.05	2.67	3.25	2.95	2.58	2.92	2.52	2.06
Fir and Western	184	4.43	4.03	3.52	4.29	3.89	3.40	3.84	3.33	2.72
Larch)	235	5.66	5.14	4.49	5.47	4.97	4.34	4.91	4.25	3.47
	286	6.88	6.25	5.46	6.65	6.04	5.28	5.97	5.17	4.22
Hem Fir	38 × 89	2.06	1.87	1.63	1.99	1.81	1.58	1.70	1.47	1.20
(includes Western	140	3.24	2.94	2.57	3.13	2.84	2.34	2.52	2.18	1.78
Hemlock and	184	4.27	3.88	3.39	4.13	3.75	3.09	3.32	2.87	2.34
Amabilis Fir)	235	5.45	4.95	4.33	5.27	4.78	3.95	4.23	3.67	2.99
	286	6.63	6.03	5.26	6.41	5.82	4.80	5.15	4.40	3.64
Eastern Hemlock	38 × 89	1.96	1.78	1.56	1.89	1.72	1.50	1.82	1.65	1.35
Tamarack	140	3.09	2.80	2.45	2.98	2.70	2.36	2.80	2.42	1.98
(includes Eastern	184	4.07	3.70	3.23	3.92	3.56	3.11	3.69	3.20	2.61
Hemlock and	235	5.19	4.72	4.12	5.01	4.55	3.97	4.71	4.08	3.33
Tamarack)	286	6.32	5.74	5.01	6.09	5.53	4.83	5.73	4.96	4.05
Coast Species	38 × 89	2.06	1.87	1.63	1.99	1.81	1.58	1.46	1.46	1.19
(includes Douglas	140	3.24	2.94	2.57	3.13	2.83	2.31	2.48	2.15	1.75
Fir, Western Larch,	184	4.27	3.88	3.39	4.13	3.73	3.04	3.27	2.83	2.31
Western Hemlock,	235	5.45	4.95	4.33	5.27	4.76	3.89	4.18	3.62	2.95
Amabilis Fir and	286	6.63	6.03	5.26	6.41	5.79	4.73	5.08	4.40	3.59
Coast Sitka Spruce)										
Spruce Pine Fir	38 × 89	1.94	1.76	1.54	1.88	1.70	1.49	1.66	1.44	1.17
(includes Spruce — all	140	3.05	2.77	2.42	2.95	2.68	2.27	2.45	2.12	1.73
species except Coast	184	4.03	3.66	3.20	3.89	3.54	3.00	3.23	2.80	2.28
Sitka Spruce — Jack	235	5.14	4.67	4.08	4.97	4.51	3.82	4.12	3.57	2.91
Pine, Lodgepole Pine,	286	6.25	5.68	4.96	6.04	5.49	4.65	5.01	4.34	3.54
Balsam Fir and										
Alpine Fir)										
Western Cedars	38 × 89	1.87	1.70	1.48	1.81	1.64	1.43	1.66	1.44	1.17
(includes Western	140	2.94	2.67	2.33	2.84	2.58	2.25	2.45	2.12	1.73
Red Cedar and Pacific	184	3.88	3.52	3.08	3.75	3.41	2.97	3.23	2.80	2.28
Coast Yellow Cedar)	235	4.95	4.50	3.93	4.78	4.35	3.80	4.12	3.57	2.91
	286	6.02	5.47	4.78	5.82	5.29	4.62	5.01	4.34	3.54
Northern Species	38 × 89	1.87	1.70	1.48	1.81	1.64	1.43	1.60	1.38	1.13
(includes all softwood	140	2.94	2.67	2.33	2.84	2.58	2.20	2.34	2.03	1.66
species covered by	184	3.88	3.52	3.08	3.75	3.41	2.90	3.09	2.68	2.18
NLGA Standard	235	4.95	4.50	3.93	4.78	4.35	3.70	3.95	3.42	2.79
Grading Rules)	286	6.02	5.47	4.78	5.82	5.29	4.50	4.80	4.16	3.39
Northern Aspen	38 × 89	1.90	1.72	1.51	1.83	1.66	1.45	1.66	1.44	1.17
(Includes Aspen Poplar,	140	2.99	2.71	2.37	2.88	2.62	2.27	2.45	2.12	1.73
Large Tooth Aspen	184	3.94	3.58	3.13	3.80	3.45	3.00	3.23	2.80	2.28
and Balsam Poplar)	235	5.03	4.57	3.99	4.85	4.40	3.82	4.12	3.57	2.91
	286	6.11	5.55	4.85	5.90	5.36	4.65	5.01	4.34	3.54

*See Note preceding Table 11.

Table 16
Roof Joist Spans — Supporting Ceiling
(Live Load 1.5 kN/m²)

Grade*		No. 1			No. 2			No 3		
Joist Spacing (mm)		300	400	600	300	400	600	300	400	600
SPECIES	Size, mm	ALLOWABLE SPANS IN METRES								
Douglas Fir Larch	38 × 89	2.35	2.14	1.87	2.27	2.07	1.80	2.18	1.91	1.56
(includes Douglas	140	3.70	3.36	2.94	3.58	3.25	2.84	3.26	2.82	2.30
Fir and Western	184	4.88	4.43	3.87	4.72	4.29	3.74	4.30	3.72	3.04
Larch)	235	6.23	5.66	4.94	6.02	5.47	4.78	5.49	4.75	3.88
	286	7.57	6.88	6.01	7.32	6.65	5.81	6.67	5.78	4.72
Hem Fir	38 × 89	2.27	2.06	1.80	2.19	1.99	1.74	1.90	1.65	1.34
(includes Western	140	3.57	3.24	2.83	3.44	3.13	2.62	2.81	2.44	1.99
Hemlock and	184	4.70	4.27	3.73	4.54	4.13	3.46	3.71	3.21	2.62
Amabilis Fir)	235	6.00	5.45	4.76	5.80	5.27	4.41	4.73	4.10	3.35
	286	7.30	6.63	5.79	7.05	6.41	5.37	5.76	4.99	4.07
Eastern Hemlock	38 × 89	2.16	1.96	1.71	2.08	1.89	1.65	2.01	1.82	1.51
Tamarack	140	3.40	3.09	2.70	3.28	2.98	2.60	3.13	2.71	2.21
(includes Eastern	184	4.48	4.07	3.55	4.32	3.92	3.43	4.13	3.57	2.92
Hemlock and	235	5.72	5.19	4.54	5.51	5.01	4.37	5.27	4.56	3.72
Tamarack)	286	6.95	6.32	5.52	6.70	6.09	5.32	6.41	5.55	4.53
Coast Species	38 × 89	2.27	2.06	1.80	2.19	1.99	1.74	1.88	1.63	1.33
(includes Douglas	140	3.57	3.24	2.83	3.44	3.13	2.58	2.78	2.40	1.96
Fir, Western Larch,	184	4.70	4.27	3.73	4.54	4.13	3.40	3.66	3.17	2.59
Western Hemlock,	235	6.00	5.45	4.76	5.80	5.27	4.34	4.67	4.05	3.30
Amabilis Fir and	286	7.30	6.63	5.79	7.05	6.41	5.29	5.68	4.92	4.02
Coast Sitka Spruce)										
Spruce Pine Fir	38 × 89	2.14	1.94	1.70	2.07	1.88	1.64	1.86	1.61	1.31
(includes Spruce — all	140	3.36	3.05	2.67	3.25	2.95	2.54	2.74	2.37	1.93
species except Coast	184	4.43	4.03	3.52	4.29	3.89	3.35	3.61	3.13	2.55
Sitka Spruce — Jack	235	5.66	5.14	4.49	5.47	4.97	4.28	4.61	3.99	3.26
Pine, Lodgepole Pine,	286	6.88	6.25	5.46	6.65	6.04	5.20	5.61	4.85	3.96
Balsam Fir and										
Alpine Fir)										
Western Cedars	38 × 89	2.06	1.87	1.63	1.99	1.81	1.58	1.86	1.61	1.31
(includes Western	140	3.24	2.94	2.57	3.13	2.84	2.48	2.74	2.37	1.93
Red Cedar and Pacific	184	4.27	3.88	3.39	4.13	3.75	3.27	3.61	3.13	2.55
Coast Yellow Cedar)	235	5.45	4.95	4.32	5.27	4.78	4.18	4.61	3.99	3.26
	286	6.63	6.02	5.26	6.41	5.82	5.08	5.61	4.85	3.96
Northern Species	38 × 89	2.06	1.87	1.63	1.99	1.81	1.58	1.79	1.55	1.26
(includes all softwood	140	3.24	2.94	2.57	3.13	2.84	2.46	2.62	2.27	1.85
species covered by	184	4.27	3.88	3.39	4.13	3.75	3.24	3.46	2.99	2.44
NLGA Standard	235	5.45	4.95	4.32	5.27	4.78	4.14	4.41	3.82	3.12
Grading Rules)	286	6.63	6.02	5.26	6.41	5.82	5.03	5.37	4.65	3.79
Northern Aspen	38 × 89	2.09	1.90	1.66	2.02	1.83	1.60	1.86	1.61	1.31
(includes Aspen Poplar,	140	3.29	2.99	2.61	3.17	2.88	2.52	2.74	2.37	1.93
Large Tooth Aspen	184	4.34	3.94	3.44	4.18	3.80	3.32	3.61	3.13	2.55
and Balsam Poplar)	235	5.53	5.03	4.39	5.33	4.85	4.23	4.61	3.99	3.26
	286	6.73	6.11	5.34	6.49	5.90	5.15	5.61	4.85	3.96

*See Note preceding Table 11.

Table 17
Roof Joist Spans — Supporting Ceiling
(Live Load 1.0 kN/m^2)

SPECIES	Size, mm	No. 1 300	No. 1 400	No. 1 600	No. 2 300	No. 2 400	No. 2 600	No 3 300	No 3 400	No 3 600
Grade*										
Joist Spacing (mm)		300	400	600	300	400	600	300	400	600
		ALLOWABLE SPANS IN METRES								
Douglas Fir Larch	38 × 89	2.69	2.45	2.14	2.60	2.37	2.07	2.50	2.21	1.80
(includes Douglas	140	4.24	3.85	3.36	4.10	3.72	3.25	3.77	3.26	2.66
Fir and Western	184	5.59	5.08	4.43	5.40	4.91	4.29	4.96	4.30	3.51
Larch)	235	7.13	6.48	5.66	6.89	6.26	5.47	6.34	5.49	4.48
	286	8.67	7.88	6.88	8.38	7.62	6.65	7.71	6.67	5.45
Hem Fir	38 × 89	2.60	2.36	2.06	2.51	2.28	1.99	2.20	1.90	1.55
(includes Western	140	4.08	3.71	3.24	3.94	3.58	3.03	3.25	2.81	2.30
Hemlock and	184	5.38	4.89	4.27	5.20	4.72	3.99	4.28	3.71	3.03
Amabilis Fir)	235	6.87	6.24	5.45	6.64	6.03	5.10	5.47	4.73	3.87
	286	8.36	7.59	6.63	8.07	7.33	6.20	6.65	5.76	4.70
Eastern Hemlock	38 × 89	2.47	2.25	1.96	2.38	2.17	1.89	2.30	2.09	1.74
Tamarack	140	3.89	3.53	3.09	3.75	3.41	2.98	3.61	3.13	2.55
(includes Eastern	184	5.13	4.66	4.07	4.94	4.49	3.92	4.77	4.13	3.37
Hemlock and	235	6.55	5.95	5.19	6.31	5.73	5.01	6.08	5.27	4.30
Tamarack)	286	7.96	7.23	6.32	7.68	6.97	6.09	7.40	6.41	5.23
Coast Species	38 × 89	2.60	2.36	2.06	2.51	2.28	1.99	2.17	1.88	1.53
(includes Douglas	140	4.08	3.71	3.24	3.94	3.58	2.98	3.21	2.78	2.27
Fir, Western Larch,	184	5.38	4.89	4.27	5.20	4.72	3.93	4.23	3.66	2.99
Western Hemlock,	235	6.87	6.24	5.45	6.64	6.03	5.02	5.40	4.67	3.81
Amabilis Fir and	286	8.36	7.59	6.63	8.07	7.33	6.10	6.56	5.68	4.64
Coast Sitka Spruce)										
Spruce Pine Fir	38 × 89	2.45	2.22	1.94	2.37	2.15	1.88	2.15	1.86	1.52
(includes Spruce — all	140	3.85	3.50	3.05	3.72	3.38	2.93	3.16	2.74	2.23
species except Coast	184	5.08	4.61	4.30	4.91	4.46	3.87	4.17	3.61	2.95
Sitka Spruce — Jack	235	6.48	5.88	5.14	6.26	5.69	4.94	5.32	4.61	3.76
Pine, Lodgepole Pine,	286	7.88	7.16	6.25	7.62	6.92	6.01	6.47	5.61	4.58
Balsam Fir and										
Alpine Fir)										
Western Cedars	38 × 89	2.36	2.14	1.87	2.28	2.07	1.81	2.15	1.86	1.52
(includes Western	140	3.71	3.37	2.94	3.58	3.25	2.84	3.16	2.74	2.23
Red Cedar and Pacific	184	4.89	4.44	3.88	4.72	4.29	3.75	4.17	3.61	2.95
Coast Yellow Cedar)	235	6.24	5.66	4.95	6.03	5.48	4.78	5.32	4.61	3.76
	286	7.58	6.80	6.02	7.33	6.66	5.82	6.47	5.61	4.58
Northern Species	38 × 89	2.36	2.14	1.87	2.28	2.07	1.81	2.07	1.79	1.46
(includes all softwood	140	3.71	3.37	2.94	3.58	3.25	2.84	3.03	2.62	2.14
species covered by	184	4.89	4.44	3.88	4.72	4.29	3.74	3.99	3.46	2.82
NLGA Standard	235	6.24	5.66	4.95	6.03	5.48	4.78	5.10	4.41	3.60
Grading Rules)	286	7.58	6.89	6.02	7.33	6.66	5.81	6.20	5.37	4.38
Northern Aspen	38 × 89	2.39	2.17	1.90	2.31	2.10	1.83	2.15	1.86	1.52
(includes Aspen Poplar,	140	3.76	3.42	2.99	3.63	0.00	2.88	3.16	2.74	2.23
Large Tooth Aspen	184	4.96	4.51	3.94	4.79	4.35	3.80	4.17	3.61	2.95
and Balsam Poplar)	235	6.33	5.75	5.03	6.11	5.55	4.85	5.32	4.61	3.76
	286	7.70	7.00	6.11	7.43	6.75	5.90	6.47	5.61	4.58

*See Note preceding Table 11

Table 18
Rafters — Not Supporting Ceiling
(Ground Snow Loads 4.2 and 3.3 kPa)

Species	Grade	Size mm	Ground Snow Loads	4.2 kPa		3.3 kPa		
			Rafter Spacing, mm 300	400	600	300	400	600
			ALLOWABLE SPANS IN METRES					
Douglas Fir Larch (includes Douglas Fir and Western Larch)	No. 1	38 × 89	2.50	2.27	1.96	2.69	2.45	2.14
		× 140	3.93	3.50	2.86	4.24	3.85	3.16
		× 184	5.19	4.62	3.77	5.59	5.08	4.16
		× 235	6.62	5.90	4.81	7.13	6.48	5.31
		× 286	8.05	7.17	5.86	8.67	7.88	6.46
	No. 2	38 × 89	2.42	2.19	1.79	2.60	2.37	1.97
		× 140	3.64	3.15	2.57	4.02	3.48	2.84
		× 184	4.80	4.16	3.39	5.30	4.59	3.74
		× 235	6.13	5.30	4.33	6.76	5.85	4.78
		× 286	7.45	6.45	5.27	8.22	7.12	5.81
	No. 3	38 × 89	1.87	1.62	1.32	2.06	1.78	1.46
		× 140	2.75	2.38	1.95	3.04	2.63	2.15
		× 184	3.63	3.15	2.57	4.01	3.47	2.83
		× 235	4.64	4.01	3.28	5.12	4.43	3.62
		× 286	5.64	4.88	3.99	6.22	5.39	4.40
Hem Fir (includes Western Hemlock and Amabilis Fir)	No. 1	38 × 89	2.39	2.07	1.69	2.60	2.29	1.86
		× 140	3.49	3.03	2.47	3.86	3.34	2.72
		× 184	4.61	3.99	3.26	5.08	4.40	3.59
		× 235	5.88	5.09	4.16	6.49	5.62	4.59
		× 286	7.15	6.19	5.06	7.89	6.83	5.58
	No. 2	38 × 89	2.17	1.88	1.53	2.39	2.07	1.69
		× 140	3.13	2.71	2.21	3.46	2.99	2.44
		× 184	4.13	3.58	2.92	4.56	3.95	3.22
		× 235	5.27	4.57	3.73	5.82	5.04	4.11
		× 286	6.42	5.56	4.54	7.08	6.13	5.00
	No. 3	38 × 89	1.61	1.39	1.14	1.77	1.54	1.25
		× 140	2.38	2.06	1.68	2.62	2.27	1.85
		× 184	3.13	2.71	2.22	3.46	3.00	2.44
		× 235	4.00	3.46	2.83	4.41	3.82	3.12
		× 286	4.87	4.21	3.44	5.37	4.65	3.80
Eastern Hemlock Tamarack (includes Eastern Hemlock and Tamarack)	No. 1	38 × 89	2.30	2.09	1.82	2.47	2.25	1.96
		× 140	3.61	3.28	2.75	3.89	3.53	3.04
		× 184	4.76	4.33	3.63	5.13	4.66	4.01
		× 235	6.08	5.52	4.64	6.55	5.95	5.12
		× 286	7.39	6.71	5.64	7.96	7.23	6.22
	No. 2	38 × 89	2.21	2.01	1.72	2.38	2.17	1.89
		× 140	3.48	3.03	2.47	3.75	3.34	2.72
		× 184	4.59	3.99	3.26	4.94	4.40	3.59
		× 235	5.86	5.09	4.16	6.31	5.62	4.59
		× 286	7.12	6.19	5.06	7.68	6.83	5.58
	No. 3	38 × 89	1.80	1.56	1.27	1.99	1.72	1.40
		× 140	2.64	2.29	1.87	2.92	2.53	2.06
		× 184	3.49	3.02	2.46	3.85	3.33	2.72
		× 235	4.45	3.85	3.15	4.91	4.25	3.47
		× 286	5.41	4.69	3.83	5.97	5.17	4.22

Table 18 (Cont'd)
Rafters — Not Supporting Ceiling
(Ground Snow Loads 4.2 and 3.3 kPa)

Species	Grade	Size mm	4.2 kPa			3.3 kPa		
			300	400	600	300	400	600
			ALLOWABLE SPANS IN METRES					
Coast Species (includes Douglas Fir, Western Larch, Western Hemlock, Amabilis Fir and Coast Sitka Spruce)	No. 1	38 × 89	2.37	2.05	1.67	2.60	2.26	1.85
		× 140	3.45	2.99	2.44	3.81	3.30	2.69
		× 184	4.55	3.94	3.22	5.02	4.35	3.55
		× 235	5.81	5.03	4.11	6.41	5.55	4.53
		× 286	7.06	6.12	4.99	7.79	6.75	5.51
	No. 2	38 × 89	2.14	1.85	1.51	2.36	2.04	1.67
		× 140	3.09	2.67	2.18	3.41	2.95	2.41
		× 184	4.07	3.52	2.88	4.49	3.89	3.17
		× 235	5.19	4.50	3.67	5.73	4.96	4.05
		× 286	6.32	5.47	4.47	6.97	6.04	4.93
	No. 3	38 × 89	1.59	1.38	1.12	1.75	1.52	1.24
		× 140	2.35	2.03	1.66	2.59	2.24	1.83
		× 184	3.09	2.68	2.19	3.41	2.96	2.41
		× 235	3.95	3.42	2.79	4.36	3.77	3.08
		× 286	4.80	4.16	3.39	5.30	4.59	3.75
Spruce Pine Fir (includes Spruce — all species except Coast Sitka Spruce — Jack Pine, Lodgepole Pine, Balsam Fir and Alpine Fir)	No. 1	38 × 89	2.27	2.00	1.64	2.45	2.21	1.80
		× 140	3.39	2.93	2.39	3.74	3.23	2.64
		× 184	4.46	3.87	3.16	4.93	4.27	3.48
		× 235	5.70	4.93	4.03	6.29	5.44	4.44
		× 286	6.93	6.00	4.90	7.65	6.62	5.41
	No. 2	38 × 89	2.10	1.81	1.48	2.31	2.00	1.63
		× 140	3.04	2.63	2.15	3.35	2.90	2.37
		× 184	4.01	3.47	2.83	4.42	3.83	3.12
		× 235	5.11	4.43	3.61	5.64	4.88	3.99
		× 286	6.22	5.38	4.40	6.86	5.94	4.85
	No. 3	38 × 89	1.57	1.36	1.11	1.73	1.50	1.22
		× 140	2.31	2.00	1.63	2.55	2.21	1.80
		× 184	3.05	2.64	2.16	3.37	2.92	2.38
		× 235	3.89	3.37	2.75	4.30	3.72	3.04
		× 286	4.74	4.10	3.35	5.23	4.53	3.69
Western Cedars (includes Western Red Cedar and Pacific Coast Yellow Cedar)	No. 1	38 × 89	2.19	1.99	1.65	2.36	2.14	1.83
		× 140	3.43	2.97	2.42	3.71	3.28	2.67
		× 184	4.52	3.92	3.20	4.89	4.32	3.53
		× 235	5.77	5.00	4.08	6.24	5.51	4.50
		× 286	7.02	6.08	4.96	7.58	6.71	5.48
	No. 2	38 × 89	2.11	1.84	1.50	2.28	2.03	1.66
		× 140	3.06	2.65	2.16	3.38	2.93	2.39
		× 184	4.04	3.50	2.85	4.46	3.86	3.15
		× 235	5.15	4.46	3.64	5.69	4.92	4.02
		× 286	6.27	5.43	4.43	6.92	5.99	4.89
	No. 3	38 × 89	1.57	1.36	1.11	1.73	1.50	1.22
		× 140	2.31	2.00	1.63	2.55	2.21	1.80
		× 184	3.05	2.64	2.16	3.37	2.92	2.38
		× 235	3.89	3.37	2.75	4.30	3.72	3.04
		× 286	4.74	4.10	3.35	5.23	4.53	3.69

Ground Snow Loads — Rafter Spacing, mm

Table 18 (Cont'd)
Rafters — Not Supporting Ceiling
(Ground Snow Loads 4.2 and 3.3 kPa)

Species	Grade	Size mm	4.2 kPa			3.3 kPa		
			300	400	600	300	400	600
			ALLOWABLE SPANS IN METRES					
Northern Species (includes all softwood species covered by NLGA Standard Grading Rules)	No. 1	38 × 89	2.19	1.95	1.59	2.36	2.14	1.75
		× 140	3.27	2.83	2.31	3.61	3.13	2.55
		× 184	4.32	3.74	3.05	4.76	4.12	3.37
		× 235	5.51	4.77	3.89	6.08	5.26	4.30
		× 286	6.70	5.80	4.74	7.39	6.40	5.23
	No. 2	38 × 89	2.04	1.76	1.44	2.25	1.95	1.59
		× 140	2.94	2.54	2.08	3.24	2.81	2.29
		× 184	3.87	3.35	2.74	4.27	3.70	3.02
		× 235	4.94	4.28	3.49	5.46	4.72	3.86
		× 286	6.01	5.21	4.25	6.64	5.75	4.69
	No. 3	38 × 89	1.51	1.31	1.07	1.67	1.44	1.18
		× 140	2.21	1.92	1.56	2.44	2.12	1.73
		× 184	2.92	2.53	2.06	3.22	2.79	2.28
		× 235	3.73	3.23	2.63	4.11	3.56	2.91
		× 286	4.54	3.93	3.21	5.00	4.33	3.54
Northern Aspen (includes Aspen Poplar, Large Tooth Aspen and Balsam Poplar)	No. 1	38 × 89	2.22	2.00	1.64	2.39	2.17	1.80
		× 140	3.39	2.93	2.39	3.74	3.23	2.64
		× 184	4.46	3.87	3.16	4.93	4.27	3.48
		× 235	5.70	4.93	4.03	6.29	5.44	4.44
		× 286	6.93	6.00	4.90	7.65	6.62	5.41
	No. 2	38 × 89	2.11	1.83	1.49	2.31	2.02	1.65
		× 140	3.04	2.63	2.15	3.35	2.90	2.37
		× 184	4.01	3.47	2.83	4.42	3.83	3.12
		× 235	5.11	4.43	3.61	5.64	4.88	3.99
		× 286	6.22	5.38	4.40	6.86	5.94	4.85
	No. 3	38 × 89	1.57	1.36	1.11	1.73	1.50	1.22
		× 140	2.31	2.00	1.63	2.55	2.21	1.80
		× 184	3.05	2.64	2.16	3.37	2.92	2.38
		× 235	3.89	3.37	2.75	4.30	3.72	3.04
		× 286	4.74	4.10	3.35	5.23	4.53	3.69

Table 19
Rafters — Not Supporting Ceiling
(Ground Snow Loads 2.5 and 1.7 kPa)

Species	Grade	Size mm	2.5 kPa			1.7 kPa		
			300	400	600	300	400	600
			ALLOWABLE SPANS IN METRES					
Douglas Fir Larch (includes Douglas Fir and Western Larch)	No. 1	38 × 89	2.97	2.69	2.35	3.40	3.09	2.69
		× 140	4.66	4.24	3.57	5.34	4.85	4.20
		× 184	6.15	5.59	4.71	7.04	6.40	5.54
		× 235	7.85	7.13	6.01	8.98	8.16	7.07
		× 286	9.54	8.67	7.31	10.93	9.93	8.60
	No. 2	38 × 89	2.87	2.60	2.23	3.28	2.98	2.60
		× 140	4.51	3.93	3.21	5.16	4.63	3.78
		× 184	5.94	5.19	4.23	6.81	6.10	4.98
		× 235	7.59	6.62	5.40	8.68	7.79	6.36
		× 286	9.23	8.05	6.57	10.56	9.47	7.73
	No. 3	38 × 89	2.33	2.02	1.65	2.74	2.38	1.94
		× 140	3.44	2.98	2.43	4.04	3.50	2.86
		× 184	4.53	3.92	3.20	5.33	4.62	3.77
		× 235	5.78	5.01	4.09	6.81	5.89	4.81
		× 286	7.03	6.09	4.97	8.28	7.17	5.85
Hem Fir (includes Western Hemlock and Amabilis Fir)	No. 1	38 × 89	2.86	2.58	2.11	3.27	2.97	2.48
		× 140	4.36	3.77	3.08	5.13	4.44	3.63
		× 184	5.75	4.98	4.06	6.76	5.86	4.78
		× 235	7.33	6.35	5.18	8.63	7.47	6.10
		× 286	8.92	7.73	6.31	10.50	9.09	7.42
	No. 2	38 × 89	2.70	2.34	1.91	3.16	2.76	2.25
		× 140	3.91	3.39	2.76	4.60	3.98	3.25
		× 184	5.16	4.46	3.64	6.07	5.25	4.29
		× 235	6.58	5.70	4.65	7.74	6.71	5.47
		× 286	8.00	6.93	5.66	9.42	8.16	6.66
	No. 3	38 × 89	2.01	1.74	1.42	2.36	2.04	1.67
		× 140	2.97	2.57	2.10	3.49	3.02	2.47
		× 184	3.91	3.39	2.76	4.60	3.99	3.25
		× 235	4.99	4.32	3.53	5.87	5.09	4.15
		× 286	6.07	5.26	4.29	7.15	6.19	5.05
Eastern Hemlock Tamarack (includes Eastern Hemlock and Tamarack)	No. 1	38 × 89	2.72	2.47	2.16	3.12	2.83	2.47
		× 140	4.28	3.89	3.40	4.90	4.45	3.89
		× 184	5.65	5.13	4.48	6.46	5.87	5.13
		× 235	7.21	6.55	5.72	8.25	7.49	6.55
		× 286	8.76	7.96	6.95	10.03	9.12	7.96
	No. 2	38 × 89	2.62	2.38	2.08	3.01	2.73	2.38
		× 140	4.13	3.75	3.08	4.73	4.29	3.63
		× 184	5.44	4.94	4.06	6.23	5.66	4.78
		× 235	6.95	6.31	5.18	7.95	7.22	6.10
		× 286	8.45	7.68	6.31	9.67	8.79	7.42
	No. 3	38 × 89	2.25	1.95	1.59	2.65	2.29	1.87
		× 140	3.30	2.86	2.33	3.88	3.36	2.74
		× 184	4.35	3.77	3.07	5.12	4.43	3.62
		× 235	5.55	4.81	3.92	6.53	5.66	4.62
		× 286	6.75	5.85	4.77	7.95	6.88	5.62

Table 19
Rafters — Not Supporting Ceiling
(Ground Snow Loads 2.5 and 1.7 kPa)

Species	Grade	Size mm	Ground Snow Loads 2.5 kPa			1.7 kPa		
			Rafter Spacing, mm 300	400	600	300	400	600
			ALLOWABLE SPANS IN METRES					
Coast Species (includes Douglas Fir, Western Larch, Western Hemlock, Amabilis Fir and Coast Sitka Spruce)	No. 1	38 × 89	2.86	2.56	2.09	3.27	2.97	2.46
		× 140	4.31	3.73	3.04	5.07	4.39	3.58
		× 184	5.68	4.92	4.01	6.68	5.79	4.72
		× 235	7.24	6.27	5.12	8.53	7.38	6.03
		× 286	8.81	7.63	6.23	10.37	8.98	7.33
	No. 2	38 × 89	2.67	2.31	1.89	3.14	2.72	2.22
		× 140	3.85	3.33	2.72	4.53	3.92	3.20
		× 184	5.08	4.40	3.59	5.98	5.17	4.22
		× 235	6.48	5.61	4.58	7.62	6.60	5.39
		× 286	7.88	6.82	5.57	9.27	8.03	6.56
	No. 3	38 × 89	1.98	1.72	1.40	2.33	2.02	1.65
		× 140	2.93	2.53	2.07	3.44	2.98	2.43
		× 184	3.86	3.34	2.73	4.54	3.93	3.21
		× 235	4.93	4.26	3.48	5.80	5.02	4.10
		× 286	5.99	5.19	4.23	7.05	6.11	4.98
Spruce Pine Fir (includes Spruce — all species except Coast Sitka Spruce — Jack Pine, Lodgepole Pine, Balsam Fir and Alpine Fir)	No. 1	38 × 89	2.69	2.45	2.04	3.09	2.80	2.40
		× 140	4.22	3.66	2.99	4.85	4.30	3.51
		× 184	5.57	4.82	3.94	6.40	5.68	4.63
		× 235	7.11	6.15	5.02	8.16	7.24	5.91
		× 286	8.64	7.49	6.11	9.93	8.81	7.19
	No. 2	38 × 89	2.60	2.26	1.85	2.98	2.67	2.18
		× 140	3.79	3.28	2.68	4.46	3.86	3.15
		× 184	5.00	4.33	3.53	5.88	5.09	4.16
		× 235	6.38	5.52	4.51	7.50	6.50	5.31
		× 286	7.76	6.72	5.48	9.13	7.90	6.45
	No. 3	38 × 89	1.96	1.70	1.38	2.31	2.00	1.63
		× 140	2.89	2.50	2.04	3.40	2.94	2.40
		× 184	3.81	3.30	2.69	4.48	3.88	3.17
		× 235	4.86	4.21	3.43	5.72	4.95	4.04
		× 286	5.91	5.12	4.18	6.95	6.02	4.92
Western Cedars (includes Western Red Cedar and Pacific Coast Yellow Cedar)	No. 1	38 × 89	2.59	2.36	2.06	2.97	2.70	2.36
		× 140	4.08	3.70	3.02	4.67	4.24	3.56
		× 184	5.38	4.88	3.99	6.16	5.59	4.69
		× 235	6.86	6.23	5.09	7.86	7.14	5.99
		× 286	8.35	7.58	6.19	9.56	8.68	7.29
	No. 2	38 × 89	2.51	2.28	1.87	2.87	2.61	2.20
		× 140	3.82	3.31	2.70	4.50	3.89	3.18
		× 184	5.04	4.36	3.56	5.93	5.13	4.19
		× 235	6.43	5.57	4.54	7.56	6.55	5.35
		× 286	7.82	6.77	5.53	9.20	7.97	6.51
	No. 3	38 × 89	1.96	1.70	1.38	2.31	2.00	1.63
		× 140	2.89	2.50	2.04	3.40	2.94	2.40
		× 184	3.81	3.30	2.69	4.48	3.88	3.17
		× 235	4.86	4.21	3.43	5.72	4.95	4.04
		× 286	5.91	5.12	4.18	6.95	6.02	4.92

Table 19 (Cont'd)
Rafters — Not Supporting Ceiling
(Ground Snow Loads 2.5 and 1.7 kPa)

Species	Grade	Size mm	2.5 kPa 300	400	600	1.7 kPa 300	400	600
			Ground Snow Loads					
			Rafter Spacing, mm					
			ALLOWABLE SPANS IN METRES					
	No. 1	38× 89	2.59	2.36	1.98	2.97	2.70	2.33
		× 140	4.08	3.54	2.89	4.67	4.16	3.40
		× 184	5.38	4.66	3.81	6.16	5.49	4.48
		× 235	6.86	5.95	4.86	7.86	7.00	5.72
		× 286	8.35	7.24	5.91	9.56	8.52	6.95
Northern Species (includes all softwood species covered by NLGA Standard Grading Rules)	No. 2	38× 89	2.51	2.20	1.80	2.87	2.59	2.11
		× 140	3.67	3.17	2.59	4.31	3.74	3.05
		× 184	4.83	4.18	3.42	5.69	4.93	4.02
		× 235	0.17	5.34	4.36	7.26	6.29	5.13
		× 286	7.50	6.50	5.30	8.83	7.65	6.24
	No. 3	38× 89	1.89	1.63	1.33	2.22	1.92	1.57
		× 140	2.76	2.39	1.95	3.25	2.82	2.30
		× 184	3.64	3.16	2.58	4.29	3.71	3.03
		× 235	4.65	4.03	3.29	5.47	4.74	3.87
		× 286	5.66	4.90	4.00	6.66	5.77	4 71
	No. 1	38× 89	2.64	2.39	2.04	3.02	2.74	2.39
		× 140	4.14	3.66	2.99	4.74	4.30	3.51
		× 184	5.46	4.82	3.94	6.26	5.68	4.63
		× 235	6.97	6.15	5.02	7.98	7.24	5.91
		× 286	8.48	7.49	6.11	9.71	8.81	7.19
Northern Aspen (includes Aspen Poplar, Large Tooth Aspen and Balsam Poplar)	No. 2	38× 89	2.54	2.28	1.86	2.91	2.64	2.19
		× 140	3.79	3.28	2.68	4.46	3.86	3.15
		× 184	5.00	4.33	3.53	5.88	5.09	4.16
		× 235	6.38	5.52	4.51	7.50	6.50	5.31
		× 286	7.76	6.72	5.48	9.13	7.90	6.45
	No. 3	38× 89	1.96	1.70	1.38	2.31	2.00	1.63
		× 140	2.89	2.50	2.04	3.40	2.94	2 40
		× 184	3.81	3.30	2.69	4.48	3.88	3.17
		× 235	4.86	4.21	3.43	5.72	4.95	4.04
		× 286	5.91	5.12	4.18	6.95	6.02	4.92

Table 20
Maximum Spans for Built-Up Wood Beams
Supporting not more than one Floor[2] in Houses

Species	Grade[1]	Supported Joist Length, m[3][4]	ALLOWABLE SPANS IN METRES FOR:					
			38 × 184		38 × 235		38 × 286	
			3 pc	4 pc	3 pc	4 pc	3 pc	4 pc
Douglas Fir Larch (includes Douglas Fir and Western Larch)	No. 1	2.4	3.70	4.27	4.72	5.45	5.74	6.63
		3 0	3.31	3.82	4.22	4.87	5.13	5.93
		3.6	3.02	3.49	3.85	4.45	4.69	5.41
		4.2	2.76	3.23	3.53	4.12	4.29	5.01
		4.8	2.46	3.02	3.14	3.85	3.82	4.69
	No. 2	2.4	3.33	3.84	4.24	4.90	5.16	5.96
		3 0	2.97	3.44	3.79	4.38	4.62	5.33
		3.6	2.71	3.14	3.46	4.00	4.22	4.87
		4.2	2.51	2.90	3.20	3.70	3.90	4.51
		4.8	2.35	2.71	3.00	3.46	3.65	4.22
Hem Fir (includes Western Hemlock and Amabilis Fir)	No. 1	2.4	3.19	3.69	4.10	4.71	4.96	5.72
		3 0	2.85	3.30	3.64	4.21	4.43	5.12
		3.6	2.61	3.01	3.33	3.84	4.05	4.67
		4.2	2.30	2.79	2.93	3.56	3.57	4.33
		4.8	2.06	2.61	2.62	3.33	3.19	4.05
	No. 2	2.4	2.86	3.31	3.65	4.22	4.45	5.13
		3 0	2.56	2.96	3.27	3.77	3.98	4.59
		3.6	2.34	2.70	2.98	3.45	3.63	4.19
		4.2	2.16	2.50	2.76	3.19	3.36	3.88
		4.8	2.02	2.34	2.58	2.98	3.14	3.63
Eastern Hemlock Tamarack (includes Eastern Hemlock and Tamarack)	No. 1	2.4	3.56	4.11	4.54	5.25	5.53	6.38
		3 0	3.18	3.68	4.06	4.69	4.94	5.71
		3.6	2.91	3.36	3.71	4.28	4.51	5.21
		4.2	2.69	3.11	3.43	3.97	4.18	4.82
		4.8	2.46	2.91	3.14	3.71	3.82	4.51
	No. 2	2.4	3.19	3.69	4.07	4.71	4.96	5.72
		3 0	2.85	3.30	3.64	4.21	4.43	5.12
		3.6	2.61	3.01	3.33	3.84	4.05	4.67
		4.2	2.41	2.79	3.08	3.56	3.75	4.33
		4.8	2.26	2.61	2.88	3.33	3.50	4.05
Coast Species (includes Douglas Fir, Western Larch, Western Hemlock, Amabilis Fir and Coast Sitka Spruce)	No. 1	2.4	3.15	3.64	4.02	4.65	4.90	5.65
		3 0	2.64	3.26	3.37	4.16	4.10	5.06
		3.6	2.26	2.89	2.88	3.69	3.51	4.49
		4.2	1.99	2.53	2.54	3.23	3.09	3.93
		4.8	1.79	2.26	2.28	2.88	2.77	3.51
	No. 2	2.4	2.82	3.26	3.60	4.16	4.38	5.06
		3 0	2.52	2.91	3.22	3.72	3.92	4.52
		3.6	2.26	2.66	2.88	3.39	3.51	4.13
		4.2	1.99	2.46	2.54	3.14	3.09	3.82
		4.8	1.79	2.26	2.28	2.88	2.77	3.51
Spruce Pine Fir (includes Spruce — all species except Coast Sitka Spruce — Jack Pine, Lodgepole Pine, Balsam Fir and Alpine Fir)	No. 1	2.4	3.09	3.57	3.95	4.56	4.80	5.55
		3 0	2.77	3.19	3.53	4.08	4.30	4.96
		3.6	2.44	2.92	3.11	3.72	3.79	4.53
		4.2	2.14	2.70	2.74	3.45	3.33	4.19
		4.8	1.92	2.44	2.45	3.11	2.98	3.79
	No. 2	2.4	2.78	3.21	3.54	4.09	4.31	4.98
		3 0	2.48	2.87	3.17	3.66	3.85	4.45
		3.6	2.26	2.62	2.89	3.34	3.52	4.06
		4.2	2.10	2.42	2.68	3.09	3.26	3.76
		4.8	1.92	2.26	2.45	2.89	2.98	3.52

Table 20 (Cont'd)
Maximum Spans for Built-Up Wood Beams
Supporting not more than one Floor[2] in Houses

Species	Grade[1]	Supported Joist Length, m[3] [4]	ALLOWABLE SPANS IN METRES FOR:					
			38 × 184		38 × 235		38 × 286	
			3 pc	4 pc	3 pc	4 pc	3 pc	4 pc
Western Cedars (includes Western Red Cedar and Pacific Coast Yellow Cedar)	No. 1	2.4	3.13	3.62	4.00	4.62	4.86	5.62
		3 0	2.80	3.24	3.58	4.13	4.35	5.02
		3.6	2.56	2.95	3.26	3.77	3.97	4.59
		4.2	2.26	2.73	2.88	3.49	3.51	4.25
		4.8	2.02	2.56	2.58	3.26	3.14	3.97
	No. 2	2.4	2.80	3.23	3.57	4.12	4.34	5.02
		3 0	2.50	2.89	3.19	3.69	3.88	4.49
		3.6	2.28	2.64	2.91	3.37	3.55	4.10
		4.2	2.11	2.44	2.70	3.12	3.28	3.79
		4.0	1.98	2.27	2.52	2.91	3.07	3.55
Northern Species (includes all softwood species covered by NLGA Standard Grading rules)	No. 1	2.4	2.99	3.45	3.82	4.41	4.64	5.36
		3 0	2.64	3.09	3.37	3.94	4.10	4.80
		3 6	2.26	2.82	2.88	3.60	3.51	4.38
		4.2	1.99	2.53	2.54	3.23	3.09	3.93
		4.8	1.79	2.26	2.28	2.88	2.77	3.51
	No. 2	2.4	2.68	3.10	3.43	3.96	4.17	4.81
		3 0	2.40	2.77	3.07	3.54	3.73	4.30
		3.6	2.19	2.53	2.80	3.23	3.40	3.93
		4.2	1.99	2.34	2.54	2.99	3.09	3.64
		4.8	1.79	2.19	2.28	2.80	2.77	3.40
Northern Aspen (includes Aspen Poplar, Large Tooth Aspen and Balsam Poplar)	No. 1	2.4	3.09	3.57	3.95	4.56	4.80	5.55
		3 0	2.69	3.19	3.44	4.08	4.18	4.96
		3.6	2.30	2.92	2.94	3.72	3.58	4.53
		4.2	2.03	2.58	2.59	3.29	3.15	4.01
		4.8	1.82	2.30	2.32	2.94	2.83	3.58
	No. 2	2.4	2.78	3.21	3.54	4.09	4.31	4.98
		3 0	2.48	2.87	3.17	3.66	3.85	4.45
		3.6	2.26	2.62	2.89	3.34	3.52	4.06
		4.2	2.03	2.42	2.59	3.09	3.15	3.76
		4.8	1.82	2.26	2.32	2.89	2.83	3.52

Notes to Table 20.
[1] Graded in conformance with 1984 "NLGA Standard Grading Rules for Canadian Lumber" published by the National Lumber Grades Authority, Vancouver.
[2] These tables provide maximum allowable spans for main beams or girders which are built-up from 38 mm members in the species, sizes and grades indicated. Allowable spans for solid wood beams or built-up beams in sizes or grades other than those shown must be determined from standard engineering formulae.
[3] Supported joist length means $1/2$ the sum of the joist spans on both sides of the beam.
[4] For supported joist lengths intermediate between those shown in the tables, straight line interpolation may be used in determining the maximum beam span.
[5] Where built-up wood beams are employed over a single span, the length of each individual piece used to fabricate the beam must equal the length of the beam.
[6] Where built-up beams are continued over more than 1 span, and where lengths of individual pieces are less than the total length of the complete beam, butt joints must be located over or near a support.

Table 21
Maximum Spans for Built-Up Wood Beams
Supporting not more than two Floors[2] in Houses

		Supported Joist Length, m[3] [4]	ALLOWABLE SPANS IN METRES FOR:					
			38 × 184		38 × 235		38 × 286	
Species	Grade[1]		3 pc	4 pc	3 pc	4 pc	3 pc	4 pc
Douglas Fir Larch (includes Douglas Fir and Western Larch)	No. 1	2.4	2.78	3.24	3.55	4.13	4.32	5.03
		3 0	2.30	2.90	2.93	3.70	3.57	4.50
		3.6	1.97	2.51	2.52	3.21	3.07	3.90
		4.2	1.74	2.20	2.23	2.81	2.71	3.42
		4.8	1.57	1.97	2.01	2.52	2.44	3.07
	No. 2	2.4	2.52	2.91	3.21	3.72	3.92	4.52
		3 0	2.26	2.61	2.87	3.33	3.50	4.05
		3.6	1.97	2.38	2.52	3.04	3.07	3.69
		4.2	1.74	2.20	2.23	2.81	2.71	3.42
		4.8	1.57	1.97	2.01	2.52	2.44	3.07
Hem Fir (includes Western Hemlock and Amabilis Fir)	No. 1	2.4	2.31	2.80	2.95	3.57	3.59	4.34
		3 0	1.92	2.44	2.45	3.12	2.99	3.79
		3.6	1.66	2.10	2.12	2.68	2.58	3.25
		4.2	1.48	1.85	1.89	2.36	2.29	2.87
		4.8	1.34	1.66	1.71	2.12	2.08	2.58
	No. 2	2.4	2.17	2.51	2.77	3.20	3.37	3.89
		3 0	1.92	2.24	2.45	2.86	2.99	3.48
		3.6	1.66	2.05	2.12	2.62	2.58	3.18
		4.2	1.48	1.85	1.89	2.36	2.29	2.87
		4.8	1.34	1.66	1.71	2.12	2.08	2.58
Eastern Hemlock Tamarack (includes Eastern Hemlock and Tamarack)	No. 1	2.4	2.70	3.12	3.45	3.98	4.19	4.84
		3 0	2.30	2.79	2.93	3.56	3.57	4.33
		3.6	1.97	2.51	2.52	3.21	3.07	3.90
		4.2	1.74	2.20	2.23	2.81	2.71	3.42
		4.8	1.57	1.97	2.01	2.52	2.44	3.07
	No. 2	2.4	2.42	2.80	3.09	3.56	3.76	4.34
		3 0	2.16	2.51	2.76	3.19	3.36	3.88
		3.6	1.97	2.28	2.52	2.91	3.07	3.54
		4.2	1.74	2.11	2.23	2.70	2.71	3.28
		4.8	1.57	1.97	2.01	2.52	2.44	3.07
Coast Species (includes Douglas Fir, Western Larch, Western Hemlock, Amabilis Fir and Coast Sitka Spruce)	No. 1	2.4	2.00	2.55	2.55	3.25	3.11	3.95
		3 0	1.67	2.11	2.14	2.69	2.60	3.28
		3.6	1.45	1.82	1.86	2.32	2.26	2.82
		4.2	1.30	1.61	1.66	2.06	2.02	2.50
		4.8	1.18	1.45	1.51	1.86	1.84	2.26
	No. 2	2.4	2.00	2.47	2.55	3.15	3.11	3.84
		3 0	1.67	2.11	2.14	2.69	2.60	3.28
		3.6	1.45	1.82	1.86	2.32	2.26	2.82
		4.2	1.30	1.61	1.66	2.06	2.02	2.50
		4.8	1.18	1.45	1.51	1.86	1.84	2.26
Spruce Pine Fir (includes Spruce — all species except Coast Sitka Spruce — Jack Pine, Lodgepole Pine, Balsam Fir and Alpine Fir)	No. 1	2.4	2.16	2.71	2.75	3.46	3.35	4.21
		3 0	1.80	2.28	2.30	2.91	2.79	3.53
		3.6	1.56	1.96	1.99	2.50	2.42	3.04
		4.2	1.39	1.73	1.77	2.21	2.16	2.69
		4.8	1.26	1.56	1.61	1.99	1.96	2.42
	No. 2	2.4	2.10	2.43	2.69	3.10	3.27	3.77
		3 0	1.80	2.17	2.30	2.77	2.79	3.38
		3.6	1.56	1.96	1.99	2.50	2.42	3.04
		4.2	1.39	1.73	1.77	2.21	2.16	2.69
		4.8	1.26	1.56	1.61	1.99	1.96	2.42

Table 21 (Cont'd)
Maximum Spans for Built-Up Wood Beams
Supporting not more than two Floors[2] in Houses

Species	Grade[1]	Supported Joist Length, m[3] [4]	ALLOWABLE SPANS IN METRES FOR:					
			38 × 184		38 × 235		38 × 286	
			3 pc	4 pc	3 pc	4 pc	3 pc	4 pc
Western Cedars (includes Western Red Cedar and Pacific Coast Yellow Cedar)	No. 1	2.4	2.27	2.74	2.90	3.50	3.53	4.26
		3.0	1.89	2.40	2.41	3.06	2.94	3.73
		3.6	1.64	2.06	2.09	2.63	2.54	3.20
		4.2	1.45	1.82	1.86	2.32	2.26	2.82
		4.8	1.32	1.64	1.68	2.09	2.05	2.54
	No. 2	2.4	2.12	2.45	2.71	3.13	3.29	3.81
		3.0	1.89	2.19	2.41	2.80	2.94	3.40
		3.6	1.64	2.00	2.09	2.55	2.54	3.11
		4.2	1.45	1.82	1.86	2.32	2.26	2.82
		4.8	1.32	1.64	1.68	2.09	2.05	2.42
Northern Species (includes all softwood species covered by NLGA Standard Grading Rules)	No. 1	2.4	2.00	2.55	2.55	3.25	3.11	3.95
		3.0	1.67	2.11	2.14	2.69	2.60	3.28
		3.6	1.45	1.82	1.86	2.32	2.26	2.82
		4.2	1.30	1.61	1.66	2.06	2.02	2.50
		4.8	1.18	1.45	1.51	1.86	1.84	2.26
	No. 2	2.4	2.00	2.35	2.55	3.00	3.11	3.65
		3.0	1.67	2.10	2.14	2.68	2.60	3.26
		3.6	1.45	1.82	1.86	2.32	2.26	2.82
		4.2	1.30	1.61	1.66	2.06	2.02	2.50
		4.8	1.18	1.45	1.51	1.86	1.84	2.26
Northern Aspen (Includes Aspen Poplar, Large Tooth Aspen and Balsam Poplar)	No. 1	2.4	2.04	2.60	2.60	3.32	3.17	4.03
		3.0	1.70	2.15	2.18	2.75	2.65	3.34
		3.6	1.48	1.85	1.89	2.37	2.30	2.88
		4.2	1.32	1.64	1.69	2.09	2.05	2.55
		4.8	1.20	1.48	1.53	1.89	1.87	2.30
	No. 2	2.4	2.04	2.43	2.60	3.10	3.17	3.77
		3.0	1.70	2.15	2.18	2.75	2.65	3.34
		3.6	1.48	1.85	1.89	2.37	2.30	2.88
		4.2	1.32	1.64	1.69	2.09	2.05	2.55
		4.8	1.20	1.48	1.53	1.89	1.87	2.30

Notes to Table 21.
[1] Graded in conformance with 1984 "NLGA Standard Grading Rules for Canadian Lumber" published by the National Lumber Grades Authority, Vancouver.
[2] These tables provide maximum allowable spans for main beams or girders which are built-up from 38 mm members in the species, sizes and grades indicated. Allowable spans for solid wood beams or built-up beams in sizes or grades other than those shown must be determined from standard engineering formulae.
[3] Supported joist length means $1/2$ the sum of the joist spans on both sides of the beam.
[4] For supported joist lengths intermediate between those shown in the tables, straight line interpolation may be used in determining the maximum beam span.
[5] Where built-up wood beams are employed over a single span, the length of each individual piece used to fabricate the beam must equal the length of the beam.
[6] Where built-up beams are continued over more than 1 span, and where lengths of individual pieces are less than the total length of the complete beam, butt joints must be located over or near a support.

Table 22
Minimum Thickness of Subflooring

	Minimum Subflooring Thickness in mm for Maximum Joist Spacing at		
	300 mm	400 mm	600 mm
Plywood	15.5	15.5	18.5
Waferboard	15.9	15.9	19.0
Particleboard	15.9	15.9	25.4
Lumber	17.0	17.0	19.0

Table 23
Sheathing and Subfloor Attachment

Element	Minimum Length of Fasteners for Sheathing and Subfloor Attachment, mm				Min. No. or Max. Spacing of Fasteners
	Common or Spiral Nails	Ring Thread Nails	Roofing Nails	Staples	
Plywood or waferboard up to 10 mm thick	51	45	N/A	38	
Plywood or waferboard from 10 mm to 20 mm thick	51	45	N/A	51	150 mm (o.c.) along edges and 300 mm (o.c.) along intermediate supports
Plywood or waferboard over 20 mm thick	57	51	N/A	N/A	
Fibreboard sheathing up to 13 mm thick	N/A	N/A	44	38	
Gypsum sheathing up to 13 mm thick	N/A	N/A	44	N/A	
Board lumber 184 mm or less wide	51	N/A	N/A	51	2 per support
Board lumber more than 184 mm wide	51	N/A	N/A	51	3 per support

Table 24
Nailing for Framing

Construction Detail	Minimum Length of Nails, mm	Minimum Number or Maximum Spacing of Nails
Floor joist to plate — toenail	82	2
Wood or metal strapping to underside of floor joists	57	2
Cross-bridging to joists	57	2 each end
Double header or trimmer joists	76	300 mm (o.c.)
Floor joist to stud (balloon construction)	76	2
Ledger strip to wood beam	82	2 per joist
Joist to joist splice (see also Table 27)	76	2 at each end
Tail joist to adjacent header joist (end nailed) around openings	{ 82 / 101	5 / 3
Each header joist to adjacent trimmer joist (end nailed) around openings	{ 82 / 101	5 / 3
Stud to wall plate (each end) toenail or end nail	{ 63 / 82	4 / 2
Doubled studs at openings, or studs at partition or wall intersections and corners	76	750 mm (o.c.)
Doubled top wall plates	76	600 mm (o.c.)
Bottom wall plate or sole plate to joists or blocking (exterior walls)[1]	82	400 mm (o.c.)
Interior partitions to framing or subflooring	82	600 mm (o.c.)
Horizontal member over openings in partitions — each end	82	2
Lintels to studs	82	2 at each end
Ceiling joist to plate — toenail each end	82	2
Roof rafter, roof truss or roof joist to plate — toenail	82	3
Rafter plate to each ceiling joist	101	2
Rafter to joist (with ridge supported)	76	3
Rafter to joist (with ridge unsupported)	76	see Table 27
Gusset plate to each rafter at peak	57	4
Rafter to ridge board — toenail	57	4
— end nail	82	3
Collar tie to rafter — each end	76	3
Collar tie lateral support to each collar tie	57	2
Jack rafter to hip or valley rafter	82	2
Roof strut to rafter	76	3
Roof strut to bearing partition — toenail	82	2
38 × 140 mm or less plank decking to support	82	2
Plank decking wider than 38 × 140 mm to support	82	3
38 mm edge laid plank decking to support (toenail)	76	1
38 mm edge laid plank to each other	76	450 mm (o.c.)

Note to Table 24.
[1] Alternatively, the exterior wall may be fastened to the floor framing by having plywood or waferboard sheathing extend down over floor framing and fastened to the floor framing by nails or staples conforming to Table 23, or by tying the wall framing to the floor framing by 50 mm wide galvanized metal strips of at least 0.41 mm thickness, spaced not more than 1.2 m apart, and fastened at each end with at least two 63 mm nails.

Table 25
Size and Spacing of Studs —
Exterior and Interior Wall Construction for Various Load Conditions

Exterior Wall

Stud Size mm	Maximum spacing in mm and unsupported height in metres (unsupported height in parentheses)			
	Roof with or without attic	Plus one floor	Plus two floors	Plus three floors
38 × 64	400 (2.4)	—	—	—
38 × 89	600 (3.0)	400 (3.0)	300 (3.0)	—
38 × 140	600 (3.0)	600 (3.0)	400 (3.6)	300 (1.8)

Interior Wall

Stud Size, mm	Maximum spacing in mm and unsupported height in metres (unsupported height in parentheses)					
	No load	Attic (not acces- sible)	Plus one floor	Plus two floors	Roof plus two floors	Roof plus three floors
38 × 38	400 (2.4)	—	—	—	—	—
38 × 64	600 (3.0)	600 (3.0)	400 (2.4)	—	—	—
38 × 89 (flat)	400 (3.6)	400 (2.4)	—	—	—	—
38 × 89	600 (3.6)	600 (3.6)	600 (3.6)	400 (3.6)	300 (3.6)	—
38 × 140	600 (3.6)	600 (3.6)	600 (3.6)	600 (3.6)	400 (4.2)	300 (4.2)

Table 26
Spans for Various Depths of Lintels

Location of Lintels	Supported Loads Including Dead Loads and Ceiling	Depth of Lintels, mm	Maximum Allowable Spans, m
Interior Walls	Attic not accessible by stairway	89	1.22
		140	1.83
		184	2.44
		235	3.05
		286	3.81
	Attic accessible by stairway Roof load Attic not accessible by stairway plus 1 floor	89	0.61
		140	0.91
		184	1.22
		235	1.52
		286	1.83
	Attic accessible by stairway plus 1 floor Roof load plus 1 floor Attic not accessible by stairway plus 2 or 3 floors	89	—
		140	0.76
		184	0.91
		235	1.22
		286	1.52
	Attic accessible by stairway plus 2 or 3 floors Roof load plus 2 or 3 floors	89	—
		140	0.61
		184	0.91
		235	1.07
		286	1.22
Exterior Walls	Roof with or without accessible attic	89	1.12
		140	1.68
		184	2.24
		235	2.79
		286	3.35
	Roof with or without accessible attic plus 1 floor	89	0.56
		140	1.40
		184	1.96
		235	2.24
		286	2.51
	Roof with or without accessible attic plus 2 or 3 floors	89	0.56
		140	1.12
		184	1.68
		235	1.96
		286	2.24

Table 27
Minimum Rafter-to-Joist Nailing[1] [2]
(Unsupported Ridge)

Roof Snow Load, kPa

Roof Slope	Rafter Spacing, mm	Rafter Tied to Every Joist						Rafter Tied to Joist Every 1.2 m					
		Building Width up to 8 m			Building Width up to 9.8 m			Building Width up to 8 m			Building Width up to 9.8 m		
		1 or less	1.5	2.0 or more	1 or less	1.5	2.0 or more	1 or less	1.5	2.0 or more	1 or less	1.5	2.0 or more
1:3	400	4	5	6	5	7	8	11	—	—	—	—	—
1:3	600	6	8	9	8	—	—	11	—	—	—	—	—
1:2.4	400	4	4	5	5	6	7	7	10	—	9	—	—
1:2.4	600	5	7	8	7	9	11	7	10	—	9	—	—
1:2	400	4	4	4	4	4	5	6	8	9	8	—	—
1:2	600	4	5	6	5	7	8	6	8	9	8	—	—
1:1.71	400	4	4	4	4	4	4	5	6	7	7	9	11
1:1.71	600	4	4	5	5	6	7	5	6	7	7	9	11
1:1.33	400	4	4	4	4	4	4	4	5	5	5	6	7
1:1.33	600	4	4	4	4	4	5	4	5	5	5	6	7
1:1	400	4	4	4	4	4	4	4	4	4	4	4	5
1:1	600	4	4	4	4	4	4	4	4	4	4	4	5

Notes to Table 27.
(1) Nails not less than 79 mm.
(2) Ceiling joists must be fastened together with at least 1 more nail per joist splice than required for the rafter-to-joist connection.

Table 28
Minimum Thickness of Roof Sheathing for Sloping Roofs[1]

		Sheathing Thickness in mm for Truss or Rafter Spacing at		
		300 mm	400 mm	600 mm
Plywood	Supported[2] edges	7.5	7.5	9.5
	Unsupported edges	9.5	9.5	12.5
Waferboard	Supported edges	9.5	9.5	11.1
	Unsupported edges	9.5	11.1	12.7
Lumber[3]		17.0	17.0	19.0

Notes for Table 28.
[1] The thickness of sheathing for flat roofs used as walking decks is the same as for subfloors (Table 22.)
[2] Supported edges between panels by means of H clips or minimum 38 × 38 mm blocking between trusses or rafters.
[3] The minimum lumber grades for sheathing are as follows and must bear the paragraph number of the National Lumber Grades Authority or the equivalent grade for other rules:
No. 3 or Common — Paragraph 113
Standard — Paragraph 114
No. 4 or Common — Paragraph 118

Table 29
Stapling Table

A) Asphalt Shingles to Wood Decks —
  (1) 1.6 mm thick, 22.2 mm long, 11.1 mm crown.
  Corrosion resistant.
  1/3 more staples than the number of nails required.
  (2) 1.6 mm thick, 19 mm long. 25.4 mm crown.
  Corrosion resistant.
  Equivalent to number of nails required.

B) Cedar Shingles to Wood Decks —
  1.6 mm thick, 28.6 mm long, 9.5 mm crown.
  Corrosion resistant.

C) Gypsum Plaster Lath, 9.5 mm thick —
  1.6 mm thick, 25.4 mm long, 19 mm crown.
  Gypsum Plaster Lath, 12.7 mm thick —
  1.6 mm thick, 28.6 mm long, 19 mm crown.

D) 7.5 mm and 9.5 mm Plywood Wall Sheathing —
  1.6 mm thick, 38.1 mm long, 9.5 mm crown.

E) 9.5 mm Plywood Roof Sheathing —
  1.6 mm thick, 38.1 mm long, 9.5 mm crown.

F) 11.1 mm and 12.7 mm Fibreboard Wall Sheathing —
  1.6 mm thick, 38.1 mm long, 9.5 mm crown.

G) 6.4 mm Underlayment —
  1.2 mm thick, 28.6 mm long, 9.5 mm crown.

H) 7.9 mm and 9.5 mm Hardboard Underlayment —
  1.2 mm thick, 28.6 mm long, 7.9 mm crown.

I) Metal Plaster Lath —
  2 mm thick, 38.1 mm long, 19 mm crown.

Table 30
Roofing Types and Slope Limits for Roofs

Type of Roofing	Minimum Slope	Maximum Slope
Built-up Roofing		
Asphalt base (gravelled)	1 in 50	1 in 4
Asphalt base (without gravel)	1 in 25	1 in 2
Asphalt base (surfaced with wide selvage asphalt roofing)	1 in 6	no limit
Coal-tar base (gravelled)	1 in 50	1 in 25
Cold process	1 in 25	1 in 1.33
Asphalt Shingles		
Normal application	1 in 3	no limit
Low slope application	1 in 6	no limit
Roll Roofing		
Smooth and mineral surfaced	1 in 4	no limit
480 mm wide selvage asphalt roofing	1 in 6	no limit
Cold application felt	1 in 50	1 in 1.33
Wood Shingles	1 in 4	no limit
Handsplit Shakes	1 in 3	no limit
Corrugated Metal Roofing	1 in 4	no limit
Sheet Metal Shingles	1 in 4	no limit
Clay Tile	1 in 2	no limit
Glass Fibre Reinforced Polyester Roofing Panels	1 in 4	no limit

Table 31
Maximum Exposure of Wood Shingles — Roofs

	Maximum Shingle Exposure mm		
Roof Slope	400 mm Shingles	450 mm Shingles	600 mm Shingles
1:3 or less	95 mm	105 mm	145 mm
Over 1:3	125 mm	140 mm	190 mm

Table 32
Material Combinations for Built-Up Roofs

Type of Roof	Amount of Bitumen Per Square Metre of Roof Surface		Number of Plies of Dry Sheathing, Roofing Felts			Minimum Amount of Aggregate Surfacing Per Square Metre of Roof Surface
	Mopping Coats between plies	Flood Coat	Wood Board or Plywood Deck		All Other Decks	
			Dry Sheath-ing	Roofing Felts	Roofing Felts	
Asphalt and aggregate	1.0 kg	3.0 kg	1	4(1)	3(2)	20 kg gravel or crushed rock or 15 kg slag on level roof, 15 kg gravel or crush-ed rock or 10 kg slag on 1:4 slope. Proportional masses for intermediate roof slopes.
Coalt-tar pitch and aggregate	1.2 kg	3.6 kg	1	4(1)	3(?)	
Glass felt and aggregate	1.2 kg	3.0 kg	—	3(3)	2(4)	
Asphalt — smooth surface	1.0 kg	1.2 kg	1	4(1)	3(2)	—
Glass felt — smooth surface	1.0 kg	1.0 kg	—	3(3)	3(4)	—
Cold process roofing	0.75 L Cold process cement	2.0 L Cold process top coating	—	2	—	—

Notes to Table 32.
(1) Two layers of felt laid dry over the sheathing and two layers mopped with bitumen. Where the deck consists of plywood or waferboard, no dry felts or dry sheathing paper need be provided where the joints in the plywood or waferboard are taped, the plywood or waferboard deck primed with asphalt and three plies of asphalt paper mopped with asphalt and flood coated as described in the table.
(2) All layers of felt mopped with bitumen.
(3) One combination felt laid dry and two layers of glass felt mopped with bitumen.
(4) All layers of glass felt mopped with bitumen.

Table 33
Minimum Thickness of Wall Sheathing

Type of Sheathing	Minimum Thickness (mm)	
	With Supports 400 mm on centre	With Supports 600 mm on centre
Structural		
Fibreboard	9.5	11.1
Gypsum board	9.5	12.7
Plywood (exterior type)	6.0	7.5
Waferboard	6.35	7.9
Lumber	17.5	17.5
Non-Structural		
Expanded polystrene (Types 1 and 2)	38	38
Expanded polystrene (Types 3 and 4)	25	25
Urethane and Isocyanurate (Types 1, 2 and 4)	38	38
Urethane and Isocyanurate (Type 3)	25	25
Phenolic, faced	25	25

Table 34
Exposure and Thickness of Wood Shingles and Machine-Grooved Shakes — Walls

Shake or Shingle Length, mm	Maximum Exposure, mm		Minimum Butt Thickness, mm
	Single Coursing	Double Coursing	
400	190	305	10
450	216	356	11
600	292	406	13

Table 35
Stucco Mixes (by volume)

Portland Cement	Masonry Cement Type H	Lime	Aggregate
1	—	1/4 to 1	3 1/4 to 4 parts per part of cementitious material
1	1	—	

Table 36
Minimum RSI values for Houses and Small Buildings

Minimum Thermal Resistance (RSI Value), m² · °C/W

| Building Assembly | Maximum Number of Celsius Degree Days[1] | | | |
	up to 3500	5000	6500	8000 and over
Wall assemblies above ground level (other than foundation walls) separating heated space from unheated space or the outside air	3.0	3.6	4.1	4.5
Foundation wall assemblies separating heated space from unheated space, outside air or adjacent earth[2]	2.2	2.2	2.2	2.2
Roof or ceiling assemblies separating heated space from unheated space or the exterior	4.7	5.6	6.4	7.1
Floor assemblies separating heated space from unheated space or the exterior	4.7	4.7	4.7	4.7
Perimeters of slab-on-ground floors that are less than 600 mm below adjacent ground level (insulation only) a) slabs where heating ducts, pipes or resistance wiring are embedded in or beneath the slabs	1.3	1.7	2.1	2.5
b) slabs other than those described in (a)	0.8	1.3	1.7	2.1

Notes to Table 36.
[1] Where the number of degree days for a particular area is different from those listed, interpolation between values shown in the Table may be made to obtain the minimum required thermal resistance values for that area.
[2] Every foundation wall face having more than 50 per cent of its area exposed to outside air and those parts of foundation walls of wood-frame construction above exterior ground level must have a thermal resistance conforming to the requirements for wall assemblies above ground level.

Table 37
Dimensions for Wood-Strip Flooring

Type of Flooring	Maximum Joist Spacing, mm	Minimum Thickness of Flooring, mm	
		With Subfloor	No Subfloor
Matched hardwood (interior use only)	400	7.9	19.0
	600	7.9	33.3
Matched softwood (interior or exterior use)	400	19.0	19.0
	600	19.0	31.7
Square edge softwood (exterior use only)	400	—	25.4
	600	—	38.1

Table 38
Nailing of Wood-Strip Flooring

Finish Floor Thickness, mm	Minimum Length of Flooring Nails, mm	Maximum Spacing of Flooring Nails, mm
7.9	38[1]	200
11.1	51	300
19.0	57	400
25.4	63	400
31.7	70	600
38.1	83	600

Note to Table 38.
[1] Staples not less than 29 mm long with 1.19 mm shank diameter or thickness and with 4.76 mm crowns may be used in lieu of nails.

Appendix B
Roof Truss Designs
With Nailing Schedules

This section provides guidance on standard designs relating to nailed "W" type trusses and deals with a broad range of conditions including details for trusses having:

Spans:	4.98 to 11.08 m
Roof slopes:	1:2.4, 1:3 and 1:4
Roof snow loads:	1.08, 1.44 and 1.79 kPa
Truss spacing:	600 mm on centre

Roof snow loads are calculated as being 60 per cent of the ground snow load. Ground snow loads for a number of locations in Canada are given in Table B.4 of this Appendix. Reducing the spacing of the trusses increases the roof snow load they can support.

The designs are based on the use of lumber graded in accordance with 1984 NLGA Standard Grading Rules for Canadian Lumber as follows:

Chords (top and bottom members)	No. 1 Grade Spruce or equivalent
Webs (interior members)	No. 2 Grade Spruce or equivalent

The following species are considered equivalent to spruce: Balsam Fir, Lodgepole Pine, Ponderosa Pine and Alpine Fir.

The designs can also be used with the following stronger species: Douglas Fir, Pacific Coast Yellow Cedar, Western Larch, Tamarack, Pacific Coast Hemlock, Jack Pine, Amabilis Fir, Eastern Hemlock and Grand Fir. However, the designs cannot be used with the following weaker species: Western Red Cedar, Red Pine, Western White Pine, Eastern White Pine, Poplar and Eastern White Cedar.

All gussets (plywood connector plates) must be 12.5 mm thick sheathing grade (or better) Douglas Fir Plywood conforming to CSA 0121. The grain of the plywood faces must be parallel to the bottom chord, except for the gussets joining the short web members to the top chord where the face grain must be parallel to the web members.

The trusses must be installed in a plumb position, and each end must be toenailed to the wall with three 82 mm nails. The top chord must be laterally supported by sheathing or by furring spaced at 450 mm on centre or less.

Figure B.4 outlines the method of reinforcing necessary when one or both ends of the truss are to be cantilevered.

Truss members must not be notched, drilled or otherwise weakened to facilitate the installation of services such as plumbing, heating or electrical wiring or for any other reason.

The designs are not intended for use in buildings with attics accessible by stairway or where the bottom chord may be subject to concentrated loads.

Table B.1
Slope 1:2.4 only — Nailed "W" Truss
Spans: 4.98 to 9.15 m — Gussets: 12.5 mm plywood

Nailing Schedule:

Top Chord Size, mm	Bottom Chord Size, mm	Roof Snow Load, kPa	Span m	Number of Nails at Joint Location					
				1	2	3	4	5	6
38 × 89	38 × 89	1.08	4.98	7	7	2	2	3	5
			5.59	8	7	2	3	3	5
			6.20	9	8	2	3	4	6
			6.81	10	9	2	3	4	6
			7.42	10	10	2	3	4	7
			8.03	11	10	3	4	5	7
			8.64	12	11	3	4	5	8
			9.15	12	12	3	4	5	8
38 × 89	38 × 89	1.44	4.98	10	9	2	3	4	6
			5.59	11	10	3	4	4	7
			6.20	12	11	3	4	5	8
			6.81	13	12	3	4	5	8
			7.42	14	13	3	4	6	9
			8.03	15	14	4	5	6	10
			8.64	16	15	4	5	6	10
38 × 89	38 × 89	1.79	4.98	14	13	3	4	5	9
			5.59	16	14	4	5	6	10
			6.20	17	16	4	5	7	11
			6.81	19	17	4	6	7	12
			7.42	20	19	4	6	8	13
			8.03	22	20	5	7	9	14
38 × 140	38 × 89	1.44	9.15	15	14	4	5	5	10
38 × 140	38 × 89	1.79	8.64	17	16	4	5	5	12
			9.15	18	17	4	5	5	12

Notes

Lumber   • No. 1 Grade Spruce or equivalent for top and bottom chords.
         • No. 2 Grade Spruce or equivalent for web members.

Nails   • All nails to be 76 mm common steel wire.
         • All rows of nails to be staggered and clinched perpendicular to direction of plywood face grain.
         • See Figure B.5 for method of fabricating joints.

Plywood • 12.5 mm sheathing grade Douglas Fir throughout.
         • Grain direction of plywood faces to be parallel to bottom chord excepting plates joining web to top chord at quarter points.

General • To ensure maximum stiffness, the upper chords must be in good bearing contact at peak.
         • Trusses with spans between those listed may be used provided the nailing is not less than that shown for the larger span.

Loading • Roof snow load — 0.6 × ground snow load.

Spacing • Trusses spaced 600 mm on centre.

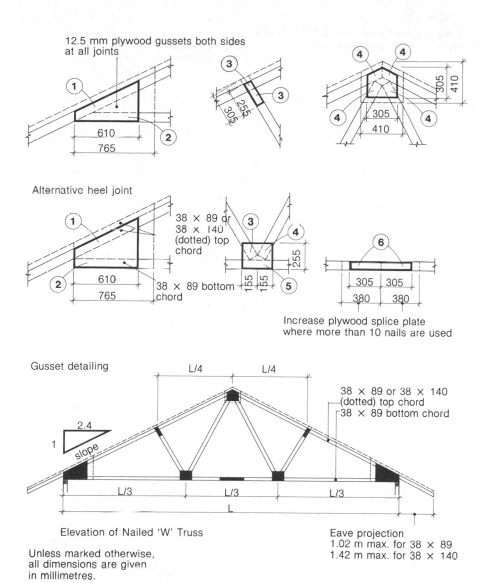

12.5 mm plywood gussets both sides at all joints

Alternative heel joint

38 × 89 or 38 × 140 (dotted) top chord

38 × 89 bottom chord

Increase plywood splice plate where more than 10 nails are used

Gusset detailing

38 × 89 or 38 × 140 (dotted) top chord
38 × 89 bottom chord

Elevation of Nailed 'W' Truss

Unless marked otherwise, all dimensions are given in millimetres.

Eave projection
1.02 m max. for 38 × 89
1.42 m max. for 38 × 140

Figure B.1   Slope: 1:2.4

Table B.2
Slope 1:3 only — Nailed "W" Truss
Spans: 4.98 to 9.15 m — Gussets: 12.5 mm plywood

Nailing Schedule:

Top Chord Size, mm	Bottom Chord Size, mm	Roof Snow Load, kPa	Span m	Number of Nails at Joint Location					
				1	2	3	4	5	6
38 × 89	38 × 89	1.08	4.98	9	8	2	3	3	5
			5.59	10	9	2	3	4	6
			6.20	11	10	2	3	4	7
			6.81	12	11	2	4	4	7
			7.42	13	12	3	4	5	8
			8.03	14	13	3	4	5	9
			8.64	15	14	3	4	5	9
38 × 89	38 × 89	1.44	4.98	12	11	2	4	4	7
			5.59	13	12	3	4	5	8
			6.20	15	13	3	4	5	9
			6.81	16	14	3	5	6	10
			7.42	17	16	4	5	6	11
			8.03	19	17	4	6	7	11
			8.64	20	18	4	6	7	12
38 × 89	38 × 89	1.79	4.98	17	16	3	5	6	11
			5.59	19	18	4	5	7	12
			6.20	21	20	4	6	7	13
			6.81	23	21	4	7	8	14
			7.42	25	23	5	7	9	16
			8.03	27	25	5	8	10	17
38 × 140	38 × 89	1.08	9.15	15	14	3	4	5	10
38 × 140	38 × 89	1.44	9.15	18	17	4	5	6	12
38 × 140	38 × 89	1.79	8.64	21	20	5	6	7	14
			9.15	22	21	5	6	7	15

Notes

Lumber
• No. 1 Grade Spruce or equivalent for top and bottom chords.
• No. 2 Grade Spruce or equivalent for web members.

Nails
• All nails to be 76 mm common steel wire.
• All rows of nails to be staggered and clinched perpendicular to direction of plywood face grain.
• See Figure B.5 for method of fabricating joints.

Plywood
• 12.5 mm sheathing grade Douglas Fir throughout.
• Grain direction of plywood faces to be parallel to bottom chord excepting plates joining web to top chord at quarter points.

General
• To ensure maximum stiffness, the upper chords must be in good bearing contact at peak.
• Trusses with spans between those listed may be used provided the nailing is not less than that shown for the larger span.

Loading
• Roof snow load — 0.6 × ground snow load.

Spacing
• Trusses spaced 600 mm on centre.

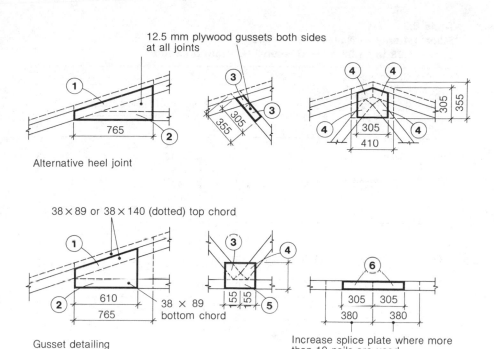

12.5 mm plywood gussets both sides
at all joints

Alternative heel joint

38 × 89 or 38 × 140 (dotted) top chord

38 × 89
bottom chord

Gusset detailing

Increase splice plate where more
than 10 nails are used

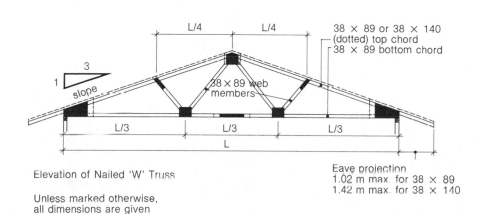

38 × 89 or 38 × 140
(dotted) top chord
38 × 89 bottom chord

38 × 89 web
members

Elevation of Nailed 'W' Truss

Unless marked otherwise,
all dimensions are given
in millimetres.

Eave projection
1.02 m max. for 38 × 89
1.42 m max. for 38 × 140

Figure B.2   Slope: 1:3

Table B.3
Slope 1:4 only — Nailed "W" Truss
Spans: 4.98 to 11.08 m — Gussets: 12.5 mm plywood

Nailing Schedule:

Top Chord Size, mm	Bottom Chord Size, mm	Roof Snow Load, kPa	Span m	Number of Nails at Joint Location					
				1	2	3	4	5	6
38 × 89	38 × 89	1.08	4.98	17	17	4	6	6	12
			5.59	20	18	4	6	6	13
			6.20	22	21	4	7	7	14
			6.81	24	24	4	8	8	16
			7.42	26	26	4	9	9	17
			8.03	29	28	5	9	9	19
			8.64	31	30	5	9	9	20
38 × 89	38 × 89	1.44	4.98	21	21	4	7	7	14
			5.59	24	23	4	7	7	16
			6.20	27	26	5	8	8	17
			6.81	29	29	5	9	9	19
			7.42	32	31	5	10	10	21
			8.03	35	34	6	11	11	23
38 × 140	38 × 89	1.08	4.98	13	13	3	5	5	9
			5.59	15	14	3	5	5	10
			6.20	16	16	3	5	5	11
			6.81	18	18	3	6	6	12
			7.42	20	19	3	6	6	13
			8.03	21	21	4	7	7	14
			8.64	22	22	4	7	7	15
38 × 140	38 × 89	1.44	4.98	16	16	3	5	5	11
			5.59	18	17	3	5	5	12
			6.20	20	19	4	6	6	13
			6.81	22	22	4	7	7	14
			7.42	24	23	4	8	8	16
			8.03	26	25	5	8	8	17
			8.64	27	27	5	8	8	18
38 × 140	38 × 89	1.79	4.98	18	18	4	6	6	12
			5.59	21	20	4	6	6	14
			6.20	24	23	5	7	7	15
			6.81	26	25	5	8	8	17
			7.42	28	27	5	9	9	18
			8.03	30	30	6	10	10	20
38 × 140	38 × 140	1.08	9.25	24	23	4	6	7	16
			9.86	26	25	5	6	8	17
			10.47	28	27	6	7	9	18
			11.08	30	29	7	8	10	19
38 × 140	38 × 140	1.44	9.25	30	29	6	7	9	20
			9.86	32	31	6	7	10	21
			10.47	34	33	7	8	11	22
			11.08	36	35	8	9	12	23
38 × 140	38 × 140	1.79	9.25	35	34	7	8	11	24
			9.86	37	36	7	8	11	25
			10.47	39	38	8	9	12	26
			11.08	41	40	9	10	13	27

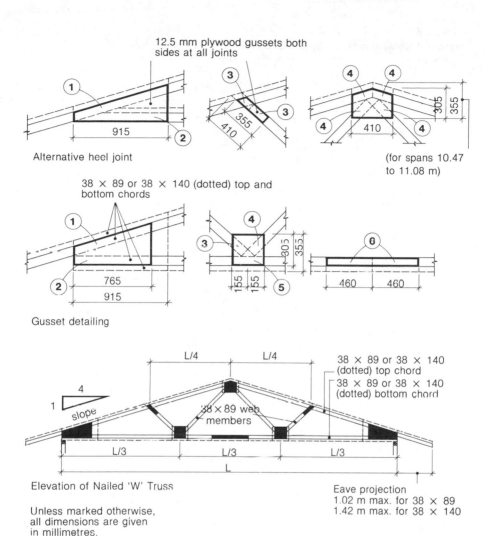

12.5 mm plywood gussets both
sides at all joints

Alternative heel joint

(for spans 10.47
to 11.08 m)

38 × 89 or 38 × 140 (dotted) top and
bottom chords

Gusset detailing

38 × 89 or 38 × 140
(dotted) top chord
38 × 89 or 38 × 140
(dotted) bottom chord

38 × 89 web
members

Elevation of Nailed 'W' Truss

Eave projection
1.02 m max. for 38 × 89
1.42 m max. for 38 × 140

Unless marked otherwise,
all dimensions are given
in millimetres.

Figure B.3   Slope: 1:4 only

Notes

Lumber • No. 1 Grade Spruce or equivalent for top and bottom chords.
• No. 2 Grade Spruce or equivalent for web members.

Nails • All nails to be 76 mm common steel wire.
• All rows of nails to be staggered and clinched perpendicular to direction of plywood face grain.
• See Figure B.5 for method of fabricating joints.

Plywood • 12.5 mm sheathing grade Douglas Fir throughout.
• Grain direction of plywood faces to be parallel to bottom chord excepting plates joining web to top chord at quarter points.

General • To ensure maximum stiffness, the upper chords must be in good bearing contact at peak.
• Trusses with spans between those listed may be used provided the nailing is not less than that shown for the larger span.

Loading • Roof snow load — 0.6 × ground snow load.

Spacing • Trusses spaced 600 mm on centre.

Table B.4
Ground Snow Loads for Urban Centres

Province and Location	Ground Snow Load (kPa)	Province and Location	Ground Snow Load (kPa)
Alberta		**Ontario**	
Calgary	0.9	Cornwall	2.5
Edmonton	1.5	Hamilton	1.6
Grande Prairie	2.1	Kapuskasing	2.9
Jasper	2.4	Kingston	2.2
Medicine Hat	1.4	Kitchener	2.9
Red Deer	1.5	London	1.9
		North Bay	2.7
British Columbia		Oshawa	2.1
Dawson Creek	2.0	Ottawa	2.9
Fort Nelson	2.4	Owen Sound	3.8
Kamloops	1.8	St. Catharines	1.7
New Westminster	2.1	Sault Ste. Marie	3.0
Prince George	2.6	Sudbury	3.0
Prince Rupert	2.6	Toronto	1.8
Vancouver	1.9	Windsor	1.1
Victoria	1.5		
		Prince Edward Island	
Manitoba		Charlottetown	3.3
Brandon	1.8	Summerside	3.0
Churchill	2.9		
Flin Flon	2.3	**Québec**	
Portage la Prairie	1.6	Bagotville	3.4
The Pas	2.6	Chicoutimi	3.6
Winnipeg	2.1	Drummondville	3.2
		Hull	3.0
New Brunswick		Montréal	2.7
Edmundston	3.5	Québec	3.8
Fredericton	3.1	Rimouski	4.6
Moncton	3.8	St. Jean	2.7
Saint John	3.0	St. Jérôme	3.5
		Shawinigan	4.0
Newfoundland		Sherbrooke	2.8
Corner Brook	4.4	Thetford Mines	3.8
Gander	3.3	Trois Rivières	4.0
Goose Bay	5.0	Val d'Or	3.4
St. John's	3.5		
		Saskatchewan	
Northwest Territories		Moose Jaw	1.3
Fort Smith	2.0	Prince Albert	1.9
Inuvik	2.2	Regina	1.7
Iqualuit	2.2	Saskatoon	1.5
Resolute	1.3	Yorkton	2.2
Yellowknife	2.0		
		Yukon Territory	
Nova Scotia		Dawson	2.6
Amherst	2.8	Whitehorse	1.7
Halifax	2.2		
New Glasgow	3.2		
Sydney	2.8		
Yarmouth	2.6		

Unless marked otherwise,
all dimensions are given
in millimetres.

38 × 89 bracing as required.
See Note 7.

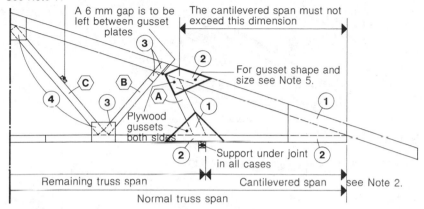

Part Elevation of Typical Truss Showing Cantilever Detail

Figure B.4
Cantilever Details for Nailed 'W' Trusses with Plywood Gussets

Notes:
1. Top and bottom chord sizes to be those required for normal truss span.
2. The cantilevered span is not to exceed 1.83 m for trusses with 38 × 140 top chords, or 1.52 m for trusses with 38 × 89 top chords.
3. The additional web member (Member A) must be of the same lumber size as the top chord.
4. Gusset plates and nailing required for additional member (Member A) must be equivalent to those at the heel joint as noted (Joints 1 and 2).
5. The shape and size of gusset plates should be chosen with regard to the space limitations and required nailing area for individual designs.
6. Number of nails at connections for Member B (Joint 3) to be increased to that used for Member C (Joint 4). Number of nails at all other connections to be those required for normal truss span.
7. For trusses having roof slopes of 1:2.4, bracing must be provided for Member C. (Lateral bracing can be achieved by tying together the midpoints of Member C of the cantilevered trusses with a 38 × 89 extending to at least two normally-supported trusses.)
If desired, both ends can be cantilevered, providing the above procedure is followed for each end.

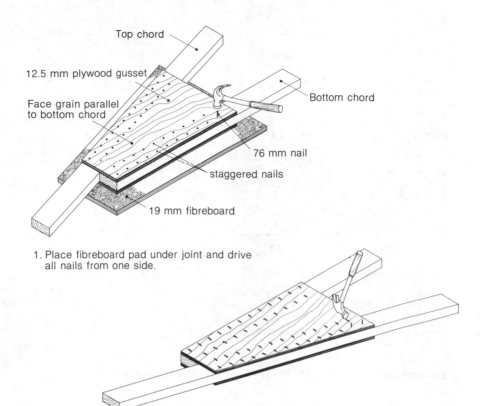

Top chord

12.5 mm plywood gusset

Face grain parallel
to bottom chord

Bottom chord

76 mm nail

staggered nails

19 mm fibreboard

1. Place fibreboard pad under joint and drive
   all nails from one side.

2. Flip truss. Remove fibreboard pads. Bend over projecting tips
   of nails at right angles to plywood face grain.

Figure B.5
Method of Fabricating Joints for
'W' Trusses with Nailed Plywood Gussets

Glossary

Aggregate. Coarse material, such as gravel, broken stone or sand, with which cement and water are mixed to form concrete. Crushed stone is usually designated as coarse aggregate, and sand as fine aggregate.

Air-Entrained Concrete. Concrete in which air in the form of minute bubbles has been occluded during the mixing period as a result of the use of an air-entraining agent as an admixture.

Anchor Bolt. A steel bolt used to secure a structural member against uplift. It is usually deformed at one end to ensure a good grip in the concrete or masonry in which it is embedded.

Apron. A plain or moulded finish piece below the sill of a window, installed to cover the rough edge of the wall finish. Also an extension of the concrete floor of a garage or other structure beyond the face of the building.

Attic or Roof Space. The space between the top floor ceiling and roof and between a dwarf partition and sloping roof.

Backfill. The material used to re-fill an excavation around the outside of a foundation wall or pipe trench.

Balloon Framing. A method of wood-frame construction in which the studs extend in one piece from the foundation sill to the top plate supporting the roof.

Baseboard. A moulded board placed against the wall around a room next to the floor to conceal the joint between the floor and wall finish.

Base Course. In masonry, the first or bottom course of brick or concrete blocks.

Batten. A narrow strip of wood used to cover joints between boards or panels.

Batter Board. Boards set at right angles to each other at each corner of an excavation, used to indicate the level and alignment of the foundation wall.

Beam. A horizontal structural member usually wood, steel or concrete used to support vertical loads.

Beam Pocket. A notch formed at the top of a foundation wall to receive and support the end of a beam.

Bearing. The part of a joist, rafter, truss or beam which actually rests on its support and the area of the support on which it rests.

Bearing Wall. A wall that supports any vertical load in addition to its own weight. Also called loadbearing wall.

Bed. In masonry, the horizontal layer of mortar on which each course of masonry are laid. Generally, any horizontal surface which has been prepared to receive the element(s) it will support.

Bevel. The sloping surface formed when two surfaces meet at an angle which is not a right angle.

Bevel Siding. Boards tapered to a thin edge and used as exterior wall covering.

Bleed Water. Excess water in the concrete mixture which surfaces after placing.

Blind-Nailing. Nailing in such a way that the nailheads are not visible on the face of the finished work.

Bond. In masonry, the pattern in which bricks or blocks are laid to tie the individual units together so that the entire wall they comprise will tend to act as a complete unit.

Bottom Plate. The lower horizontal member of a wood-frame wall nailed to the bottom of the wall studs and to the floor framing members.

Breaking Joints. The manner of laying masonry units so as to prevent vertical joints in adjacent courses from lining up. Also the distribution of joints in boards, flooring, lath and panels so no two adjacent end-joints are directly in line.

Brick Veneer. A facing of brick tied to a wood-frame or masonry wall, serving as a wall covering only and carrying no structural loads.

Built-Up Roof. A roof covering composed of three or more layers of roofing felt or glass fibre saturated with coal tar or asphalt. The top is finished with crushed stone, gravel, or a cap sheet. Generally used on flat or low-pitched roofs.

Bull Float. A board of wood, aluminum or magnesium mounted on a pole which is used to spread and smooth freshly placed horizontal concrete surfaces.

Butt Joint. Any joint made by fastening two members together without overlapping.

Cant Strip. A wedge or triangular-shaped piece of lumber generally installed in the deck of a flat roof around the perimeter or at the junction of the roof and an adjoining wall.

Casing. A form of moulded trim used around window and door openings.

Ceramic Tiles. Vitreous clay tile used for a surface finish.

Chimney Flue. A passage housed in a chimney through which smoke and gases are carried from a fuel-burning appliance, fireplace or incinerator to the exterior.

Collar Brace. A horizontal piece of lumber used to provide intermediate support for opposite roof rafters, usually located in the middle third of the rafters. Also called collar beam or collar tie.

Common Rafter. One of a series of rafters extending from the top of an exterior wall to the ridge of a roof.

Control Joint. A joint tooled or cut into the surface of concrete in order to control the location of cracks.

Corner Bead. In gypsumboard finish, a strip of metal or wood fixed to external corners to protect the corners from damage.

Corner Boards. A built-up wood member installed vertically on the external corners of a house or other frame structure against which the ends of the siding are butted.

Counterflashing. A flashing applied above another flashing to shed water over the top of the under-flashing and to allow some differential movement without damage to the flashing.

Course. A continuous layer of bricks or masonry units in buildings; the term is also applicable to shingles.

Cove. To splay off the right angle between a horizontal and vertical surface. Carried out particularly when applying roofing materials.

Crawl Space. A shallow space between the lowest floor of a house and the ground beneath.

Cricket. A small roof structure at the junction of a chimney and a roof to divert rain water around the chimney. Also known as a saddle.

Cross Bridging. Small wood or metal members that are inserted in a diagonal position between adjacent floor or roof joists.

Curing (of Concrete). The maintenance of proper temperature and moisture conditions to promote the continued chemical reaction which takes place between the water and the cement.

Dado. A rectangular groove in a board or plank. In interior decoration, a special type of wall treatment.

Dampproof Course. A dampproof material placed just above the ground level in a brick or stone wall to prevent ground moisture from seeping up through the structure.

Dampproofing. The process of coating the outside of a foundation wall with a special preparation to resist passage of moisture through the wall. Material used to resist the passage of moisture through concrete floor slabs and from masonry to wood.

Darby Float. A hand float or trowel used by concrete finishers and plasterers in preliminary floating and levelling operations. Also called a derby flicker.

Dead Load. The aggregate weight of the structural components, the fixtures and the permanently attached equipment of a building and its foundation.

Deflection. The bending of a structural member as a result of its own weight or an applied load. Also the amount of displacement resulting from this bending.

Dormer. Framing which projects from a sloping roof, providing an internal recess in the roof space.

Double Glazing. Two panes of glass in a door or window, with an air space between the panes. They may be sealed hermetically as a single unit, or each pane may be installed separately in the door or window sash.

Drywall Finish. Interior wall and ceiling finish other than plaster, for example, gypsum board, plywood and fibreboard panels.

Dwarf Wall. A framed wall of less than the normal full height. Also known as knee or pony wall.

Eaves. The lower part of a roof which projects beyond the face of the walls.

Eaves Soffit. The under surface of the eaves.

Eaves Trough. A trough fixed to an eave to collect and carry away the runoff from the roof. Also called a gutter.

Edge Grained. When lumber is sawn along the radius of the annual rings or at an angle less than 45 degrees to the radius. Also described as quartersawed.

End Grain. The face of a piece of lumber which is exposed when the fibres are cut transversely.

End Matched. Having tongued and grooved ends.

Exterior Trim. That part of the exterior finish other than the wall covering.

Face Nailing. Fastening a member by driving nails through it at right angles to its exposed surface.

Fascia Board. A finish member around the face of eaves and roof projections.

Feathering. Reducing gradually to a very thin edge.

Fire Clay. A clay of high heat-resisting qualities used to make fire brick and the mortar in which the fire brick is laid.

Fire Stop. A complete obstruction placed across a concealed air space in a wall, floor or roof to retard or prevent the spread of flame and hot gases.

Flange. A projecting edge, rib or rim; the top and bottom of I-beams and channels are called flanges.

Flashing. Sheet metal or other material used in roof and wall construction to shed water.

Flooring. Material used in the construction of floors. The surface material is known as finish flooring while the base material is called subflooring.

Flue. See chimney flue.

Flue Lining. The material (usually tile pipe in 610 mm lengths) which lines the flue to protect the chimney walls from hot gases.

Footing. The widened section, usually concrete, at the base or bottom of a foundation wall, pier or column.

Formwork. Temporary sheets or boards (metal or wood) carefully fixed and braced to form the required profile into which concrete is poured, for example, a concrete foundation wall. Removed when concrete is properly set.

Foundation. The lower portion, usually concrete or masonry and including the footings, which transfers the weight of, and loads on, a building to the ground.

Furring. Strips of wood applied to a wall or other surface as nailing support for the finish material, or to give the wall an appearance of greater thickness.

Gable. The upper triangular-shaped portion of the end wall of a house.

Gable End. The entire wall of a house having a gable roof.

Gauge. A standard for measuring, for example, diameter of nails or wire and thickness of metal sheets.

Grade (Lumber). To separate lumber into different established classifications depending upon its suitability for different uses. A classification of lumber.

Grade. The surface slope. The level of the ground surface around the foundation wall. To modify the ground surface by cut and fill.

Grade Line. A pre-determined line indicating the proposed elevation of the ground surface around a building.

Grout. A thin mixture of cement mortar and additional water.

Gusset. A wood or metal plate attached to one or both sides of a joint to increase its holding power.

Header (Framing). A wood member at right angles to a series of joists or rafters at which the joists or rafters terminate. When used at openings in the floor or roof system, the header supports the joist or rafters and acts as a beam.

Hearth. The floor of the fireplace, including the area in front of the fireplace.

Hip. The sloping ridge of a roof formed by two intersecting roof slopes.

Hip-Rafter. The rafter which forms the hip of the roof.

I-Beam. A steel beam with a cross section resembling the capital letter I.

Insulation. Material used to resist heat transmission through walls, floors and roofs.

Interior Finish. The covering used on interior walls and ceilings.

Jack Rafter. A short rafter that spans from the wallplate to a hip rafter or from a valley rafter to the roof ridge.

Jack Stud. A block or short stud nailed to rough door or window studding to add strength and provide a solid bearing and nailing member for the finished door jamb or window frame.

Jamb. The side post or lining of a doorway, window or other opening.

Joint Cement. A powder which is mixed with water and applied to the joints between sheets of gypsum wallboard.

Joist. One of a series of horizontal wood members, usually of 38 mm thickness, used to support a floor, ceiling or roof.

Joist Hanger. A steel section shaped like a stirrup, bent so it can be fastened to a beam to provide end support for joists, headers, etc.

Kerf. The groove formed in wood by a saw cut.

Ledger Strip. A strip of lumber fastened along the bottom of the side of a beam on which joists rest.

Lintel. A horizontal structural (beam) that supports the load over an opening such as a door or window.

Live Load. The weight that is superimposed on the structural components by the use and occupancy of the building, such as furniture, appliances and people.

Lookout Rafters. Short wood members cantilevered over a wall to support an overhanging portion of a roof.

Louvre. A slatted opening for ventilation in which the slats are so placed to exclude rain, sunlight or vision.

Mesh. Expanded metal or woven wire used as a reinforcement for concrete, plaster or stucco.

Metal Lath. Expanded metal or woven wire used to provide a base for plaster or stucco.

Millwork. Building materials made of finished wood including such items as internal and external doors, windows and door frames, panel work, mouldings and interior trim. It does not include flooring, ceiling or siding.

Mineral Wool. A material used for insulating buildings, produced by sending a blast of steam through molten slag or rock; common types now in use include rock, wool, glass wool and slag wool.

Mitre Joint. A joint formed by cutting and butting two pieces of board on a line bisecting the angle of their junction.

Mortar. A substance produced from prescribed proportions of cementing agents, aggregates and water which gradually sets hard after mixing.

Mortar Bed. Layer of mortar on which any structural member, masonry unit or tile is bedded.

Nail Set. A special tool used to complete final driving of nails and avoid damage to the material, for example, in tongued and grooved wood flooring or siding.

Nosing. The rounded and projecting edge of a stair tread, window sill, etc.

O.G. or Ogee. A moulding with a profile in the form of a letter *S*; having the outline of a reversed curve.

On Centre. A term used to define the point from which measurements are taken — from the centre of one member to the centre of the adjacent member as in the spacing of studs, joists or nails. Also centre-to-centre. OC and o.c. are common abbreviations.

Panel. A large, thick board or sheet of lumber, plywood or other material. A thin board with all its edges inserted in a groove of a surrounding frame of thick material. A portion of a flat surface recessed or sunk below the surrounding area, distinctly set off by moulding or some other decorative device. Also a section of floor, wall, ceiling or roof, usually prefabricated and of a large size, handled as a single unit in the operations of assembly and erection.

Parapet Wall. That part of an exterior, party or fire wall extending above the roof line; a wall which serves as a guard at the edge of a balcony or roof.

Parging. A coat of plaster or cement mortar applied to concrete or masonry walls.

Partition. A wall which separates space into rooms, but supports no vertical load except its own weight.

Pier. A column of masonry, usually rectangular in horizontal cross section, used to support other structural members.

Pilaster. A pier forming an integral part of a wall and partially projecting from the wall face.

Pitch. Inclination to the horizontal plane. Also known as slope.

Pitched Roof. A roof which has one or more surfaces sloping at angles greater than necessary for drainage.

Plain Concrete. Unreinforced concrete.

Plenum. An enclosed chamber used to circulate or gather heated or cooled air in a forced-air heating/cooling system.

Plough. To cut a groove.

Plumb. Vertical. To make vertical.

Plumbing. The pipes, fixtures and other apparatus for the water supply and the removal of waterborne wastes.

Portland Cement. A hydraulic cement consisting of silica, lime and alumina mixed in the proper proportions and then burned in a kiln. The clinkers or vitrified product, when finely ground, form an extremely strong cement.

Pressure Treatment. Impregnation of wood or plywood with chemicals under pressure to prevent decay and insect attack.

Purlin. A horizontal member in a roof supporting the rafters.

Rabbet. A groove cut in the surface along the edge of a board, plank or other timber. The recess in a brick jamb which receives a window frame. Also the recess in a door frame to receive the door.

Radiant Heating. A method of heating, usually consisting of coils, pipes or electric heating elements, placed in the floor, wall or ceiling.

Rafter. One of the series of structural members of a roof, usually of 38 mm thickness, designed to support roof loads, but not ceiling finish.

Rail. A traverse piece of wood or metal extending from one vertical member to another in the construction of doors, fences, balustrades, staircases, etc. In framing and panelling, the horizontal pieces are called rails, and the perpendicular are called stiles.

Rake. An incline as in a pitched roof. A slope.

Raked Joint. Joints in masonry veneer where the mortar is grooved out to behind the face of the wall.

Ribbon. A narrow board let into studs to support joists.

Ridge Beam. A horizontal structural member, usually 38 mm thick, supporting the upper ends of the rafters.

Ridge Board. A horizontal structural member, usually 19 mm thick, at the upper end of the rafters, to which these rafters are nailed.

RSI. A metric measurement of the capacity of a material or assembly to impede the flow of heat.

Scribing. Fitting woodwork to an irregular surface.

Sealer. A liquid applied directly over uncoated wood for the purpose of sealing the surface.

Segregation. The separation of the coarse aggregate from the mortar fraction of the concrete which usually results in the formation of rock pockets or honeycombing.

Shake. A shingle split (not sawn) from a block of wood and used for roofing and siding.

Sheathing Paper. Paper treated with tar or asphalt used under exterior wall cladding as protection against the passage of water or air.

Shed Roof. A sloping roof having its surface in one plane.

Shiplap. A form of matching lumber in which a section one-half the thickness of a board is cut from the upper side of one edge and a similar section from the lower side of the opposite edge.

Shoe Moulding. For interior, a moulding strip placed against the baseboard at the floor; also called base shoe or carpet strip.

Siding. In wood-frame construction, the material other than masonry or stucco used as an exterior wall covering.

Sill. The horizontal member forming the bottom of an opening such as a door or window.

Sill Plate. A structural member, anchored to the top of a foundation wall, upon which the floor joists rest.

Sleeper. Any horizontal timber laid on the ground to distribute a load from a post. Also a strip of wood fastened to the top of a concrete slab to support a wood floor.

Smoke Alarm. An electrical device which sounds an alarm when sensing the presence of the products of combustion.

Smoke Pipe. A pipe conveying the products of combustion from a solid or liquid fuel-fired appliance to a chimney flue.

Soffit. The underside of elements of a building, such as staircases, roof overhangs, beams, etc.

Span. The horizontal distance between supports for beams, joists, rafters, etc.

Splash Block. A small masonry block laid with the top close to the ground surface to receive roof drainage and divert it away from the building.

Stair Landing. A platform between flights of stairs.

Step Flashing. Rectangular or square pieces of flashing used at the junction of shingled roof and walls. Also called shingle flashing.

Stoop. A low platform, with or without steps, outside the entrance door of a house.

Storm Door. An extra outside door for protection against inclement weather.

Strike Plate. The part of a door lock set which is fastened to the jamb.

Stile. A vertical piece of a sash, door or piece of framing or panelling to which the ends of rails are attached.

Strongback. A wood batten fixed at right angles to the tops of cross framing members or ceiling joists in order to align and level them.

Strut. A structural member which is designed to resist longitudinal compressive stress such as members supporting a ridge beam or rafters; a short column.

Stud. One of a series of wood structural members, usually 38 mm thick, used as supporting elements in walls and partitions. (Plural: studs or studding.)

Subfloor. Boards or sheet material laid on joists under finish flooring.

Taping. In gypsum board construction, the masking of joints between sheets by means of paper tape which is smoothed over with joint cement.

Three-Way Switch. A switch used in house wiring when one or more lights are controlled from two places. A three-way switch must be used at each location.

Threshold. A strip of wood, metal or other material bevelled on each edge and used at the junction of two different floor finishes under doors or on top of the door sill at exterior doors.

Toenailing. Nailing at an angle to the first member so as to ensure penetration into a second member.

Tongue-and-Groove Lumber. Any lumber, such as boards or planks, machined in such a manner that there is a groove on one edge and a corresponding tongue on the other.

Top Plate. In building, the horizontal member nailed to the top of the partition or wall studs.

Trimmer. A beam or joist alongside an opening and into which a header is framed.

Truss. A structural component composed of a combination of members usually in a triangular arrangement to form a rigid framework. Often used to support a roof.

Valley. The internal angle formed by the junction of two sloping sides of a roof.

Valley Rafters. Rafters which are located at the centre of roof valleys to support the jack rafters.

Vapour Barrier. Material used to retard the passage of water vapour or moisture.

Wall Plates. In wood-frame construction, the horizontal members attached to the ends of the studs. Also called top or bottom plates, depending on their location.

Water Table. The level below which the ground is saturated with water.

Weatherstripping. Strips of felt, rubber, metal or other material, fixed along the edges of doors or windows to keep out drafts and reduce heat loss.

Weephole. A small hole, as at the bottom of a retaining wall or masonry veneer, to drain water to the exposed face.

INDEX

Air barriers. *See* Vapour and air barriers

Anchor bolts, masonry, 12–13

Asphalt shingles, 70–74, 76
 finish at ridge and hips, 76
 installing on low slopes, 73–74
 installing on slopes 1:3 or
  greater, 71–73

Attic
 ceiling joist spans for attic not
  accessible by stairway, 187
 floor joist spans for attic
  accessible by stairway, 189
 ventilating, 132–34

Backfilling, foundation, 4–5

Balloon construction, 35, 51–52

Base mouldings, installing, 148

Basement
 drainage, 26–28
 headroom, 37
 pouring concrete floors, 7
 slab floors, 21–23
 stairs, 157
 windows and window wells, 13,
  26–28

Batt insulation, definition of, 117

Batter boards, establishing building
 lines and elevation with, 1–4

Beam and joist, installing, 37–38

Brick veneer. *See* Masonry veneer

Building materials
 protecting on site, 29

Building paper. *See* Wall sheathing
 paper

Built-up roofing
 installing, 76–77
 material combinations for, 211

Carpeting, installing, 142

Carports. *See* Garages and carports

Cast-in-place foundation walls,
 building, 12–16

Ceiling and roof framing, 53–67. *See
 also*
  Flat roofs; Pitched roofs;
  Roof trusses
 for flat roofs, 66–67
 for gable-ends, 63–65
 for pitched roofs, 44–65
 for roof trusses, 55–56

Ceiling finishes. *See* Interior wall and
 ceiling finishes

Ceiling joists
 ceiling joist spans for attic not
  accessible by stairway, 187

Ceramic tile
 flooring, 142–43
 in showers, 143

Chimneys, 166–70
 flashing for, 159–62
 openings in roof sheathing for,
  69

Clay tile roofing. *See* Concrete and
 clay tile roofing

Closets, building, 149–51

Columns and beams
 in floor framing, 36–37

Concrete. *See also* Concrete
  Blocks; Footings; Foundations;
  Slabs
 concrete mixes, 177
 curing, 7–8
 formwork, 12–16
 on-site mixing, 6
 placing, 7
 ready-mix, 6

Concrete blocks
 foundation walls of, 16–18
 mortar mix proportions for
  laying, 179

Concrete and clay tile roofing, 78

Concrete slab foundation, 21–24
 basement floor slabs, 21–23
 slabs on ground, 23–24

Control joints
 in basement floor slabs, 22–23
 in driveways, 171–72

Crawl Spaces
    footing and foundations for,
        24–25
    insulating of floors over, 121–22
    ventilating of, 134
    warm-air furnace, installing in,
        108

Dampproofing
    concrete floor slabs, 22
    crawl spaces, 25
    foundation walls, 16, 18

Decay, protecting against, 13, 29, 173

Dimension lumber. See Lumber

Doors
    exterior frames and doors,
        98–100
    garage, 164–65
    hardware, installing, 146–48
    interior frames and trim, 144–46
    sliding, exterior, 100
    sliding, interior, 149–51

Dormers
    framing for, 63–64

Downspouts. See Eaves troughs and
    downspouts

Drain tile, laying, 26–28

Drainage
    around the foundation, 26–28
    surface, 171–72

Driveways, constructing, 171–72

Drywall. See Gypsum board

Dwarf walls, use of, 57–62

Eaves
    eave and gable-end intersections,
        96–97
    finishing projections, 94–96

Eaves troughs and downspouts,
    installing, 163

Electric baseboard heating system,
    108

Electrical installation. See Wiring

Excavation, 1–5
    size and depth of, 1–3

Exterior Wall Finishes, 83–93
    corner treatment of siding, 89–90
    hardboard panels, 89
    hardboard siding. 85
    lumber, 85–88
    masonry veneer, 92–93
    metal and vinyl, 83–85
    plywood panels, 88–89
    stucco side-wall finish, 91–92,
        212
    wood shingles and shakes, 90–91

Fibreboard
    definition of, 32
    as a wall sheathing, 80

Fire control, building for, 129–31

Fireplaces, 166–70

Flashing, 159–62
    at chimneys, 159–62
    on roofs, 159
    at valleys, 160–61
    at walls, 159

Flat roofs, 66–67. See also Ceiling
        and roof framing; Built-up
        roofs
    covering, 76–77
    insulating, 126–28
    ventilating, 133

Floor coverings, 139–43
    carpeting, 142
    ceramic tile, 142–43
    resilient flooring, 141–42
    seamless resin constituent,
        141–42
    wood strip flooring, 139–41
    wood tile flooring, 141

Floor framing, 36–46. See also Floor
        joists; Subfloor
    beams in, 36–38
    columns in, 36–38
    improving floor performance, 44
    insulating, 121–23
    projections, 45–46
    sill anchors in, 36

Floor joists, 42–46. *See also* Subfloor;
    Beam and Joist
    allowable spans for bedrooms
        and attics accessible by
        stairways, 189
    allowable spans for living
        quarters, 188
    connecting the foundation wall
        and joist, 38–41
    installing beams and joists,
        37–39
    notching and drilling, 101–2

Floor projections, framing, 45–46

Foamed-in-place insulation, 118

Formwork, concrete, use of, 12–14

Footings, 9–11. *See also*
        Foundations; Concrete slabs
    column, 10
    minimum footing sizes, 178
    stepped, 11
    wall, 9–10

Foundation wall and joist
    connecting, 38–41

Foundations, 11–21. *See also*
        Footings, Concrete slabs
    cast-in-place, 12–16
    concrete block, 16–18
    dampproofing, 16, 18
    drainage, 26–28
    insulating, 118–21
    minimum depths of, 178
    minimum thickness of walls, 177
    notches for wood beams, 13–14
    preserved wood, 18–21

Gable-end framing and projections,
        63–65

Garages and carports, 164–65
    doors, 164–65
    floors, slab, 21–23, 25
    footings and foundations, 25

Ground snow loads
    for urban centres, 222

Gutters. *See* Eaves troughs and
    downspouts

Gypsum board
    as a wall and ceiling finish,
        135–38
    as a wall sheathing, 80

Handsplit shakes, installing, 75–76

Hardboard
    definition of, 33
    as a finish, exterior, 85, 89
    as a finish, interior, 138

Heating systems, 101–8
    electric baseboard, 108
    hot-water, 108
    notching and drilling framing
        members, 101–3
    warm-air, 106–8

Hot water heating system, 108

Ice and snow dams on roofs, 71–72

Insulation, 117–28, 213
    floors, 121–23
    floor projections, 45–46
    foundations, 118–21
    joist-type roof-ceilings, 126–28
    rafter-type roof-ceilings, 125–26
    recommended minimum RSI
        values, 118, 213
    trusses, 125–26
    types, 117–18
    wall sheathing, 81–82
    walls, 122–25

Interior wall and ceiling finishes,
        135–38
    gypsum board, 135–38
    nailing support for, 49–51
    other finishes, 138

Joists. *See* Ceiling joists; Floor
    joists; Roof joists

Kitchen cabinets, arranging, 149–50

Knee wall. *See* Dwarf wall

Lintels, 47–48
    spans for various depths, 207

Location of house,
    marking the site, 1–4

Loose fill insulation, 117

Lumber, 30–33, 179–86
    commercial species, 184–85
    facsimiles of lumber grade
        marks, 181–83
    facsimiles of MSR lumber grade
        marks, 183
    as a finish, interior, 138
    grade marks, 30
    grades and uses, 30–31, 179–80
    metric sizes for dimension
        lumber and boards, 186
    as a roof sheathing, 68–69
    as a siding, exterior, 85–88
    as a subfloor, 44–45
    as a wall sheathing, 82

Maintenance, importance of, 175

Masonry veneer, as an exterior
    cladding, 92–93

Measurements, metric, ix,
    metric sizes for dimension
        lumber and boards, 186

Measures for Energy Conservation in
    New Buildings, 1983, 118

Metal and vinyl sidings, installing,
    83–85

Millwork, interior, 148–49

Mortar mix, proportions, 179

Mouldings. See Base mouldings.

Nailing
    framing, 205
    gypsum board, 135–38
    minimum nail lengths and nail
        spacing for flooring, 214
    minimum rafter-to-joist nailing,
        208
    roofing, 70–78
    subfloors, 45
    trusses, 215–21, 223

National Building Code of Canada, ix,
    118, 130, 187

Painting, 174

Particleboard, definition of, 32

Partitions, 47–51
    framing intersections with
        exterior walls, 49–51
    installing a vapour barrier on, 115

Pitched roofs, 53–65
    building on site, 56–65
    building with trusses, 55–56
    types of, 58

Platform construction, 35, 47–51
    exterior corner and wall
        intersection details, 49–51
    using joist-embedded method,
        39–41
    using sill-plate method, 38–39

Plumbing, 101–5
    notching and drilling framing
        members, 101–3
    roughing-in, 103–5

Plywood
    definition of, 32
    as a finish, interior, 138
    formwork for concrete, 12–13
    as a roof sheathing, 68–69
    as a siding, exterior, 88–89
    as a subfloor, 44–45
    as an underlay, 44–45
    as a wall sheathing, 80

Preservatives, wood, 19, 173

Preserved wood foundations
    building, 18–21

Rafters
    allowable spans when not
        supporting ceiling, 194–99
    dormer rafters, 63
    hip and valley rafters, 63
    intermediate support for, 62
    minimum rafter-to-joist nailing,
        208

Resilient flooring
    installing, 141–42
    seamless resin constituent, 142
    underlay, 141

Rigid insulation, 117
    attaching to foundation walls,
        118–21

Roofs. See Flat Roofs; Pitched Roofs

Roof-ceilings
    insulation for joist-type, 126–28
    insulation for rafter-type, 125–26

Roof coverings, 70–79
  asphalt shingles, 71–74, 76
  built-up, 76–77
  concrete and clay tile, 78
  finish at ridge and hips, 76
  handsplit shakes, 75–76
  sheet metal roofing, 78–79
  slope limits for various types,
    210
  wood shingles, 74–76

Roof joists. See also Rafters
  allowable spans when supporting
    ceiling, 190–93

Roof sheathing, 68–70
  details, 69–70
  installing, 68–69
  minimum thickness of, 209

Roof snow loads, 215–21

Roof trusses, 31–32, 55–56, 215–24
  bracing, 56–57
  cantilevered trusses, 223
    reinforcing, 223
  designs and nailing schedules,
    215–24
  fabricating joints, method of, 224
  insulating, 125–26

RSI values, 117–25. See also
    Insulation
  minimum values for houses and
    small buildings, 213

Shakes. See Wood shingles and
    shakes

Sheet metal roofing, installing, 78–79

Siding. See Exterior wall finishes

Sill anchors, in concrete
    foundations, 36

Slabs, See Concrete slab foundation

Smoke alarms, installing, 130–31

Soffits. See Eaves

Soundproofing, designs for, 129–30

Stairs, 152–58
  basement, 154, 157
  design terminology, 152–53
  designs for, 154–56
  exterior steps and stoops, 158
  newels, handrails and guards in,
    157
  ratio of rise-to-run in, 154
  stringers in, 156–57

Staples
  stapling details for various
    construction materials, 209

Stone veneer. See Masonry veneer

Stucco
  applying, 91–92
  flashing, 159–60
  mixes, 212

Studs
  notching and drilling of, 101–3
  size and spacing of, 206

Subfloor, 44–45. See also Underlay
  minimum length of
    fasteners, 204
  minimum number and maximum
    spacing of fasteners, 204
  minimum thickness, 204

Termites, protecting against, 173

Tile
  ceiling, 138
  ceramic, 142–43
  concrete and clay roofing, 78
  drain, 26–28
  resilient flooring, 141–42
  wood flooring, 141

Underlay, 44–45. See also Subfloor
  for resilient flooring, 141

Vapour and air barriers, 113–16. See
    also Insulation; Ventilation
  proper placement, 114–16

Ventilation, 132–34. See also
    Insulation; Vapour and air
    barriers
  of crawl space, 134
  of roof space, 132–33
  size of vents for, 133–34

Vinyl siding. *See* Metal and vinyl sidings

Waferboard
  definition of, 32
  as a roof sheathing, 68
  as a subfloor, 44–45
  as a wall sheathing, 80

Walkways, constructing, 171–72

Wall finishes. *See* Interior wall and ceiling finishes

Wall sheathing, 80–82, 212
  minimum thickness of, 212
  types and installation, 80–82

Wall sheathing paper, placement of, 83

Wallboard. *See* Gypsum board

Wall framing, 47–52. *See also* Platform Construction; Balloon Construction

Warm-air heating system, 106–8

Windows
  basement windows and wells, 13, 26–28
  frames and sashes, exterior, 96–99
  trim, interior, 148

Wiring, electrical, 108–12
  box location, 112
  codes, 111
  notching and drilling framing members, 101–3
  switches, 112

Wood beams, built-up
  in floor framing, 36–37
  maximum span when supporting not more than one floor, 200–201
  maximum span when supporting not more than two floors, 202–3

Wood shingles, roof
  installing, 74–76
  maximum exposure of, 210

Wood shingles and shakes, walls, installing, 90–91
  maximum exposure and minimum butt for, 212

Wood strip flooring, laying, 139–41
  minimum thickness of, 214
  nailing of, 214

Wood tile flooring, laying, 141